HERITAGE
IMPORTANT CIVIL WAR AUCTION
June 24-25, 2007 | Gettysburg, Pennsylvania

LOT VIEWING LOCATION

Eisenhower Inn
2634 Emmitsburg Road
Gettysburg Road
Gettysburg, PA 17325
www.eisenhower.com
(717) 334-6363

LOT VIEWING

Friday, June 22, 5pm - 9pm ET
Saturday, June 23, 10am - 5pm ET
Sunday, June 24, 10am - 2pm ET

RECEPTION

Sunday, June 24, 1:30pm - 3pm ET

BIDS VIA FAX

Deadline: Friday, June 22, 12pm CT

BIDS VIA INTERNET

HA.com/CivilWar
Bid@HA.com
Internet bidding closes at 10:00pm CT
the night prior to each session

LIVE PHONE BIDDING

Client Services: 866-835-3243
Must be arranged on or before Friday, June 22, 12pm CT

AUCTION LOCATION

Wyndham Gettysburg Hotel
95 Presidential Circle
Gettysburg, PA 17325
www.wyndhamgettysburg.com
(717) 339-0020
Sunday, June 24 – Presidential Ballroom
Monday, June 25 – Presidential Ballroom Salon D

AUCTION SESSIONS

Session 1 - Sunday, June 24, 3pm ET
Lots 72001 - 72279

Session 2 - Monday, June 25, 10am ET
Lots 72280 - 72600
(see separate catalog mailing at later date)

AUCTIONEER

Samuel W. Foose, PA License #AS009993
Robert Merrill, PA License #AS009992

LOT PICK UP

Gettysburg Civil War Show location at Eisenhower Inn
(same location as lot viewing)
Sunday, June 24, 6pm - 8pm ET
Monday, June 25, 10am - 4pm ET
Also available during and between sessions

AUCTION RESULTS

Immediately available at HA.com/CivilWar

View lots online at HA.com/CivilWar
This auction is subject to a 19.5% Buyer's Premium.

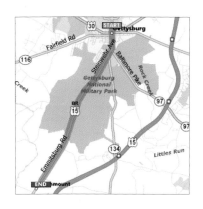

HERITAGE HA.com
Auction Galleries

3500 Maple Avenue, 17th Floor • Dallas, Texas 75219-3941
214.528.3500 • 800.872.6467 • 214.443.8425 (fax)
Direct Client Service Line: Toll-Free 866.835.3243

CATALOGUED BY: Gary Hendershott, Dr. Douglass Brown, Michael Riley, Marsha Dixey, Dave Golemon, Sandra Palomino, Joe Fay and Eric Smylie
GUEST EXPERTS/CATALOGERS: Rob Golan, Bill Beard, Kent Wall and Howard Madaus
EDITED BY: Gary Hendershott, Dr. Douglass Brown, Marsha Dixey and Michael Riley
IMAGING AND PHOTOGRAPHY BY: Abel Privado, Matt Roppolo, James Elliott, Kevin Gaddis Jr., Ray Proska, Roy Richardson, Terry Thibeau, David Kuykendall, Billy Coleman, Leticia Crawford, Beatriz Faustino, Andrew Fitzpatrick, Brian Connor, Lindsey Johnson, Lucas Garritson, Patric Glenn, Haley Hagen, Craig Smith and Lori McKay
OPERATIONS: Julie Gonzalez, Whitny Wooten, Meagan Galbraith, Alex Perez and Teia Baber
PRODUCTION AND DESIGN: Cindy Brenner, Mary Hermann and Michael Puttonen

HERITAGE HA.com
Auction Galleries

World Headquarters
3500 Maple Avenue, 17th Floor
Dallas, Texas 75219-3941
800-872-6467

UNITED STATES COINS

HA.com/Coins
U.S. Coins

Leo Frese, Ext. 294
Leo@HA.com

Charles Clifford, Ext. 477
CharlesC@HA.com

Sam Foose, Ext. 227
SamF@HA.com

Jim Jelinski, Ext. 257
JimJ@HA.com

Katherine Kurachek, Ext. 389
KKurachek@HA.com

David Lewis, Ext. 520
DLewis@HA.com

David Lisot, Ext. 303
DavidL@HA.com

Bob Marino, Ext. 374
BobMarino@HA.com

David Mayfield, Ext. 277
DavidM@HA.com

Bob Phillips, Ext. 588
BobP@HA.com

Mike Sadler, Ext. 332
MikeS@HA.com

UNITED STATES COINS PRIVATE TREATY SALES

HA.com/Coins

Todd Imhof, Ext. 313
Todd@HA.com

CURRENCY

HA.com/Currency
Paper Money

Len Glazer, Ext. 390
Len@HA.com

Allen Mincho, Ext. 327
Allen@HA.com

Dustin Johnston, Ext. 302
Dustin@HA.com

Jim Fitzgerald, Ext. 348
JimF@HA.com

Michael Moczalla, Ext. 481
MichaelM@HA.com

WORLD COINS

HA.com/Coins
World Coins & Currencies

Warren Tucker, Ext. 287
WTucker@HA.com

Scott Cordry, Ext. 369
ScottC@HA.com

Harvey Gamer, Ext. 676
HarveyG@HA.com

CIVIL WAR HISTORICAL MATERIAL

HA.com/Civil War
*Artifacts, Documents and Memorabilia
Related to the American Civil War*

Gary Hendershott, Ext. 182
GaryH@HA.com

Douglass Brown, Ext. 165
DouglassB@HA.com

CORPORATE OFFICERS

R. Steven Ivy, Co-Chairman
James L. Halperin, Co-Chairman
Gregory J. Rohan, President
Paul Minshull, Chief Operating Officer

COMICS

HA.com/Comics
*Comics, Original Comic Art
and Related Memorabilia*

Ed Jaster, Ext. 288
EdJ@HA.com

Lon Allen, Ext. 261
LonA@HA.com

MUSIC & ENTERTAINMENT MEMORABILIA

HA.com/Entertainment
*Stage-Worn Costumes, Records,
Signed Photos & Memorabilia*

Doug Norwine, Ext. 452
DougN@HA.com

John Hickey, Ext. 264
JohnH@HA.com

Jim Steele, Ext. 328
JimSt@HA.com

POLITICAL MEMORABILIA & AMERICANA

HA.com/Americana
*Historical & Pop Culture Americana,
Vintage Toys, Presidential & Political Memorabilia,
Buttons & Medals, Books & Manuscripts,
First Editions and Collectible Autographs*

Tom Slater, Ext. 441
TomS@HA.com

Marsha Dixey, Ext. 455
MarshaD@HA.com

John Hickey, Ext. 264
JohnH@HA.com

Sandra Palomino, Ext. 107
SandraP@HA.com

Michael Riley, Ext. 467
MichaelR@HA.com

SPORTS COLLECTIBLES

HA.com/Sports
*Sports Cards, Artifacts,
Game-Used Jerseys & Equipment*

Chris Ivy, Ext. 319
CIvy@HA.com

Stephen Carlisle, Ext. 292
StephenC@HA.com

Jonathan Scheier, Ext. 314
JonathanS@HA.com

Mark Jordan, Ext. 187
MarkJ@HA.com

Mike Gutierrez, Ext. 183
MikeG@HA.com

VINTAGE MOVIE POSTERS

HA.com/MoviePosters
Posters, Lobby Cards, and Hollywood Ephemera

Grey Smith, Ext. 367
GreySm@HA.com

Bruce Carteron, Ext. 551
BruceC@HA.com

TRUSTS AND ESTATES

HA.com/Estates

Steven Roach, Ext. 694
Roach@HA.com

HA.com/CivilWar

Gary Hendershott, Director
Ext. 182 • GaryH@HA.com

Norma Gonzalez, Vice President Operations
Ext. 242 • Norma@HA.com

Jared Green, Vice President, Business Development
Ext. 279 • JaredG@HA.com

FINE ART

HA.com/FineArt
*Impressionist, Old Masters and
Contemporary Drawings, Paintings,
Sculpture and Photography*

Edmund P. Pillsbury, Ph.D., Ext. 533
EPP@HA.com

Kathleen Guzman, Ext. 672
KathleenG@HA.com

Ed Jaster, Ext. 288
EdJ@HA.com

Christine Carmody, Ext. 521
ChristineC@HA.com

Lindsay Davis, Ext. 542
LindsayD@HA.com

TEXAS ART

HA.com/TexasArt
Early Texas Art, Drawings and Paintings

Larry Boettigheimer, Ext. 523
LarryB@HA.com

ILLUSTRATION ART/PHOTOGRAPHY

HA.com/FineArt
Pinups and Illustration Art

Ed Jaster, Ext. 288
EdJ@HA.com

DECORATIVE ARTS

HA.com/FineArt
*Art Glass, European & American Silver,
Pottery & Ceramics*

Michael Wolf, Ext. 541
MWolf@HA.com

Tim Rigdon, Ext. 119
TimR@HA.com

Christine Carmody, Ext. 521
ChristineC@HA.com

JEWELRY & TIMEPIECES

HA.com/Jewelry
Jewelry & Timepieces

Jill Burgum, Ext. 697
JillB@HA.com

Ghislain d'Humières, Ext. 157
GDH@HA.com

MEDIA RELATIONS

Marketing and Public Relations

Kelley Norwine, Ext. 583
KelleyN@HA.com

John Petty, Ext. 283
JohnP@HA.com

CREDIT DEPARTMENT

Marti Korver, Ext 248
Marti@HA.com

WIRING INSTRUCTIONS

Bank Information: JP Morgan Chase Bank, N.A.
270 Park Avenue, New York, NY 10017
Account Name: Heritage Numismatic Auctions
Master Account
ABA Number: 021000021
Account Number: 1884827674
Swift Code: CHASUS33

FOR THE EXTENSIONS ABOVE, PLEASE CALL 800-872-6467
FOR TOLL-FREE DIRECT CLIENT SERVICES, CALL 866-835-3243

5/3/07

Steve Ivy
CEO
Co-Chairman
of the Board

Jim Halperin
Co-Chairman
of the Board

Greg Rohan
President

Paul Minshull
Chief Operating Officer

Gary Hendershott
Director of
Civil War Auctions

Douglass Brown
Chief Cataloger
and Consignment
Director

Jared Green
V.P. of Business
Development

Tom Slater
Director of
Acquisitions

John Hickey
Consignment
Director

Marsha Dixey
Consignment
Director

Michael Riley
Chief Cataloger
and Consignment
Director

HERITAGE
Auction Galleries

3500 Maple Avenue, 17th Floor
Dallas, Texas 75219-3941
214.528.3500 • 800.872.6467 • 214.443.8425 (fax)

JOIN US IN GETTYSBURG!   JUNE 23, 24, & 25, 2007

I would like to extend my personal invitation for you to join us at Heritage Auction Galleries' Civil War auction in Gettysburg, Pennsylvania.

As someone with an interest in Civil War memorabilia, I know you will want to attend the greatest Civil War auction ever assembled. Valued at well over $10 million, you will be able to see this incredible treasure trove first hand for three days during our auction preview at the Gettysburg Civil War show, the most famous show of its kind in the country. Beginning on Sunday afternoon, June 24, Heritage will host the most incredible Civil War auction ever held, in the Wyndham Gettysburg Presidential Ballroom. Here you'll be able to bid on such exquisite treasures as the personal battle flag of General George Armstrong Custer, the handsome presentation sword of General and President Ulysses S. Grant, the fabled "Bonnie Blue" flag of Texas, and much, much more. Without a doubt, this will prove to be the event of the year, and one that you will no doubt want to participate in. I encourage you to bring your family and friends to this once-in-a-lifetime event and join us for an exciting weekend in Gettysburg.

If you are unable to attend the auction in person, you can join us via live telephone bidding or through the Internet. Definitely the next best thing to being there, we will be able to assist you with condition reports as well as provide provenance descriptions for any piece in the collection. Our experts have over a century of knowledge and experience between them, and they have thoroughly researched and documented each and every item. Our entire staff will be available to assist you, whether you are a private collector looking for one important piece or a museum director hoping to acquire a number of items for your institution. Let us assist you with pre-registration, deferred billing or extended payment plans, expert opinions and more on these important icons of both Civil War and American history.

The first session of this monumentally exciting auction begins at 3:00 pm on Sunday afternoon, June 24, and will be catered by the Wyndham, so join us for food, fellowship and fun as we kick off this sure-to-be historical event. Then, on Monday morning, June 25 at 10 am, we'll resume with the second session of over 400 exciting Civil War items.

I hope you'll accept our personal invitation to join us in Gettysburg for this important auction. If I can be of any assistance to you in any way, please don't hesitate to call me at 1-800-872-6467, ext. 182, or email me at GaryH@HA.com. I look forward to seeing you in June.

Sincerely,

Gary Hendershott
Director, Civil War Auctions
Heritage Auction Galleries
office: 800-872-6467, x182
cell: 972-358-4969
GaryH@HA.com

Auctioneer and Auction:

1. This Auction is presented by Heritage Auction Galleries, a d/b/a/ of Heritage Auctions, Inc., or their affiliates Heritage Numismatic Auctions, Inc. or Currency Auctions of America, Inc., d/b/a as identified with the applicable licensing information on the title page of the catalog or on the HA.com Internet site (the "Auctioneer"). The Auction is conducted under these Terms and Conditions of Auction and applicable state and local law. Announcements and corrections from the podium and those made through the Terms and Conditions of Auctions appearing on the Internet at HA.com supersede those in the printed catalog.

Buyer's Premium:

2. On bids placed through Heritage, a Buyer's Premium of fifteen percent (15%) will be added to the successful hammer price bid on lots in Coin and Currency auctions, or nineteen and one-half percent (19.5%) on lots in all other auctions. If your bid is placed through eBay Live, a Buyer's Premium equal to the normal Buyer's Premium plus an additional five percent (5%) of the hammer price will be added to the successful bid up to a maximum Buyer's Premium of Twenty Two and one-half percent (22.5%). There is a minimum Buyer's Premium of $9.00 per lot. In Gallery Auctions only, a ten percent (10%) handling fee is applied to all lots based upon the total of the hammer price plus the 19.5% Buyer's Premium.

Auction Venues:

3. The following Auctions are conducted solely on the Internet: Heritage Weekly Internet Coin, Currency, Comics, and Vintage Movie Poster Auctions; Heritage Monthly Internet Sports and Marketplace Auctions; OnLine Sessions. Signature Auctions and Grand Format Auctions accept bids on the Internet first, followed by a floor bidding session; bids may be placed prior to the floor bidding session by Internet, telephone, fax, or mail.

Bidders:

4. Any person participating or registering for the Auction agrees to be bound by and accepts these Terms and Conditions of Auction ("Bidder(s)").

5. All Bidders must meet Auctioneer's qualifications to bid. Any Bidder who is not a customer in good standing of the Auctioneer may be disqualified at Auctioneer's sole option and will not be awarded lots. Such determination may be made by Auctioneer in its sole and unlimited discretion, at any time prior to, during, or even after the close of the Auction. Auctioneer reserves the right to exclude any person it deems in its sole opinion is disruptive to the Auction or is otherwise commercially unsuitable.

6. If an entity places a bid, then the person executing the bid on behalf of the entity agrees to personally guarantee payment for any successful bid.

Credit References:

7. Bidders who have not established credit with the Auctioneer must either furnish satisfactory credit information (including two collectibles-related business references) well in advance of the Auction or supply valid credit card information. Bids placed through our Interactive Internet program will only be accepted from pre-registered Bidders; Bidders who are not members of HA.com or affiliates should pre-register at least two business days before the first session to allow adequate time to contact references.

Bidding Options:

8. Bids in Signature Auctions or Grand Format Auctions may be placed as set forth in the printed catalog section entitled "Choose your bidding method." For auctions held solely on the Internet, see the alternatives on HA.com. Review at HA.com/common/howtobid.php.

9. Presentment of Bids: Non-Internet bids (including but not limited to podium, fax, phone and mail bids) are treated similar to floor bids in that they must be on-increment or at a half increment (called a cut bid). Any podium, fax, phone, or mail bids that do not conform to a full or half increment will be rounded up or down to the nearest full or half increment and this revised amount will be considered your high bid.

10. Auctioneer's Execution of Certain Bids. Auctioneer cannot be responsible for your errors in bidding, so carefully check that every bid is entered correctly. When identical mail or FAX bids are submitted, preference is given to the first received. To ensure the greatest accuracy, your written bids should be entered on the standard printed bid sheet and be received at Auctioneer's place of business at least two business days before the Auction start. Auctioneer is not responsible for executing mail bids or FAX bids received on or after the day the first lot is sold, nor Internet bids submitted after the published closing time; nor is Auctioneer responsible for proper execution of bids submitted by telephone, mail, FAX, e-mail, Internet, or in person once the Auction begins. Internet bids may not be withdrawn until your written request is received and acknowledged by Auctioneer (FAX: 214-443-8425); such requests must state the reason, and may constitute grounds for withdrawal of bidding privileges. Lots won by mail Bidders will not be delivered at the Auction unless prearranged.

11. Caveat as to Bid Increments. Bid increments (over the current bid level) determine the lowest amount you may bid on a particular lot. Bids greater than one increment over the current bid can be any whole dollar amount. It is possible under several circumstances for winning bids to be between increments, sometimes only $1 above the previous increment. Please see: "How can I lose by less than an increment?" on our website.

The following chart governs current bidding increments.

Current Bid	Bid Increment	Current Bid	Bid Increment
< $10	$1	$3,000 - $4,999	$250
$10 - $29	$2	$5,000 - $9,999	$500
$30 - $59	$3	$10,000 - $19,999	$1,000
$60 - $99	$5	$20,000 - $29,999	$2,000
$100 - $199	$10	$30,000 - $49,999	$2,500
$200 - $299	$20	$50,000 - $99,999	$5,000
$300 - $499	$25	$100,000 - $249,999	$10,000
$500 - $999	$50	$250,000 - $499,999	$25,000
$1,000 - $1,999	$100	$500,000 - $1,499,999	$50,000
$2,000 - $2,999	$200	> $1,500,000	$100,000

12. If Auctioneer calls for a full increment, a floor/phone bidder may request Auctioneer to accept a bid at half of the increment ("Cut Bid") which will be that bidders final bid; if the Auctioneer solicits bids other the expected increment, they will not be considered Cut Bids, and bidders accepting such increments may continue to participate.

Conducting the Auction:

13. Notice of the consignor's liberty to place reserve bids on his lots in the Auction is hereby made in accordance with Article 2 of the Texas Uniform Commercial Code. A reserve is an amount below which the lot will not sell. THE CONSIGNOR OF PROPERTY MAY PLACE WRITTEN RESERVE BIDS ON HIS LOTS IN ADVANCE OF THE AUCTION; ON SUCH LOTS, IF THE HAMMER PRICE DOES NOT MEET THE RESERVE, THE CONSIGNOR MAY PAY A REDUCED COMMISSION ON THOSE LOTS. Reserves are generally posted online several days prior to the Auction closing. Any successful bid placed by a consignor on his Property on the Auction floor or by telephone during the live session, or after the reserves for an Auction have been posted, will be considered an Unqualified Bid, and in such instances the consignor agrees to pay full Buyer's Premium and Seller's Commissions on any lot so repurchased.

14. The highest qualified Bidder shall be the buyer. In the event of any dispute between floor Bidders at a Signature Auction, Auctioneer may at his sole discretion reoffer the lot. Auctioneer's decision and declaration of the winning Bidder shall be final and binding upon all Bidders.

15. Auctioneer reserves the right to refuse to honor any bid or to limit the amount of any bid which, in his sole discretion, is not submitted in "Good Faith," or is not supported by satisfactory credit, numismatic references, or otherwise. A bid is considered not made in "Good Faith" when an insolvent or irresponsible person, or a person under the age of eighteen makes it. Regardless of the disclosure of his identity, any bid by a consignor or his agent on a lot consigned by him is deemed to be made in "Good Faith".

16. Nominal Bids. The Auctioneer in its sole discretion may reject nominal bids, small opening bids, or very nominal advances. If a lot bearing estimates fails to open for 40 –60% of the low estimate, the Auctioneer may pass the item or may place a protective bid on behalf of the consignor.

17. Lots bearing bidding estimates shall open at Auctioneer's discretion (approximately 50% of the low estimate). In the event that no bid meets or exceeds that opening amount, the lot shall pass as unsold.

18. All items are to be purchased per lot as numerically indicated and no lots will be broken. Bids will be accepted in whole dollar amounts only. No "buy" or "unlimited" bids will be accepted. Off-increment bids may be accepted by the Auctioneer at Signature Auctions and Grand Format Auctions. Auctioneer reserves the right to withdraw, prior to the close, any lots from the Auction.

19. Auctioneer reserves the right to rescind the sale in the event of nonpayment, breach of a warranty, disputed ownership, auctioneer's clerical error or omission in exercising bids and reserves, or otherwise.

20. Auctioneer occasionally experiences Internet and/or Server service outages during which Bidders cannot participate or place bids. If such outage occurs, we may at our discretion extend bidding for the auction. This policy applies only to widespread outages and not to isolated problems that occur in various parts of the country from time to time. Auctioneer periodically schedules system downtime for maintenance and other purposes, which may be covered by the Outage Policy. Bidders unable to place their Bids through the Internet are directed to bid through Client Services at 1-800-872-6467.

21. The Auctioneer or its affiliates may consign items to be sold in the Auction, and may bid on those lots or any other lots. Auctioneer or affiliates expressly reserve the right to modify any such bids at any time prior to the hammer based upon data made known to the Auctioneer or its affiliates. The Auctioneer may extend advances, guarantees, or loans to certain consignors, and may extend financing or other credits at varying rates to certain Bidders in the auction.

22. The Auctioneer has the right to sell certain unsold items after the close of the Auction; Such lots shall be considered sold during the Auction and all these Terms and Conditions shall apply to such sales including but not limited to the Buyer's Premium, return rights, and disclaimers.

Payment:

23. All sales are strictly for cash in United States dollars. Cash includes: U.S. currency, bank wire, cashier checks, travelers checks, and bank money orders, all subject to reporting requirements. Checks may be subject to clearing before delivery of the purchases. Credit Card (Visa or Master Card only) and PayPal payments may be accepted up to $10,000 from non-dealers at the sole discretion of the auctioneer, subject to the following limitations: a) sales are only to the cardholder, b) purchases are shipped to the cardholder's registered and verified address, c) Auctioneer may pre-approve the cardholder's credit line, d) a credit card transaction may not be used in conjunction with any other financing or extended terms offered by the Auctioneer, and must transact immediately upon invoice presentation, e) rights of return are governed by these Terms and Conditions, which supersede those conditions promulgated by the card issuer, f) floor Bidders must present their card.

24. Payment is due upon closing of the Auction session, or upon presentment of an invoice. Auctioneer reserves the right to void an invoice if payment in full is not received within 7 days after the close of the Auction.

25. Lots delivered in the States of Texas, California, or other states where the Auction may be held, are subject to all applicable state and local taxes, unless appropriate permits are on file with us. Bidder agrees to pay Auctioneer the actual amount of tax due in the event that sales tax is not properly collected due to: 1) an expired, inaccurate, inappropriate tax certificate or declaration, 2) an incorrect interpretation of the applicable statute, 3) or any other reason. Lots from different Auctions may not be aggregated for sales tax purposes.

26. In the event that a Bidder's payment is dishonored upon presentment(s), Bidder shall pay the maximum statutory processing fee set by applicable state law.

27. If any Auction invoice submitted by Auctioneer is not paid in full when due, the unpaid balance will bear interest at the highest rate permitted by law from the date of invoice until paid. If the Auctioneer refers any invoice to an attorney for collection, the buyer agrees to pay attorney's fees, court costs, and other collection costs incurred by Auctioneer. If Auctioneer assigns collection to its in-house legal staff, such attorney's time expended on the matter shall be compensated at a rate comparable to the hourly rate of independent attorneys.

28. In the event a successful Bidder fails to pay all amounts due, Auctioneer reserves the right to resell the merchandise, and such Bidder agrees to pay for the reasonable costs of resale, including a 10% seller's commission, and also to pay any difference between the resale price and the price of the previously successful bid.

29. Auctioneer reserves the right to require payment in full in good funds before delivery of the merchandise.

30. Auctioneer shall have a lien against the merchandise purchased by the buyer to secure payment of the Auction invoice. Auctioneer is further granted a lien and the right to retain possession of any other property of the buyer then held by the Auctioneer or its affiliates to secure payment of any Auction invoice or any other amounts due the Auctioneer or affiliates from the buyer. With respect to these lien rights, Auctioneer shall have all the rights of a secured creditor under Article 9 of the Texas Uniform Commercial Code, including but not limited to the right of sale. In addition, with respect to payment of the Auction invoice(s), the buyer waives any and all rights of offset he might otherwise have against the Auctioneer and the consignor of the merchandise included on the invoice. If a Bidder owes Auctioneer or its affiliates on any account, Auctioneer and its affiliates shall have the right to offset such unpaid account by any credit balance due Bidder, and it may secure by possessory lien any unpaid amount by any of the Bidder's property in their possession.

31. Title shall not pass to the successful Bidder until all invoices are paid in full. It is the responsibility of the buyer to provide adequate insurance coverage for the items once they have been delivered.

Delivery; Shipping and Handling Charges:

32. Shipping and handling charges will be added to invoices. Please refer to Auctioneer's website www.HA.com/common/shipping.php for the latest charges or call Auctioneer. Auctioneer is unable to combine purchases from other auctions or affiliates into one package for shipping purposes.

33. Successful overseas Bidders shall provide written shipping instructions, including specified customs declarations, to the Auctioneer for any lots to be delivered outside of the United States. NOTE: Declaration value shall be the item(s) hammer price together with its buyer's premium.

34. All shipping charges will be borne by the successful Bidder. Any risk of loss during shipment will be borne by the buyer following Auctioneer's delivery to the designated common carrier or third-party shipper, regardless of domestic or foreign shipment.

35. Due to the nature of some items sold, it shall be the responsibility for the successful bidder to arrange pick-up and shipping through third-parties; as to such items Auctioneer shall have no liability.

36. Any request for shipping verification for undelivered packages must be made within 30 days of shipment by Auctioneer.

Cataloging, Warranties and Disclaimers:

37. NO WARRANTY, WHETHER EXPRESSED OR IMPLIED, IS MADE WITH RESPECT TO ANY DESCRIPTION OR CONDITION REPORT CONTAINED IN THIS AUCTION OR ANY SECOND OPINE. Any description of the items or second opine contained in this Auction is for the sole purpose of identifying the items for those Bidders who do not have the opportunity to view the lots prior to bidding, and no description of items has been made part of the basis of the bargain or has created any express warranty that the goods would conform to any description made by Auctioneer.

38. Auctioneer is selling only such right or title to the items being sold as Auctioneer may have by virtue of consignment agreements on the date of auction and disclaims any warranty of title to the Property. Auctioneer disclaims any warranty of merchantability or fitness for any particular purposes.

39. Translations of foreign language documents may be provided as a convenience to interested parties. Heritage makes no representation as to the accuracy of those translations and will not be held responsible for errors in bidding arising from inaccuracies in translation.

40. Auctioneer disclaims all liability for damages, consequential or otherwise, arising out of or in connection with the sale of any Property by Auctioneer to Bidder. No third party may rely on any benefit of these Terms and Conditions and any rights, if any, established hereunder are personal to the Bidder and may not be assigned. Any statement made by the Auctioneer is an opinion and does not constitute a warranty or representation. No employee of Auctioneer may alter these Terms and Conditions, and, unless signed by a principal of Auctioneer, any such alteration is null and void.

41. Auctioneer shall not be liable for breakage of glass or damage to frames (patent or latent); such defects, in any event, shall not be a basis for any claim for return or reduction in purchase price.

Release:

42. In consideration of participation in the Auction and the placing of a bid, Bidder expressly releases Auctioneer, its officers, directors and employees, its affiliates, and its outside experts that provide second opines, from any and all claims, cause of action, chose of action, whether at law or equity or any arbitration or mediation rights existing under

the rules of any professional society or affiliation based upon the assigned description, or a derivative theory, breach of warranty express or implied, representation or other matter set forth within these Terms and Conditions of Auction or otherwise. In the event of a claim, Bidder agrees that such rights and privileges conferred therein are strictly construed as specifically declared herein; e.g., authenticity, typographical error, etc. and are the exclusive remedy. Bidder, by non-compliance to these express terms of a granted remedy, shall waive any claim against Auctioneer.

Dispute Resolution and Arbitration Provision:

43. By placing a bid or otherwise participating in the auction, Bidder accepts these Terms and Conditions of Auction, and specifically agrees to the alternative dispute resolution provided herein. Arbitration replaces the right to go to court, including the right to a jury trial.

44. Auctioneer in no event shall be responsible for consequential damages, incidental damages, compensatory damages, or other damages arising from the auction of any lot. In the event that Auctioneer cannot deliver the lot or subsequently it is established that the lot lacks title, provenance, authenticity, or other transfer or condition issue is claimed, Auctioneer's liability shall be limited to rescission of sale and refund of purchase price; in no case shall Auctioneer's maximum liability exceed the high bid on that lot, which bid shall be deemed for all purposes the value of the lot. After one year has elapsed, Auctioneer's maximum liability shall be limited to any commissions and fees Auctioneer earned on that lot.

45. In the event of an attribution error, Auctioneer may at its sole discretion, correct the error on the Internet, or, if discovered at a later date, to refund the buyer's purchase price without further obligation.

46. If any dispute arises regarding payment, authenticity, grading, description, provenance, or any other matter pertaining to the Auction, the Bidder or a participant in the Auction and/or the Auctioneer agree that the dispute shall be submitted, if otherwise mutually unresolved, to binding arbitration in accordance with the commercial rules of the American Arbitration Association (A.A.A.). A.A.A. arbitration shall be conducted under the provisions of the Federal Arbitration Act with locale in Dallas, Texas. Any claim made by a Bidder has to be presented within one (1) year or it is barred. The prevailing party may be awarded his reasonable attorney's fees and costs. An award granted in arbitration is enforceable in any court of competent jurisdiction. No claims of any kind (except for reasons of authenticity) can be considered after the settlements have been made with the consignors. Any dispute after the settlement date is strictly between the Bidder and consignor without involvement or responsibility of the Auctioneer.

47. In consideration of their participation in or application for the Auction, a person or entity (whether the successful Bidder, a Bidder, a purchaser and/or other Auction participant or registrant) agrees that all disputes in any way relating to, arising under, connected with, or incidental to these Terms and Conditions and purchases, or default in payment thereof, shall be arbitrated pursuant to the arbitration provision. In the event that any matter including actions to compel arbitration, construe the agreement, actions in aid or arbitration or otherwise needs to be litigated, such litigation shall be exclusively in the Courts of the State of Texas, in Dallas County, Texas, and if necessary the corresponding appellate courts. The successful Bidder, purchaser, or Auction participant also expressly submits himself to the personal jurisdiction of the State of Texas.

48. These Terms & Conditions provide specific remedies for occurrences in the auction and delivery process. Where such remedies are afforded, they shall be interpreted strictly. Bidder agrees that any claim shall utilize such remedies; Bidder making a claim in excess of those remedies provided in these Terms and Conditions agrees that in no case whatsoever shall Auctioneer's maximum liability exceed the high bid on that lot, which bid shall be deemed for all purposes the value of the lot..

Miscellaneous:

49. Agreements between Bidders and consignors to effectuate a non-sale of an item at Auction, inhibit bidding on a consigned item to enter into a private sale agreement for said item, or to utilize the Auctioneer's Auction to obtain sales for non-selling consigned items subsequent to the Auction, are strictly prohibited. If a subsequent sale of a previously consigned item occurs in violation of this provision, Auctioneer reserves the right to charge Bidder the applicable Buyer's Premium and consignor a Seller's Commission as determined for each auction venue and by the terms of the seller's agreement.

50. Acceptance of these Terms and Conditions qualifies Bidder as a Heritage customer who has consented to be contacted by Heritage in the future. In conformity with "do-not-call" regulations promulgated by the Federal or State regulatory agencies, participation by the Bidder is affirmative consent to being contacted at the phone number shown in his application and this consent shall remain in effect until it is revoked in writing. Heritage may from time to time contact Bidder concerning sale, purchase, and auction opportunities available through Heritage and its affiliates and subsidiaries.

State Notices:

Notice as to an Auction in California. Auctioneer has in compliance with Title 2.95 of the California Civil Code as amended October 11, 1993 Sec. 1812.600, posted with the California Secretary of State its bonds for it and its employees, and the auction is being conducted in compliance with Sec. 2338 of the Commercial Code and Sec. 535 of the Penal Code.

Notice as to an Auction in New York City. These Terms and Conditions are designed to conform to the applicable sections of the New York City Department of Consumer Affairs Rules and Regulations as Amended. This is a Public Auction Sale conducted by Auctioneer. The New York City licensed Auctioneers are Kathleen Guzman, No.0762165-Day, and Samuel W. Foose, No.0952360-Day, No.0952361-Night, who will conduct the Auction on behalf of Heritage Auctions, Inc. ("Auctioneer"). All lots are subject to: the consignor's right to bid thereon in accord with these Terms and Conditions of Auction, consignor's option to receive advances on their consignments, and Auctioneer, in its sole discretion, may offer limited extended financing to registered bidders, in accord with Auctioneer's internal credit standards. A registered bidder may inquire whether a lot is subject to an advance or reserve. Auctioneer has made advances to various consignors in this sale.

ADDITIONAL TERMS AND CONDITIONS OF AUCTION

MEMORABILIA TERM A: Signature and Grand Format Auctions of Autographs, Sports Collectibles, Music, Entertainment, Political, Americana, Vintage Movie Posters and Pop Culture memorabilia are not on approval. When the lot is accompanied by a Certificate of Authenticity (or its equivalent) from an third-party authentication provider, buyer has no right of return. On lots not accompanied by third-party authentication or under extremely limited circumstances not including authenticity (e.g. gross cataloging error), a purchaser who did not bid from the floor may request Auctioneer to evaluate voiding a sale; such request must be made in writing detailing the alleged gross error, and submission of the lot to Auctioneer must be pre-approved by Auctioneer. A Bidder must notify the appropriate department head (check the inside front cover of the catalog or our website for a listing of department heads) in writing of the Bidder's request within three (3) days of the non-floor bidder's receipt of the lot. Any lot that is to be evaluated for return must be received in our offices within 35 days after Auction. AFTER THAT 35 DAY PERIOD, NO LOT MAY BE RETURNED FOR ANY REASONS. Lots returned must be in the same condition as when sold and must include any Certificate of Authenticity. No lots purchased by floor bidders may be returned (including those bidders acting as agents for others). Late remittance for purchases may be considered just cause to revoke all return privileges.

MEMORABILIA TERM B: When a memorabilia lot is accompanied by a Certificate of Authenticity (or its equivalent) from an independent third-party authentication provider, Auctioneer does not warrant authenticity of that lot. Bidder shall solely rely upon warranties of the authentication provider issuing the Certificate or opinion. For information as to such authentication providers' warranties the bidder is directed to: SCD Authentic, 4034 West National Ave., Milwaukee, WI 53215 (800) 345-3168; JO Sports, Inc., P.O. Box 607 Brookhaven, NY 11719 (631) 286-0970; PSA/DNA; 130 Brookshire Lane, Orwigsburg, Pa. 17961; Mike Gutierrez Autographs, 8150 Raintree Drive Suite A, Scottsdale, AZ. 85260; or as otherwise noted on the Certificate.

MEMORABILIA TERM C: Bidders who intend to challenge authenticity or provenance of a lot must notify Auctioneer in writing within thirty-five (35) days of the Auction's conclusion. Any claim as to provenance or authenticity must be first transmitted to Auctioneer by credible and definitive evidence or the opine of a qualified third party expert and there is no assurance after such presentment that Auctioneer will validate the claim. Authentication is not an exact science and contrary opinions may not be recognized by Auctioneer. Even if Auctioneer agrees with the contrary opinion of such authentication, our liability for reimbursement for such service shall not exceed $500. Provenance and authenticity are guaranteed by neither the consignor nor Auctioneer. While every effort is made to determine provenance and authenticity, it is the responsibility of the Bidder to arrive at their own conclusion prior to bidding.

MEMORABILIA TERM D: In the event Auctioneer cannot deliver the lot or subsequently it is established that the lot lacks title, or other transfer or condition issue is claimed, Auctioneer's liability shall be limited to rescission of sale and refund of purchase price; in no case shall Auctioneer's maximum liability exceed the high bid on that lot, which bid shall be deemed for all purposes the value of the lot. After one year has elapsed, Auctioneer's maximum liability shall be limited to any commissions and fees Auctioneer earned on that lot.

MEMORABILIA TERM E: On the fall of Auctioneer's hammer, buyer assumes full risk and responsibility for lot, including shipment by common carrier, and must provide their own insurance coverage for shipments.

MEMORABILIA TERM F: Auctioneer complies to all Federal and State rules and regulations relating to the purchasing, registration and shipping of firearms. A purchaser is required to provide appropriate documents and the payment of associated fees, if any. Purchaser is responsible for providing a shipping address that is suitable for the receipt of a firearm.

WIRING INSTRUCTIONS:
Bank Information: JP Morgan Chase Bank, N.A., 270 Park Avenue, New York, NY 10017
Account Name: HERITAGE NUMISMATIC AUCTIONS MASTER ACCOUNT
ABA Number: 021000021
Account Number: 1884827674
Swift Code: CHASUS33

Interactive Internet™ Bidding

You can now bid with Heritage's exclusive *Interactive Internet™* program, available only at our web site: HA.com. It's fun, and it's easy!

1. Register online at:
   HA.com

2. View the full-color photography of every single lot in the online catalog!

3. Construct your own personal catalog for preview.

4. View the current opening bids on lots you want; review the prices realized archive.

5. Bid and receive immediate notification if you are the top bidder; later, if someone else bids higher, you will be notified automatically by e-mail.

6. The *Interactive Internet™* program opens the lot on the floor at one increment over the second highest bid. As the high bidder, your secret maximum bid will compete for you during the floor auction, and it is possible that you may be outbid on the floor after Internet bidding closes. Bid early, as the earliest bird wins in the event of a tie bid.

7. After the sale, you will be notified of your success. It's that easy!

Interactive Internet™ Bidding Instructions

1. **Log Onto Website**

   Log onto **HA.com** and chose the portal you're interested in (i.e., coins, comics, movie posters, fine arts, etc.).

2. **Search for Lots**

   Search or browse for the lot you are interested in. You can do this from the home page, from the Auctions home page, or from the home page for the particular auction in which you wish to participate.

3. **Select Lots**

   Click on the link or the photo icon for the lot you want to bid on.

4. **Enter Bid**

   At the top of the page, next to a small picture of the item, is a box outlining the current bid. Enter the amount of your secret maximum bid in the textbox next to "Secret Maximum Bid." The secret maximum bid is the maximum amount you are willing to pay for the item you are bidding on (for more information about bidding and bid increments, please see the section labeled "Bidding Increments" elsewhere in this catalog). Click on the button marked "Place Absentee Bid." A new area on the same page will open up for you to enter your username (or e-mail address) and password. Enter these, then click "Place Absentee Bid" again.

5. **Confirm Absentee Bid**

   You are taken to a page labeled, "Please Confirm Your Bid." This page shows you the name of the item you're bidding on, the current bid, and the maximum bid. When you are satisfied that all the information shown is correct, click on the button labeled, "Confirm Bid."

6. **Bidding Status Notification**

   One of two pages is now displayed.

   a. If your bid is the current high bid, you will be notified and given additional information as to what might happen to affect your high bidder status over the course of the remainder of the auction. You will also receive a Bid Confirmation notice via email.

   b. If your bid is not the current high bid, you will be notified of that fact and given the opportunity to increase your bid.

Mail Bidding at Auction

Mail bidding at auction is fun and easy and only requires a few simple steps.

1. Look through the catalog, and determine the lots of interest.

2. Research their market value by checking price lists and other price guidelines.

3. Fill out your bid sheet, entering your maximum bid on each lot.

4. Verify your bids!

5. Mail Early. Preference is given to the first bids received in case of a tie. When bidding by mail, you frequently purchase items at less than your maximum bid.

Bidding is opened at the published increment above the second highest mail or Internet bid; we act on your behalf as the highest mail bidder. If bidding proceeds, we act as your agent, bidding in increments over the previous bid. This process is continued until you are awarded the lot or you are outbid.

An example of this procedure: You submit a bid of $100, and the second highest mail bid is at $50. Bidding starts at $51 on your behalf. If no other bids are placed, you purchase the lot for $51. If other bids are placed, we bid for you in the posted increments until we reach your maximum bid of $100. If bidding passes your maximum: if you are bidding through the Internet, we will contact you by e-mail; if you bid by mail, we take no other action. Bidding continues until the final bidder wins.

Telephone Bidding

To participate by telephone, please make arrangements at least one week before the sale date with Customer Service, 1-800-872-6467, Ext. 150.

We strongly recommend that you place preliminary bids by mail, fax, or Internet, even if you intend to participate by telephone. On many occasions this dual approach has helped reduce disappointments due to telephone problems, unexpected travel, late night sessions and time zone differences, etc. We will make sure that you do not bid against yourself.

Mail Bidding Instructions

1. **Name, Address, City, State, Zip**
Your address is needed to mail your purchases. We need your telephone number to communicate any problems or changes that may affect your bids.

2. **References**
If you have not established credit with us from previous auctions, you must send a 25% deposit, or list dealers with whom you have credit established.

3. **Lot Numbers and Bids**
List all lots you desire to purchase. On the reverse are additional columns; you may also use another sheet. Under "Amount" enter the maximum you would pay for that lot (whole dollar amounts only). We will purchase the lot(s) for you as much below your bids as possible.

4. **Total Bid Sheet**
Add up all bids and list that total in the appropriate box.

5. **Sign Your Bid Sheet**
By signing the bid sheet, you have agreed to abide by the Terms of Auction listed in the auction catalog.

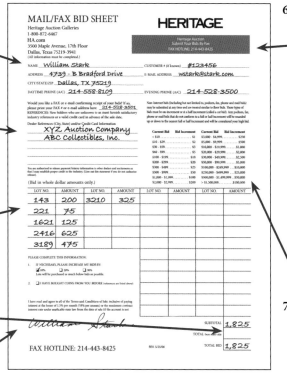

6. **Fax Your Bid Sheet**
When time is short submit a Mail Bid Sheet on our exclusive Fax Hotline. There's no faster method to get your bids to us *instantly*. Simply use the **Heritage Fax Hotline number: 214-443-8425**.

When you send us your original after faxing, mark it "Confirmation of Fax" (preferably in red!)

7. **Bidding Increments**
To facilitate bidding, please consult the following chart. Bids will be accepted on the increments or on the half increments.

The official prices realized list that accompanies our auction catalogs is reserved for bidders and consignors only. We are happy to mail one to others upon receipt of $1.00. Written requests should be directed to Customer Service.

Upcoming Auctions

HERITAGE HA.com
Auction Galleries

HA.com/Consign
Call Our Consignment Hotline
Toll Free: 800-872-6467 Ext. 222

Over 275,000 Online Registered Bidder-Members • Annual Sales Exceeding $500 Million

United States Coin Auctions	Location	Auction Dates	Consignment Deadline
Milwaukee ANA	Milwaukee, WI	August 8-12, 2007	June 29, 2007
Long Beach	Long Beach, CA	September 26-29, 2007	August 16, 2007
Dallas	Dallas, TX	November 6-9, 2007	September 30, 2007

World Coin Auctions	Location	Auction Dates	Consignment Deadline
Long Beach	Long Beach, CA	September 26-29, 2007	August 9, 2007

Currency Auctions	Location	Auction Dates	Consignment Deadline
Long Beach	Long Beach, CA	September 28-29, 2007	August 9, 2007

Fine & Decorative Arts Auctions	Location	Auction Dates	Consignment Deadline
Pre Columbian/Native American Art	Dallas, TX	October 2007	July 26, 2007
Decorative Arts	Dallas, TX	October 2007	August 4, 2007
Harrisburg Collection of Western Art and Photography	Dallas, TX	October 18-20, 2007	August 9, 2007
Fine Art	Dallas, TX	November 2007	August 29, 2007

Jewelry & Timepieces Auction	Location	Auction Dates	Consignment Deadline
Estate Jewelry & Timepieces	Dallas, TX	Dec 3, 2007	October 11, 2007

Vintage Movie Posters Auctions	Location	Auction Dates	Consignment Deadline
Vintage Movie Posters	Dallas, TX	July 13, 2007	May 21, 2007
Vintage Movie Posters	Dallas, TX	November 9-10, 2007	Spetember 17, 2007

Comics Auctions	Location	Auction Dates	Consignment Deadline
Comics & Original Comic Art	Dallas, TX	July 27-28, 2007	June 12, 2007
Comics & Original Comic Art	Dallas, TX	August 1-4, 2007	June 19, 2007

Music & Entertainment Memorabilia Auctions	Location	Auction Dates	Consignment Deadline
Music Celebrity & Hollywood Memorabilia	Dallas, TX	October 6-7, 2007	August 14, 2007

Political Memorabilia & Americana Grand Format Auctions	Location	Auction Dates	Consignment Deadline
Civil War Auction	Gettysburg, PA	June 24-25, 2007	Closed
Space Exploration	Dallas, TX	September 20, 2007	July 30, 2007
Grand Format Autographs Auction	Dallas, TX	October 25-26, 2007	September 2, 2007

Sports Collectibles Auctions	Location	Auction Dates	Consignment Deadline
Dallas	Dallas, TX	October 27, 2007	September 4, 2007

HERITAGE TUESDAY INTERNET COIN AUCTIONS • HERITAGE SUNDAY INTERNET COIN AUCTIONS • Begin and end every Tuesday and Sunday at 10 PM CT.

HERITAGE TUESDAY INTERNET CURRENCY AUCTIONS • Begin and end every Tuesday at 10 PM CT.

HERITAGE WEEKLY INTERNET COMICS AUCTIONS • Begin and end every Sunday of each month at 10 PM CT.

HERITAGE WEEKLY INTERNET MOVIE POSTER AUCTIONS • Begin and end every Sunday at 10 PM CT.

HERITAGE MONTHLY MARKETPLACE AUCTIONS • Wednesdays/Thursdays between 4 PM and 10 PM CT. This Auction has a combination of lots consisting of Americana, Sports, Comics, Fine Art/Decorative Arts, Texas Art and Music Memorabilia lots.

HERITAGE MONTHLY INTERNET SPORTS AUCTIONS • Begin and end, on the last Sunday of each month at 10 PM CT.

Heritage Numismatic Auctions, Inc.: California 3S 3062 16 63, Florida AB0000665, Ohio 2006000050. Currency Auctions of America: Florida AB 2218. Auctioneers: Leo Frese: Florida AU 0001059. California 3S 3062 16 64, NewYork City 1094965. Samuel Foose: North Carolina 8363, Texas 00011727, California 3S 3062 16 65, Florida AU3244, Ohio 2006000048, and New York City 0952360. Jim Fitzgerald: Texas Associate 16130. Mike Sadler: Texas Associate 16129. Scott Peterson: Texas 00013256, Florida AU3021. Robert Korver: North Carolina 8363, Ohio 2006000049, Texas 13754, Wisconsin 2412-52, and New York City 1096338.

5/04/07

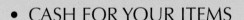

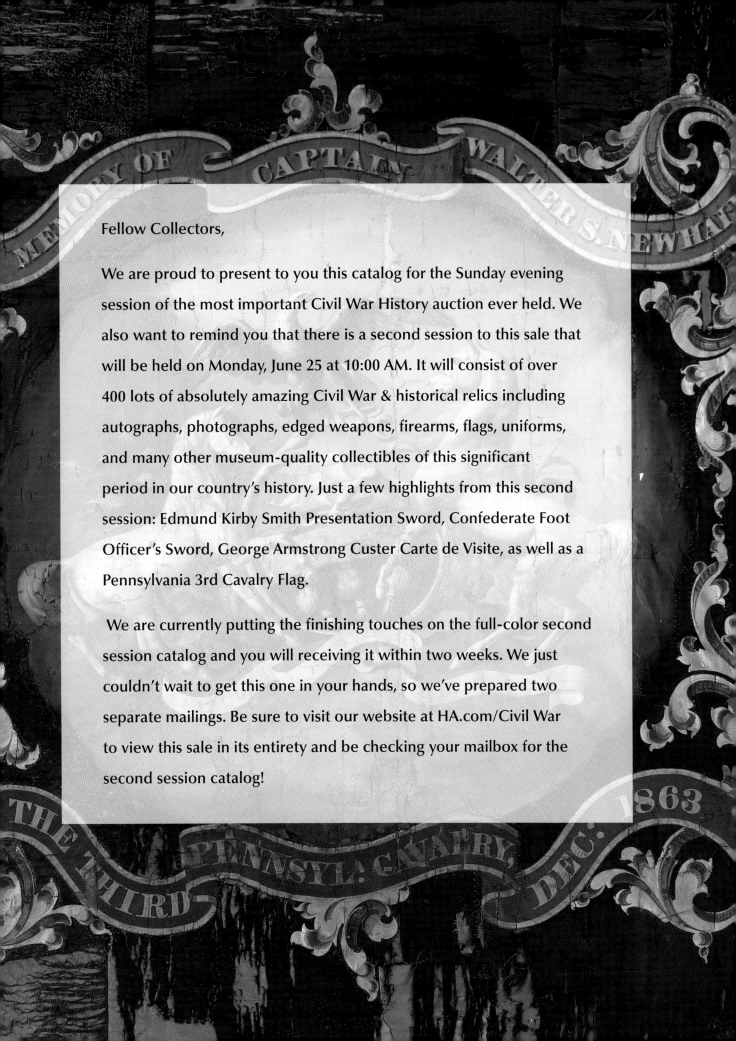

Fellow Collectors,

We are proud to present to you this catalog for the Sunday evening session of the most important Civil War History auction ever held. We also want to remind you that there is a second session to this sale that will be held on Monday, June 25 at 10:00 AM. It will consist of over 400 lots of absolutely amazing Civil War & historical relics including autographs, photographs, edged weapons, firearms, flags, uniforms, and many other museum-quality collectibles of this significant period in our country's history. Just a few highlights from this second session: Edmund Kirby Smith Presentation Sword, Confederate Foot Officer's Sword, George Armstrong Custer Carte de Visite, as well as a Pennsylvania 3rd Cavalry Flag.

We are currently putting the finishing touches on the full-color second session catalog and you will receiving it within two weeks. We just couldn't wait to get this one in your hands, so we've prepared two separate mailings. Be sure to visit our website at HA.com/Civil War to view this sale in its entirety and be checking your mailbox for the second session catalog!

CHAPTER INDEX
SESSION ONE

VIRGINIA & MOSBY

SESSION ONE
Live, Internet, and Mailbid Auction #663
Sunday, June 24, 2007, 3:00 PM ET, Lots 72001-72279
Gettysburg, Pennsylvania

A 19.5% Buyer's Premium Will Be Added To All Lots.
Visit HA.com/CivilWar to view scalable images and bid online.

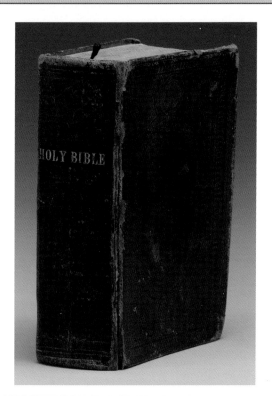

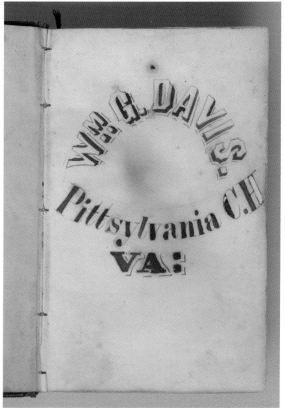

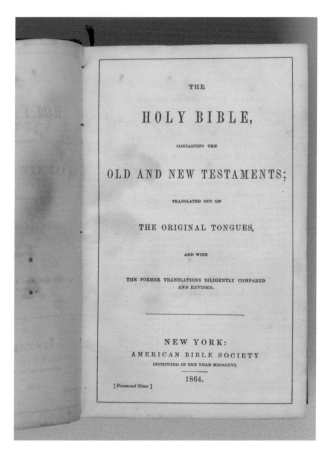

72001   THE BIBLE OF WILLIAM G. DAVIS, COMPANY E. 6TH VIRGINIA CAVALRY – Private William G. Travis owned and carried this leather bound bible as he fought with Company E the 6th Virginia Cavalry during the course of the Civil War. Organized in November 1861, the unit fought with Jackson in the Valley Campaign, at Second Manassas, Brandy Station and Spottsylvania. They took part in Early's Shenandoah Campaign and the Appomattox Campaign as well. Interestingly, only three of the men in this surrendered at Appomattox, instead making their way through the Union lines and back home.

Measuring 3½" x 5", this Holy Bible was printed by the American Bible Society at New York City in 1864. It is quite possible that this bible was taken from a Union soldier since the frontispiece has embossed upon it "Young Men's Christian Association. Elmira, NY". The YMCA gave more than one million bibles to soldiers going off to war. This is one of the few that survive, making its way into a Confederate's hands. Private Davis' name and unit are handwritten in pencil into the frontispiece while it is elaborately stenciled on the next page along with "Pittsylvania C. H." representing Pittsylvania Court House where Davis' unit once fought and likely captured this Bible.

The bible is in overall good condition with some cracking of the leather at the binding.

Provenance: *The Tharpe Collection of American Military History*

Exhibited: *The Liberty Heritage Society Museum*

Estimate: $800-$1,000

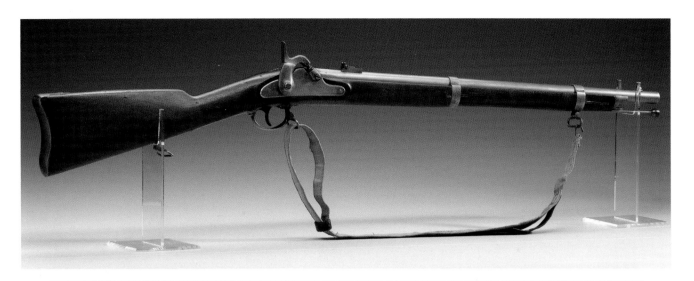

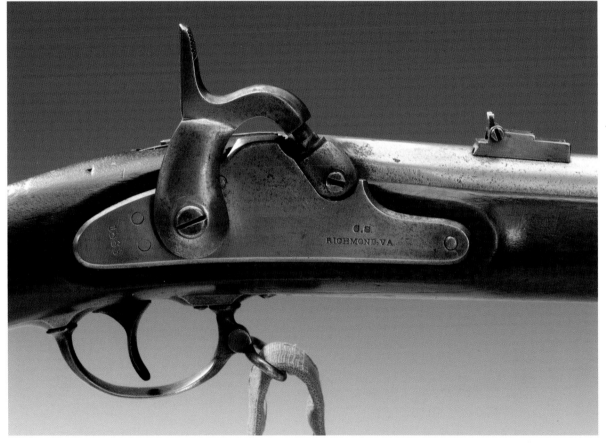

**72002   A RARE 'CS' RICHMOND CARBINE WITH ITS LINEN SLING – THE 4TH VIRGINIA CAVALRY 'BLACK HORSE TROOP',
GETTYSBURG** – This rare CS Richmond carbine was used by the famed Black Horse Troop originally formed at Fauquier County, Virginia in 1859. Serving from First Manassas to Appomattox Court House they were involved in every major battle and campaign of the Army of Northern Virginia.

This CS Richmond 25" carbine was carried by Private Courtney Washington of Company H of the 4th Virginia Cavalry, the famed Black Horse Troop. He fought at Williamsburg, Second Manassas and Gettysburg before being captured near Warrenton, Virginia on November 10, 1863. He was exchanged several months later and paroled on May 3, 1865.

This weapon is in fine condition with a nice even light gray patina and its 33" linen sling attached. The full stock of the gun is securely fastened by two barrel bands and has the distinctive third sling swivel attached at the underside of the buttstock as well as at the upper band and at the trigger guard. Measuring 41" in length, the carbine has the iron front sight that is distinctive to this cavalry weapon as well.

This is a rare cavalry carbine identified to the famous Black Horse Troop, made even more rare since it was carried by Courtney Washington, who was captured after Gettysburg in Warrenton, Virginia in 1863. This gun must have seen action in the battle of Gettysburg.

Provenance: *The Tharpe Collection of American Military History*

Exhibited: *The Liberty Heritage Society Museum*

Estimate: $15,000-$20,000

72003   PRIVATE BOWMAN, 12TH VIRGINIA CAVALRY – CASED 1/9TH PLATE TINTYPE OF A CONFEDERATE CAVALRYMAN FROM VIRGINIA. Posing here is young William Bowman, a private in Co. "K", 12th Virginia Cavalry. Hardly the glamorous stereotype of a dashing Virginia cavalier, Bowman wears simple civilian clothing that is only somewhat militarized by the addition of three uniform buttons. His low-crowned hat also carries a modest regimental designation by having "12 VA" pinned to its face. The tintype is in excellent condition. Its gutta-percha case has floral designs on both sides . Despite his mild agrarian appearance, William Bowman rode with a hard-riding rebel cavalry regiment. The 12th Virginia checked a Federal advance at Brandy Station and, the following year, participated in the famed "Beefsteak Raid" that netted some 2,000 head of Yankee cattle for the starving defenders of Petersburg. Bowman survived the war, dying in 1923. He is buried in his native Shenandoah County.

Provenance: *The Tharpe Collection of American Military History*

Exhibited: *The Liberty Heritage Society Museum*

Estimate: $1,000-$2,000

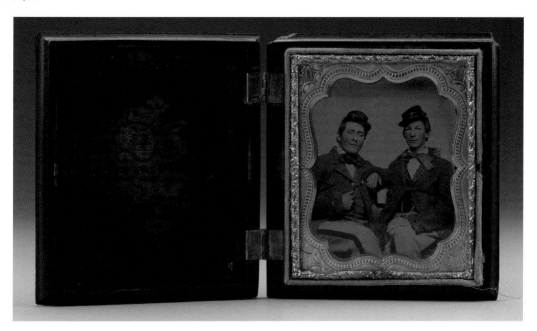

72004   CASED 1/6TH PLATE RUBY AMBROTYPE OF TWO VIRGINIA CONFEDERATES. These early war Southern volunteers wear matching non-regulation frock coats, high crowned kepis and grey trousers striped down the side. A unit designation peeks from behind the bill of one kepi, however not enough of it is visible to determine its meaning. It is possible that these young men were members of the Richmond Howitzers, an elite artillery battalion that served in the Army of Northern Virginia throughout the war. This image is in excellent condition in every respect. Its gutta-percha case is molded on both sides with a scene showing a medieval lady on horseback being followed by a child with a dog. Two corners on the back panel are chipped.

Provenance: *The Tharpe Collection of American Military History*

Exhibited: *The Liberty Heritage Society Museum*

Estimate: $600-$800

72005   PRIVATE EDWIN D. BROWN-COMPANY C, "LAUREL BRIGADE", 9TH VIRGINIA CAVALRY, MALTESE CROSS BADGE – A superb, unique and one of only a handful of Confederate insignia known to exist. Beautifully made by a Virginia jeweler in Maltese cross fashion surrounded by a wreath and engraved in the center, "E.D.B. - Co. C, 9th VA. Caval. - Con. States - 1861." Private Brown enlisted in July of 1861 and was wounded in action during the Battle of Gettysburg July 1st, 1863. An extremely rare and historically important Confederate cavalryman's insignia from the hard fighting and famous Laurel Brigade. Absolutely superb and never before on the market as the only silver Laurel brigade insignia known to exist.

Provenance: *The Flayderman Collection; The Tharpe Collection of American Military History*

Exhibited: *The Liberty Heritage Society Museum*

Estimate: $8,000-$10,000

72006   LT. WEEDON 4TH VIRGINIA CAVALRY CASED 1/9TH PLATE RUBY AMBROTYPE – Shown here is a very determined trooper, 2nd Lieutenant Robert Weedon, Co. "A", 4th Virginia Cavalry. Weedon enlisted as a sergeant shortly after Virginia seceded. He was promoted to 2nd lieutenant on September 1, 1863 and was paroled with that rank at war's end. As part of Stuart's cavalry, the 4th Virginia saw hard service with the Army of Northern Virginia. Weedon had a horse shot out from under him in 1862 and some two years later was himself wounded. He survived, received the UDC's Southern Cross of Honor and lived until 1906. Here the subject wears a plumed Hardee hat with a non-regulation brass bugle device on its face. Eagle buttons line the front of Weedon's coat and he tightly grips his sheathed saber. What appears to be a standard Model 1851 U.S. sword belt plate peeks out from behind the sword's pommel. A few peripheral scrapes to the ambrotype's emulsion, else an excellent image with good surfaces. The case is missing its lid.

Provenance: *Weedon Family of Warrenton, Virginia; The Tharpe Collection of American Military History*

Exhibited: *The Liberty Heritage Society Museum*

Estimate: $550-$750

Virginia Black Horse Troop Flag Bearer

72007   SGT. HAMILTON, 4TH VIRGINIA CAVALRY CASED 1/9TH PLATE AMBROTYPE OF IDENTIFIED CONFEDERATE CAVALRYMAN. The sitter in this portrait is Hugh Hamilton, flag bearer for The Black Horse Troop, Co. "H", 4th Virginia Cavalry. Perhaps Virginia's most famous cavalry company, the Black Horse Troop was formed in 1859 and served in every major campaign waged by the Army of Northern Virginia. Trooper Hamilton, who enlisted on March 15, 1862, is shown wearing the classic pleated "battle shirt" favored by so many rebels and is unarmed. The photographer has lightly tinted Hamilton's cheeks and green shirt giving the overall effect of this being a color image. Housed in a gutta-percha Union case embossed with foliate designs on both sides. A splendid Confederate image in very fine condition.

An old note accompanying this image states that Hamilton died in camp. Not so. He survived the war, dying in 1928 after a career of public service which included being Treasurer of Fauquier County, Virginia.

Provenance: *Hamilton family; The Tharpe Collection of American Military History*

Exhibited: *The Liberty Heritage Society Museum*

Estimate: $550-$750

"Keep this for my sake..."

72008 PRIVATE JOHN GAITHER, A VIRGINIA CONFEDERATE 1/9TH PLATE AMBROTYPE. Two notations by the portrait's sitter, one in pencil and the other penned, are written inside the case behind the image as follows: *"John R. Gaither. August the 11th 1863"* and *"presented Martha G Gaither August 12th 1863 keep this for my sake"*. Shown is a clean shaven young rebel wearing a grey jacket with shoulder straps and side pockets. Eight two-piece Virginia State Seal buttons are visible. The plate shows moderate haloing and has a few peripheral spots that do not detract in the least. The case is quite worn, however, and lacks the velvet matt on the lid's underside.

By the time this haunting portrait was made, John Gaither had been a Confederate soldier for two years and had witnessed some of the fiercest fighting of the Civil War. Private Gaither joined the "Rockingham Rangers" - Co. "B", 10th Virginia Infantry - in the valley town of Harrisonburg on July 9, 1861. His regiment made history with the Army of Northern Virginia from Second Manassas through Appomattox. Gaither himself was wounded at Cedar Run, Virginia on August 9, 1862. He recovered, fought on and was with his regiment until captured at Spotsylvania C.H. on May 12, 1864. He would never see the Old Dominion again. After a hot summer at Point Lookout, Maryland, Gaither was sent to the notorious prison camp at Elmira, New York. He died there of disease on September 9, 1864 and inhabits Gravesite 301 in Elmira's Woodlawn National Cemetery.

Provenance: *The Tharpe Collection of American Military History*

Exhibited: *The Liberty Heritage Society Museum*

Estimate: $1,500-$2,500

72009 AN AMBROTYPE OF GEORGE W. GAITHER, CO. C 10TH VIRGINIA INFANTRY – 1/9TH PLATE AMBROTYPE. The sitter here is Private George W. Gaither , Co."C", 10th Virginia Infantry. A fantastic Confederate grey kepi tops his civilian clothing. The image is in excellent condition and is housed in a partial case that has been converted to a wall frame by the addition of a small brass attachment loop. The leather cover on the case half is well worn. Private Gaither enlisted in Harrisonburg, Virginia on April 10, 1862. His regiment, the 10th Virginia, was largely recruited in the Shenandoah Valley and would see heavy action throughout the course of the war. With the exception of Sharpsburg, the 10th fought in the major campaigns endured by the Army of Northern Virginia. Only a handful of its soldiers survived to sign paroles at Appomattox.

Provenance: *The Tharpe Collection of American Military History*

Exhibited: *The Liberty Heritage Society Museum*

Estimate: $1,500-$2,500

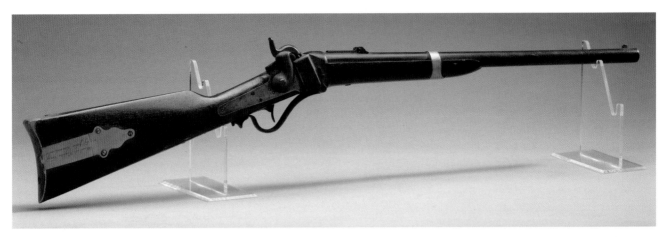

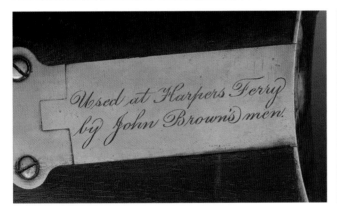

72010   A 'JOHN BROWN' SHARPS CARBINE – USED AT THE HARPER'S FERRY RAID – One of the rarest firearms with a Civil War connection, a Sharps carbine of the lot used by abolitionist John Brown and his men as they raided the federal armory at Harper's Ferry, Virginia, an event that helped spark the fire of the United States Civil War. This gun has appeared in the literature of noted firearms historian Norm Flayderman and has an excellent provenance and historical background. A Model 1853 in .52 caliber, this gun was part of the shipment sent to Brown; it eventually made its way to the famous raid on the armory. As noted in Frank Sellers' *Sharps Carbines* (Benafield Publishing) on page 97, this particular carbine is in the range of the guns that were used by the men. Brown had moved the weapons to the Kennedy farm in Maryland near Harper's Ferry and used them to execute his raid on the night of October 16, 1859. Armed with his Sharps carbines, including this one, and his 'John Brown pikes', long spear-like weapons, the party took over the U.S.armory. They were soon forced out by a troop of marines led by then-Colonel Robert E. Lee and Lieutenant J.E.B. Stuart, an irony of history that initially shocked Northerners, but eventually led to a sympathetic view of Brown's cause and directly led to the outbreak of the Civil War. Brown was wounded, tried and convicted of treason and hanged in December 1859.

This historical weapon has a 21½" barrel and is stamped 'Sharp's Manufg. Co Hartford, Conn' on the top of the barrel. It has walnut stocks, an even gray patina and bears the serial number 16150. It has an attractive brass buttplate, barrel band and patchbox which is engraved as follows: *Used at Harper's Ferry by John Brown's Men*. On the tang by the serial number 'Sharps Patent 1848' is stamped.

This is an historic Sharps carbine that was used in a singularly important event in American history.

Provenance: *The Norm Flayderman Collection; The Tharpe Collection of American Military History*

Exhibited: *The Liberty Heritage Society Museum*

Estimate: $70,000-$80,000

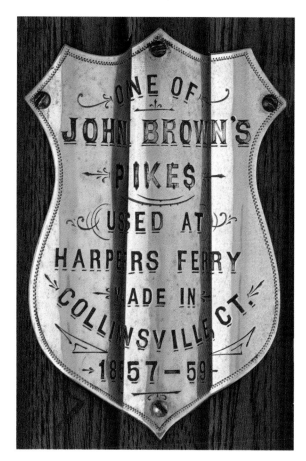

72011   A 'JOHN BROWN PIKE' USED AT THE HARPER'S FERRY RAID, SERIAL NUMBER 846
– This 80" pike was used at the famed Harper's Ferry Raid executed by abolitionist John Brown and his party of 18 men. Brown, a native of Connecticut, became an ardent abolitionist from early in life being raised by a highly religious, anti-slavery family. Having first been trained in the ministry, he became involved in the tannery business, traveled to Kansas to assist the anti-slavery movement and became a violent abolitionist, ultimately organizing his ill-fated raid on the Harper's Ferry, Virginia Armory which resulted in his wounding, capture and execution. It was during the preparation for this raid that he ordered these pikes from his native Connecticut. At 80" long, they are wooden spear-like weapons tipped with a 10" blade and were used to subdue the minimal force guarding the armory, after which Brown's forces seized their rifles and barricaded themselves inside.

This John Brown pike actually was used at the raid by Brown's forces, all of whom were either killed or captured as the raid was put down by then-Colonel Robert E. Lee and Lieutenant J. E. B. Stuart who, along with 90 Marines, stormed the armory. A silver commemorative plaque has been affixed to the pike at 6" down from the blade on the wooden shaft as follows: *One of John Brown's Pikes Used at Harpers Ferry, Made in Collinsville, Ct., 1857-1859.* The metal haft on the pike itself is numbered '846' and is in very good condition as is the wood which is of a very nice grain and completely intact.

This is a very rare weapon used at one of the most significant events in American history that sparked the outbreak of the Civil War.

Provenance: *The Norm Flayderman Collection, The Tharpe Collection of American Military History*

Exhibited: *The Liberty Heritage Society Museum*

Estimate: $15,000-$20,000

72012   AN OIL PORTRAIT OF JOHN BROWN, ABOLITIONIST AND RAIDER ON HARPER'S FERRY – John Brown was born in Connecticut in 1800, the son of parents who were religiously devout, continually teaching him the evils of slavery. While training for the ministry early in life, he eventually went into the tannery business. An incident where he witnessed the mistreatment of a black slave child spurred him to fight to rid the nation of slavery for the rest of his life, one that ended after his unsuccessful raid on the Harper's Ferry Armory on October 16, 1859. While he and his band of raiders captured the armory, within two days Colonel Robert E. Lee and Lieutenant J. E. B. Stuart had arrived with a troop of 90 marines who stormed the armory and defeated Brown's 18-man raiding party.

Brown, wounded in the assault, was tried, convicted and subsequently hanged in December of that year. This 5½" x 7½" oil portrait in the oval was completed after his death. Nicely matted with a thick linen mat, the portrait is framed in a heavy 2" walnut frame with a plaque attached reading 'John Brown 1800-1859'. It depicts Brown in the well-known pose with his long beard, black three-piece suit and collar. While the artist is unknown, the subject of the fiery Brown is captured by the face; inspired, wrinkled and serious, staring down the viewer with his passion. There is very slight crackling of the image at the bottom right, otherwise this portrait is in excellent condition.

Provenance: *The Tharpe Collection of American Military History*

Exhibited: *The Liberty Heritage Society Museum*

Estimate: $20,000-$25,000

72013   ORIGINAL PENCIL SKETCH OF SLAVES FLEEING THE BATTLE AT PETERSBURG, on paper, 8" x 5", tipped on to a folded sheet of paper, artist *"S. H. S.",* captioned *"Escape of "contrabands" from Col. Avery's estate near Petersburg Virginia."* The sketch is uniformly toned with a few light spots of foxing. There are old crease marks present with a 1.25" split and 2.5" split in two of the folds that could easily be repaired. There is an old paper tape repair on the back of the sketch. There is a negligibly small piece missing from the bottom edge that does not affect either the text or drawing. The Avery House figures prominently in the literature of the battle and siege at Petersburg. The large house was used as an observation post and at one time the headquarters of Union General Governor K. Warren. Very good condition.

Estimate: $800-$1,000

72014   A PENCIL DRAWING, CIRCA 1830'S DEPICTING AN OVERSEER LECTURING SLAVES – This fascinating scene of an overseer lecturing a line of slaves has the pencil notation 'Scene of "Ariadne Estate - Moral Lecture". The 10" x 7" sketch is made in pencil and depicts two overseers, their backs to the artist, lecturing the slaves with a dog lying on the ground behind them. The slaves are dressed in knee breeches giving this sketch a dating of the 1830's. The sketch, pencil on paper, is framed in an antique 16" x 13" heavy walnut Anthony and Scovill stamped frame secure in the back by two sturdy metal bands.

This is a very interesting piece that shows some foxing at the top and at the bottom middle. The tongue and groove frame shows wear but is very sturdy and well-made.

Estimate: $1,500-$2,500

Magnificent Early Ambrotype of Future Confederate Brigadier General Robert Doak Lilley

72015   CONFEDERATE GENERAL ROBERT D. LILLEY – COMMANDED JUBAL EARLY'S BRIGADE – CASED 1/2 PLATE AMBROTYPE – Augusta County, Virginia, ca. 1861. Two stalwart officers, wearing the dark blue frock coats of Virginia militia, pose for an unknown photographer on the eve of the Civil War. A piece of black paper taped to the underside of the image carries a penciled note identifying the men as *"Col. Rob't D. Lilley"* and *"Maj. James Templeton"*. A young Robert Doak Lilley is the smaller officer to the right. The subjects' fancy militia officer's swords have ivory grips and hang from belt rigs outfitted with two-piece Virginia plates. Their uniform coats are double-breasted and secured with fourteen Virginia State Seal buttons. An additional Virginia button is visible on Templeton's plumed cocked hat, which rests on a table by his side. Red coloring has been added to the officers' sashes and yellow has been lightly applied to their swords and epaulettes. The ambrotype is in a gutta-percha case having an embossed Elizabethan scene on the lid. The case has minimal chipping to the edges.. The image itself is in excellent condition with only a few trivial spots in the fields.

Robert D. Lilley (1836 - 1886) was a captain with the Lee Rifles of Augusta County, Virginia. This militia unit became Co. "C" of the 25th Virginia Infantry. At Sharpsburg, Lilley, although only a captain, commanded his regiment by virtue of being the senior officer on the field. By Gettysburg he was a major. A brigadier's commission was forthcoming on June 2, 1864 when Lilley was given command of Jubal Early's old brigade. The new general served the rest of the war in the Shenandoah, being captured and losing his right arm at the battle at Winchester against Sheridan, when he burned the valley. Despite his general's rank, Lilley was better known after the war and may be seen in the famous Reconstruction-era group photo with General Lee that was taken at the Greenbrier Hotel.

The other officer in this picture is Major James Templeton of Virginia, who was a surgeon for Lee's Army of Northern Virginia.

Provenance: *The Tharpe Collection of American Military History*

Exhibited: *The Liberty Heritage Society Museum*

Estimate: $20,000-$25,000

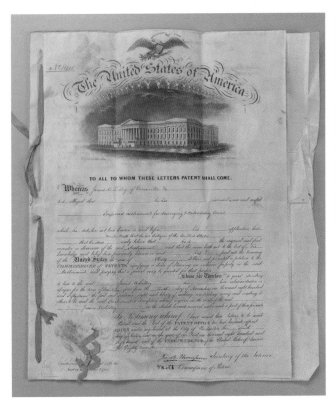

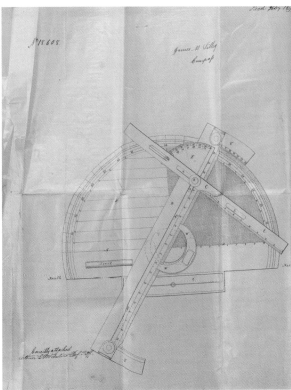

72016   CONFEDERATE STATES PATENT, MECHANICAL DRAWING AND DOCUMENT ARCHIVE TO JAMES M. LILLEY FATHER OF CSA GENERAL ROBERT DOAK LILLEY. An important archive that includes a United States patent document, number 18608, dated November 10, 1857, 14.75" x 19.75", granted to James M. Lilley of Greenville, Virginia for an improved instrument for surveying and calculating areas including the original schematic diagram illustrating the device and a hand-written description of the device. On the reverse of the official patent document is the hand-written official Confederate States patent transfer information, dated February 4, 1862, with the Confederate Patent Office wax seal and signed by Rufus R. Rhodes, commissioner of patents. These Confederate transfer patents are quite scarce. There are only about 266 known examples cataloged. The document is in very good condition with fold creases as expected and only moderate age toning to the paper. The description document has a 6" tear at the center fold. Included with this rare Confederate transfer patent is a two-page, 8.25" x 13.5", document and hand-drawing by James Lilley which describes his measuring device. It is likely that this document was produced in the early stages of the patent process. Further highlighting the group is a four-page advertising document, 8.5" x 11", circa 1866 from the Stuart, Lilley & Company, real estate agents based in Staunton, Virginia, advertising the aforementioned surveying and calculating instrument and including endorsements from satisfied users. Noteworthy among those users is General G. T. Beauregard. The document is in fine condition with only light age toning to the first page.

James M. Lilley (1802-1875) was also an important military presence in the Virginia Militia in the early part of the 19th century. Included in this lot is a one page hand-written document 12.5" x 7.75", dated 1824, county of Augusta, noting the return men and arms of the 1st Battalion of the 93rd regiment of the Virginia Militia which is endorsed by Lilley, their commander. The document is a bit rough around the edges and toned with age but still in very good condition. A similar one page oblong document, 29.5" x 8", dated November 1, 1820 to January 13, 1821, in very good condition is also included. Of particular interest is a Commonwealth of Virginia commission document, signed by Virginia governor David Campbell, 10" x 8", on parchment, with Virginia Commonwealth wax seal, dated November 14, 1838, promoting James M. Lilley to the rank of colonel of the 93rd regiment of the infantry of the line, in the seventh brigade and third division of the Virginia Militia. Lastly is a printed circular of this Lilley patent for a 'survey transom' which was endorsed by Robert E. Lee, Beauregard and others. This is an important archive to an important Virginia family. Lilley's son, Robert Doak Lilley, was a much-celebrated Confederate Brigadier General. He fought at many important battles during the war.

Provenance: The Tharpe Collection of American Military History

Exhibited: The Liberty Heritage Society Museum

Estimate: $10,000-$15,000

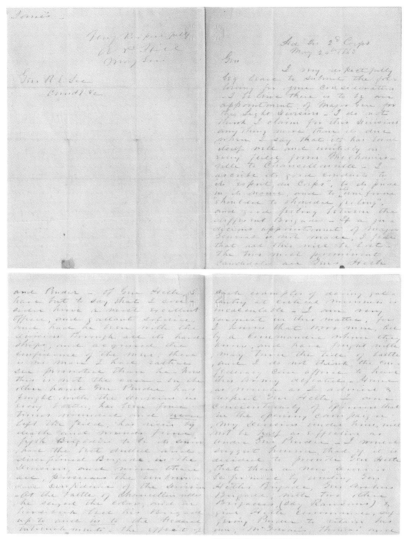

72017   A. P. HILL, AUTOGRAPH LETTER SIGNED TO ROBERT E. LEE, REQUESTS APPOINTMENT AS MAJOR GENERAL − four pages, 7.5" x 9.75", "*Hd Qrs 2d Corps*", May 24, 1863, to General Robert E. Lee. This, one of Major General A. P. Hill's few surviving Civil War letters, was written while the Army of Northern Virginia was being reorganized in the wake of Stonewall Jackson's death. Lee needed a new divisional commander before launching what would become the Gettysburg Campaign. The most likely candidates were brigadiers Harry Heth and William Pender. As it happened, both generals were promoted and led divisions into Pennsylvania. Here A. P. Hill makes a passionate recommendation as follows: "*I very respectfully beg leave to submit the following for your consideration. I believe there is to be one appointment of Major Gen for the Light Division. I do not think I claim for this Division anything more than is due, where I say that it has borne itself well and unitedly on every field from Mechanicsville to Chancellorsville. I ascribe its good conduct to its 'espirit du Corps', to its pride in its name, and to its uniform 'shoulder to shoulder feeling', and good feeling between the different Brigades. If a judicious appointment of Major General is not made, I fear that all this will be lost. The two most prominent candidates are Gens Heth and Pender. Of Gen Heth, I have but to say that I consider him a most excellent officer, and gallant soldier, and had he been with the Division through all its hardships, and acquired the confidence of the men, there is no man I had rather seen promoted than he. Now this is not the case. On the other hand Gen Pender has fought with the Divisions in every battle, he has been four times wounded and never left the field, he has risen by death and wounds from fifth Brigadier to be its senior, had the best drilled and disciplined Brigade in the Division, and more than all, possesses the unbridled confidence of the Division. At the battle of Chancellorsville he seized the colors, and on horseback led his Brigade up to and in to the Federal intrenchments(sp). The effect of such examples of daring gallantry at critical moments is incalculable. I am very earnest in this matter, for I know that 10,000 men, led by a commander whom they know and have fought with may turn the tide of battle, and I do not think the Confederacy can afford to have this army defeated. Hence, as much as I admire & respect Gen Heth, I am conscientiously of opinion that in the opening campaign my Divisions under him, will not be half as effective as under Gen Pender. I would suggest however, that if it is decided to promote Gen Heth that then a new division be formed by uniting Gen Heth's Brigade, Gen Archers Brigade, with two other Brigades, (say Ramseurs) & give Heth command, suffering Pender to retain his men, McGowan's, Thomas' and Lane's. Very Respectfully,*". Evenly toned with smoothed fold lines and still crisp. Very fine condition.

Provenance: *The William Turner Collection*

Estimate: $15,000-$20,000

72018   C.S.A. GENERAL HENRY HETH AUTOGRAPH LETTER SIGNED – A. P. HILL JOINS THE CONFEDERACY – *"H Heth Lt Col & A.Q.M.G"*. Two pages with docketing, lined 5" x 8" paper, Quartermaster Generals Office Richmond, May 7, 1861, to the governor of Virginia [John Letcher]. Just days after Heth had resigned from the U.S. Army and joined the Confederate Army, he petitions the governor to offer his friend A. P. Hill a commission. Heth, at this time, was serving as Robert E. Lee's quartermaster in Virginia. The letter reads, in part: *"I take the liberty of calling your attention to the fact that A. P. Hill late of the U.S. Army is now here...and offers his services to Va, his native state. He graduated at West Point in 1847 [as did Heth]- he brings with him great military experience, especially as an officer of Light Artillery, his standing in the Army is very high...Mr. Hill has been offered by the Governor of Ky a Colonelcy, but declined on principal, thinking it was his duty to offer his services to his Native State..."* There is an additional note beneath written and signed by John Strode Barbour, Jr., confirming and corroborating what Heth had said about Hill's qualifications. Barbour was, at the time, president of the Orange and Alexandria Railroad.

Whether influenced by Heth's recommendation or not we don't know, but Hill was commissioned colonel of the Virginia 13th Infantry Regiment two days after this letter was written. He distinguished himself at First Manassas, receiving a promotion to brigadier general the following February, to major general later in 1862, and to lieutenant general in 1863 after the death of Stonewall Jackson (at about the same time Heth was promoted to major general). Heth and Hill would both have controversial roles to play at Gettysburg and both were personal favorites of General Robert E. Lee. Hill was killed on April 2, 1865 at Petersburg, just days before Lee's surrender at Appomattox Court House. He had once said that he had no desire to see the collapse of the Confederacy and he didn't. This historical letter is in very fine condition with original folds.

Provenance: *The William Turner Collection*

Estimate: $2,500-$3,500

West Point Diploma Signed by Robert E. Lee,
Robert Selden Garnett, and Fitz-John Porter

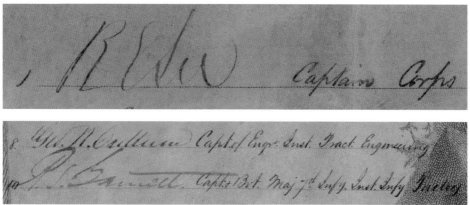

72019   FANTASTIC ASSOCIATION WEST POINT DIPLOMA SIGNED BY ROBERT E. LEE AS SUPERINTENDENT, ALSO SIGNED BY FUTURE CONFEDERATE GENERAL ROBERT S. GARNETT AND FUTURE UNION GENERAL FITZ-JOHN PORTER – An oversized vellum DS "*R E Lee*", 1 page, 17" x 23", West Point, New York, June 16, 1854, being the West Point diploma awarded to Michael R. Morgan of the State of Louisiana upon completion of his degree. Also signed by Robert Selden Garnett, the first Confederate general officer to die in action during the Civil War (he fell at Carrick's Ford on July 13, 1861); and Fitz-John Porter, who signs twice, first at the bottom as an instructor and again at top left as the recorder. Document bears usual folds and mild discoloration as is common with vellum, however all signatures remain very visible with the Lee rating about an "8". On the verso, a former owner notes how he came to have possession of the diploma: "*This diploma was taken by me from a sailor (at Pilot Town on the Mississippi river) belonging to the steam gunboat Montgomery, who was taking it as a rebel trophy. Month of April 1862 Edward S. Lamid [?].*" A highly desirable diploma valuable on many levels and in very good condition.

Estimate: $5,000-$7,000

72020   BRADY *CARTE DE VISITE* OF ROBERT E. LEE, CUSTIS LEE AND WALTER TAYLOR, M. B. Brady & Co. backmark on verso, copyright information on lower obverse margin. Shortly after the surrender at Appomattox, Matthew Brady received permission to visit General Lee's home in Richmond. The ensuing photography session resulted in some of the most enduring portraits of the general. This particular image shows General Lee with his son, Custis, and aide-de-camp Colonel Taylor. Light foxing, else fine condition.

Estimate: $1,500-$2,000

72021   ROBERT E. LEE SIGNED CDV, "*R E Lee,* Vannerson & Jones, Richmond, Virginia backmark. General Lee is shown here in profile as photographed by Julian Vannerson in 1863. Lightly toned with Lee's characteristic signature being fully legible. Very fine condition with crisp edges.

Estimate: $5,000-$6,000

72022   RARE EARLY WARTIME SIGNED CDV OF ROBERT E. LEE, with "*R E Lee*" in lower field. Matted and framed to 6.75" x 10". This rare *carte de visite* by Minnis & Cowell of Richmond carries a lithograph made from the firm's 1863 full length photograph of the great general. Lee is depicted here in his prime as a Confederate commander. Nice, large signature on an exceptionally clean print. Very fine condition.

Estimate: $4,000-$5,000

Lee notes his favorite photographic portrait:
"The best large one I have seen of myself is by Gardner of Washington City; a profile likeness."

72023   AUTOGRAPH LETTER SIGNED BY ROBERT E. LEE ACCOMPANIED BY A SIGNED *CARTE DE VISITE* OF THE GENERAL IN CONFEDERATE UNIFORM − Single page ALS "*R E Lee*", 5.25" x 8.25", Lexington, Va., April 15, 1867, to a Rev. William C. Greene enclosing a CDV. He writes: "*I have the houner* [sic] *to state in reply to your note of the 11 ulto; that I know of no good full sized photograph of Mr. Davis & Genl Beauregard. The best large one I have seen of myself is by Gardner of Washington City; a profile likeness. I enclose a small one taken during the war by Vannesian & Co., Richmond, Vir.*" Accompanied by a signed version of the CDV of Lee bearing a bold signature. Albumen is very clean save a few spots and there is evidence of minor restoration done to the mount. The letter bears mat burn at margins, and professional restoration has replaced a few spots of paper loss. Otherwise a nice pairing of Lee items, referencing one of the most noted American photographers of his time, Alexander Gardner.

Estimate: $8,000-$12,000

Facing the ultimate destruction of the Shenandoah Valley by Union General Philip H. Sheridan, Robert E. Lee expresses his frustration with independent commands: "they are worthless for the general service, and not of much value for that into which they enter. Their object is not so much to do duty as to be near their homes"

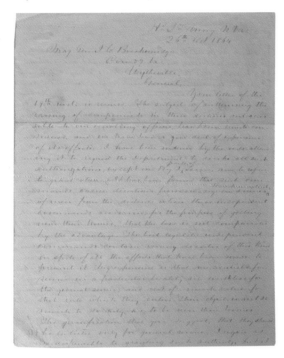
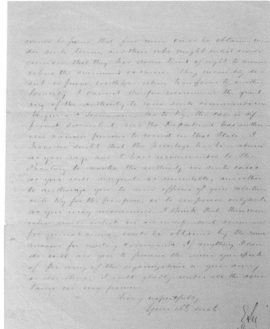

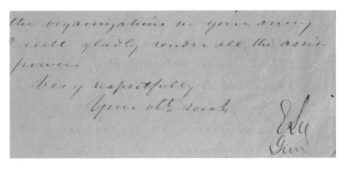

72024   EXCEPTIONAL CIVIL WAR-DATED LETTER SIGNED TO MAJ. GENERAL JOHN CABELL BRECKENRIDGE, 2 pages, 8.25" x 10.25", "*Hd Qrs Army N Va*", Oct. 26, 1864, informing him that the supposed benefits of independent commands are outweighed by their accompanying disadvantages. He writes, in large part: "*The subject of authorizing the raising of companies in those districts not accessible to our enrolling officers, has been much considered, and we have had a good deal of experience of its effects. I have been induced by the evils attending it to request the Department to revoke all such authorizations, except in Ky & parts of Tenn, and to refuse to grant others. It has been found that such commands cause desertions from our regular armies to such an extent, of men from the districts where these independent commands are raised, for the purpose of getting near their homes, that the loss is not compensated by the advantage. The best regulated independent commands contain many deserters of this kind in spite of all the efforts that have been made to prevent it. My experience is that men enlisted for service in a particular locality are worthless for the general service, and not of much value for that into which they enter. Their object is not so much to do duty as to be near their homes. the qualifications you suggest that they should be enlisted only for general service, I regard as indispensable to granting such authority, but it would be found that few men could be obtained under such terms and those who might enlist would consider that they had some kind of right to remain where the command is raised. they invariably desert or prove worthless when transferred to another locality. I cannot therefore recommend the granting of the authority to raise such commands in Virginia & Tennessee. As to Ky, the case is different somewhat, and the Department has authorized various persons to recruit in that state. I have no doubt that the privilege has been abused as you say, and I have recommended to the Secretary to revoke the authority in such cases as you will designate as unsuitable, and either to authorize you to send officers of your selection in Ky for the purpose, or to empower only such as you may recommend...*"

The Shenandoah Valley Campaign of summer and fall 1864 marked the end of Confederate rule in Virginia. It was Union Major General Sheridan's major victories there which brought President Lincoln his much needed and timely successes. In early October, the Union cavalry systematically destroyed everything in their path, including civilian property. This three day period, Oct. 6-8, 1864, would become known as "The Burning". Some resistance was provided by Confederate General Jubal A, Early, first launching an attack driving Federal forces northward, and then through a brilliant surprise attack at dawn on Oct. 19th crushing two-thirds of the Union infantry. Nevertheless, Sheridan's superior forces were able to rally and counter-attack routing the Confederates at the Battle of Cedar Creek. Sheridan's forces would go on to inflict four major defeats on Early, ultimately marking the beginning of the end for the Confederacy. Lee's only hope for the Confederacy lay in conscription and in the substitution of disabled soldiers and blacks for the still able-bodied soldiers on detail. Lee had been hopeful that replacements from farmers who had harvested their crops would help swell Confederate ranks, but by the end of October, at the time this letter is written, he accepted the futility and considered only conscription into the army as a solution. Unfortunately, conscripts were few.

An excellent letter filled with Lee's military insight and experience as he faces unavoidable defeat. The "R" in Lee's signature is light, the result of a faulty nib as the remainder is quite bold; overall the letter is in near fine condition with dark and legible text.

Estimate: $12,000-$15,000

72025   SUPERB POST-WAR PORTRAIT OF ROBERT E. LEE SIGNED, "*R E Lee*", oval albumen print, 6" x 8.25", framed to an overall 11.75" x 13.5". Lee, as President of Washington College, wears a civilian suit in this Matthew Brady portrait taken in May, 1869. The former Confederate general consented to a studio sitting while in Washington visiting his old adversary, President U. S. Grant. The image has an earlier wooden back carrying a frame-maker's label dated September 25, 1860 and made out to a Mr. W.F. Stansbury. The whole has been placed in a more recent wood and gilt frame. An attractive deep sepia toning with a large, bold signature make this a great Lee presentation. A small water stain in the lower field does not detract in the least. Accompanying this piece is a photocopy of the frame's back with a typed note of provenance that no longer exists. It reads: "W. F. Stansbury, Jr. attended Washington & Lee College in Lexington, Virginia. Was in Ford Theatre when President Lincoln was shot, 1865. The picture of Robert E. Lee belonged to him. You will note on back of frame that it has the name of W. F. Stansbury 1860, that was our grandfather, and the frame was purchased long before the picture was framed. This frame was given to me many years later by Aunt Lily Durden, the back was in an old frame."

Estimate: $12,000-$15,000

Writing to his wife during the Bermuda Hundred Campaign, General George E. Pickett details: "...Dearest we have just taken a 'fourth of July' to your sweet self while the Enemy fired their usual salute at 12 m[idnight]. the national salute to day they fired with solid shot..."

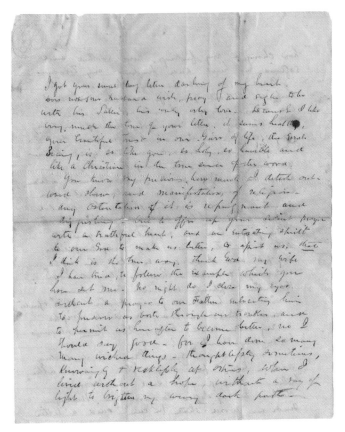
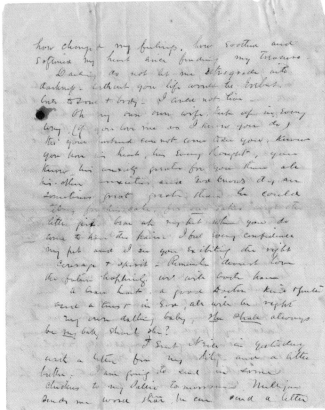

72026   GENERAL GEORGE PICKETT, EXTREMELY RARE CIVIL WAR-DATED AUTOGRAPH LETTER SIGNED TO HIS PREGNANT WIFE, LASALLE "SALLIE" CORBETT PICKETT, 4 pages, 8" x 9.75", from the Howlett Line during the Bermuda Hundred Campaign, July 4, [1864]. He pens, in part:

"I got your sweet long letter darling of my heart. does not your husband wish, pray and sigh to be with his Sallie, his only only love. Dearest I like very much the tone of your letter, it seems healthy, your bountiful trust in our Giver of life, the Great Being, is so like you, so holy, so humble and like a Christian in the true sense of the word.

You know my precious, how much I detest outward show, and manifestations of religion - any ostentation of it is unpleasant and disgusting - but it offers up your silent prayer with a truthful heart, and as untrusting spirit to our God to make is better, to assist us, that I think is the true way. Thank God my wife I have tried, to follow the example which you have set me. No night do I close my eyes without a prayer to our Father enlisting him to preserve us both through our troubles, and to permit us hereafter to becomes better, no i should say good - for I have done so many wicked things - thoughtlessly sometimes, knowingly & recklessly at others, when I lived without a hope, without a ray of light to brighten my weary dark path, ho changed my feelings, how soothed and softened my heart and finding my Treasure.

Darling to not let me retrograde into darkness - without you life would be [?] to soul and body - i could not live.

Oh my own wife, keep up in every way (if you love me as I know you do) tho' your husband cannot come to see you, know you have his heart, his every thought, you know his anxiety greater for you than all his other anxieties and God knows they are sometimes great - greater than he could tell for his sake - for our sakes - get the little girl's [?] up my pet when you do come to have this pain. I feel every confidence my pet and I see you exhibiting the right courage & spirit - Remember dearest love the future hopefully we will both have a brave heart, a good Doctor kind & gentle and a trust in Eve, all will be right my own darling baby, She shall always be my baby shant she?... Auld Dearest we have just taken a 'fourth of july' to your sweet self while the Enemy fired their usual salute at 12 m[idnight]. the national salute to day they fired with solid shot..."

Pickett is excessively rare war-dated correspondence, and such a personal missive is particularly desirable. With archival repairs at fold separations, including the addition of paper loss; however ink is very bold and all text remains legible, overall condition is very good.

Estimate: $6,000-$8,000

Pickett's Division Appomattox Surrender Document

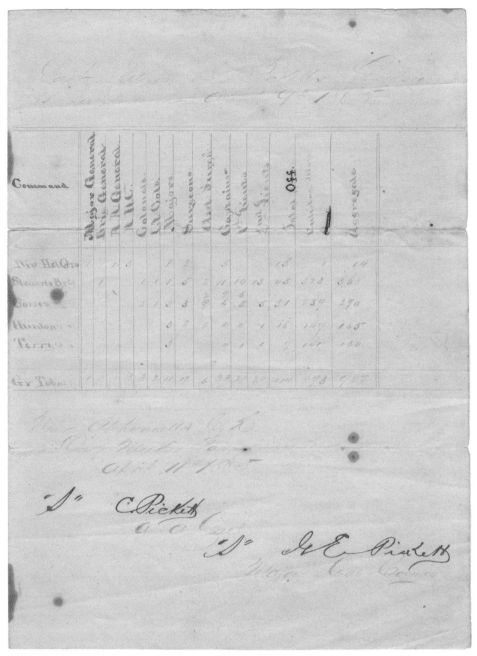

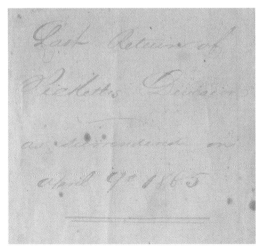

72027   RARE CONFEDERATE 'PICKETT SURRENDER' DOCUMENT SIGNED BY HIS BROTHER, "*C. Pickett*" by Major Charles F. Pickett and "G E Pickett", secretarially by Charles Pickett, one page with docketing, 7.5" x 10", April 11, 1865, Appomattox C. H., Virginia. This "*Last Return of Pickett's Division as surrendered April 9, 1865*" is composed of a hand-drawn grid on which the troops of each brigade of the division is noted. Officers and enlisted men are counted separately, with the former being further divided by rank. A total strength of just 987 makes up this tattered remnant of George Pickett's reduced division. Major General Pickett was not present to sign this final roll, leaving his brother, the division's Assistant Adjutant General, the task of doing so. Considerable fading to title, some stains, smoothed folds with small splits. Very good condition.

Provenance: *The William Turner Collection*

Estimate: $4,500-$6,500

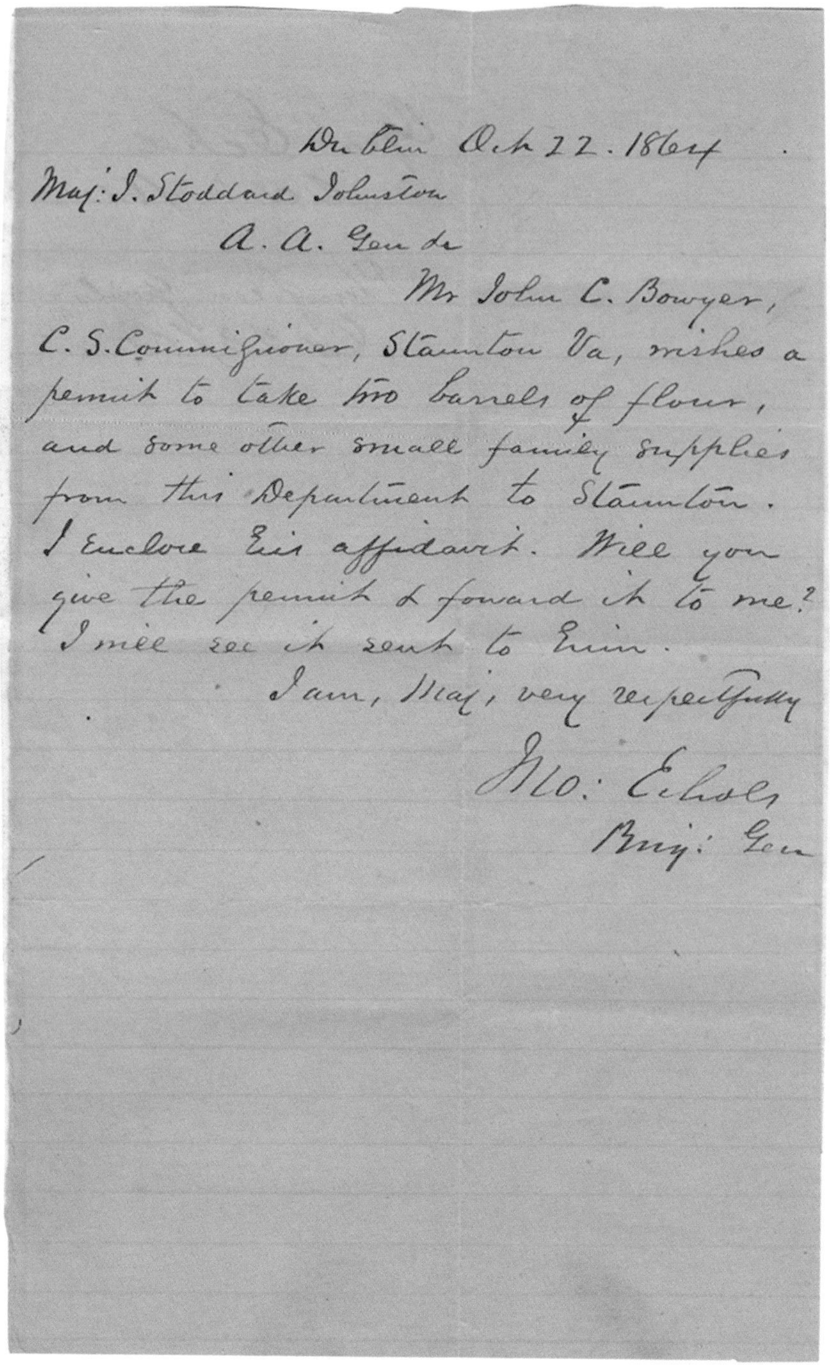

Dublin Oct 22. 1864

Maj: J. Stoddard Johnston
A. A. Gen'l

Mr. John C. Bowyer,
C. S. Commissioner, Staunton Va, wishes a
permit to take two barrels of flour,
and some other small family supplies
from this Department to Staunton.
I enclose his affidavit. Will you
give the permit & forward it to me?
I will see it sent to him.

I am, Maj, very respectfully

Jno: Echols
Brig: Gen

72028   C.S.A. GENERAL JOHN ECHOLS AUTOGRAPH LETTER SIGNED *"Jno: Echols"*. One page with verso docketing, 5" x 8", lined paper, Dublin [Virginia], October 22, 1864, to Maj. J. Stoddard Johnston, assistant adjutant general. Written while Echols was in charge of the District of Southwestern Virginia, it reads in full, *"Mr. John C. Bowyer, C.S. Commissioner, Staunton Va, wishes a permit to take two barrels of flour, and some other small family supplies from this Department to Staunton. I enclose his affidavit. Will you give the permit & forward it to me? I will see it sent to him."* Fine condition with original folds, a bit of toning away from the text and mounting tape traces on verso.

Provenance: *The William Turner Collection*

Estimate: $800-$1,000

72029 CONFEDERATE GENERAL EDWARD JOHNSON POW AUTOGRAPH LETTER SIGNED TO EMILY S.B. BRUNE, THE ANGEL OF FORT DELAWARE, 2 pages, 5" x 8", Fort Delaware, May 29, 1864, thanking her for all of the food and sundries received. He writes, in part: "*I thank you for the box you and my other friends must not send me any more clothing... as I am taxing your generosity too much. I am now well supplied with almost everything...*" Additional content includes chatty news regarding mutual friends.

Johnson (1816-1873) was a graduate of West Point and entered the Confederate service as Col. of the 12th Georgia under Robert S. Garnett. Johnson would fall prisoner twice during the war, and this letter is written during his first incarceration after he was captured at the "Bloody Angle". He would be released at the end of the summer of 1864, at which time he would be re-assigned to the 2nd Corps., Army of Tennessee. He would end the war as a POW, being released in July 1865 after being captured during the Battle of Nashville.

The letter is in very good condition with the usual mail folds, with a 1.5" tear at bottom of first page, with no paper loss and easily mended. Accompanied by the original transmittal cover, bearing a Delaware City postmark, a great association letter and relic of Emily Brune whose many good works on behalf of Confederate prisoners, earned her the nickname, "Angel of Fort Delaware".

Provenance: *The William Turner Collection*

Estimate: $1,000-$2,000

Custis Lee Writes to the Future "Beast" of Andersonville

72030   GEORGE WASHINGTON CUSTIS LEE WAR-DATED AUTOGRAPH LETTER SIGNED TO GENERAL JOHN WINDER AT 'CASTLE THUNDER' "*G.W.C. Lee*". One page, 8" x 8.75", Confederate States of America Executive Department letterhead, Richmond, Virginia, August 25, 1863, dark ink to John Henry Winder. This Lee ALS is addressed to General John Henry Winder, who was at the time commander of all Union military prisoners east of the Mississippi, later known as the "beast" of Andersonville. The letter here reads in full: "*Neither Col. Browne nor myself have any knowledge of a communication from Welsh or Wash confirmed in Castle Thunder. There is no such name recorded in our book, nor can I find such a paper on our desks. I will however search further, and inform you of the result. Col. Browne and myself are the only ones present just now. I have the honor to be very respectly G.W.C. Lee.*"

Besides being the son of Robert E. Lee, Custis Lee served as aide-de-camp to Confederate President Jefferson Davis during most of the Civil War, and had been named a brigadier general exactly two months before he wrote this letter to Winder. Castle Thunder was an infamous military prison in Richmond, where spies, political prisoners, and soldiers accused of treason were housed. The letter is fine, with minimal edge wear, light pencil initials toward the bottom, and one small crease at the bottom right of the document. Usual folds present, and three thin strips of archival tape can be seen along the edges on the verso of the letter. A wonderful correspondence from one Richmond general to another.

Provenance: *The William Turner Collection*

Estimate: $2,000-$3,000

Correspondence Between Sandie Pendleton and Jubal Early Regarding the General's Arrest

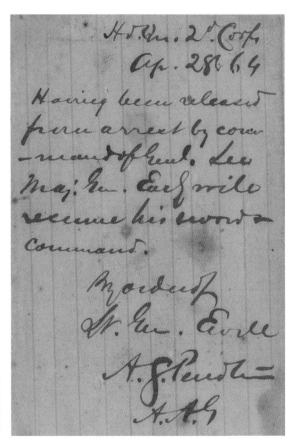

72031   ALEXANDER SWIFT (SANDIE) PENDLETON AUTOGRAPH LETTER SIGNED TO JUBAL EARLY ABOUT HIS ARREST, "*A. S. Pendleton*", one page, 7" x 9.25", Headquarters, 2nd Corps, April 25, 1864, to General Jubal Early. It reads: "*The Lieut. General commanding directs me to say, that, your remarks upon the enclosed communication of Maj. Brown and G. are considered improper. They are therefore returned for withdrawal. Your attention is now called to the enclosed paper, marked A, showing the decision of the War Dept. and the comdg. General as to the method of transmission of orders in the Staff Departments. The instructions given by Maj. Brown to Maj. Hale are in accordance with their decision.*" Stains, smoothed folds. Very good condition.

JUBAL EARLY AUTOGRAPH LETTER SIGNED TO SANDIE PENDLETON, "*JA Early*", one page, 7.5" x 10", Jamesville Ford, April 26, 1864, to Sandie Pendleton. It reads in part as follows: "*I desire to know what is the extent of the limits of my confinement. When you informed me that I was placed under arrest, the condition was that I would confine myself to the limits of my camp. I wish to know if this means the camp of my quarters or of my division…*". A verso endorsement signed "*A. S. Pendleton*" reads, "*The limits of Maj Gen J A Early's arrest are extended to embrace all points within the limits of this army.*". Backed with clear linen, old repairs with light stains.

JUBAL EARLY AUTOGRAPH LETTER SIGNED, REGARDING HIS ARREST, "*J A Early*", one page, 7.25" x 10", Jamesville Ford, April 28, 1864, to Sandie Pendleton. It reads: "*I received last night on my return the paper containing General Lee's remarks in regard to the subject of my arrest. Am I to understand that I am released from arrest and resume my command without any further delay?*" Endorsed by Pendleton on verso as follows: "*Having been released from arrest by command of Genl. Lee Maj Gen. Early will resume his sword & command. By orders of Lt Gen Ewell A.S Pendleton A,A,G.*". Fading, stains, separation along upper fold.

Provenance: *The William Turner Collection*

Estimate, all three documents as one lot: $8,000-$10,000

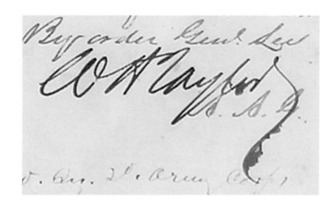

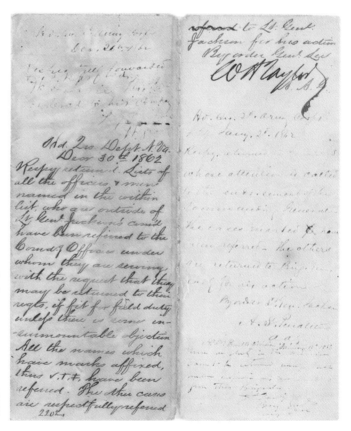

**72032   THOMAS "STONEWALL" JACKSON AND JUBAL A. EARLY AUTOGRAPH
ENDORSEMENTS SIGNED ON VERSO OF AN AUTOGRAPH LETTER SIGNED BY HARRY T. HAYS**
– AES "*T Jackson*" , Dec. 26, 1862 reading, in part: "*Respectfully forwarded & acknowledged*" on verso of an ALS
dated Nov. 19, 1862, by Hays requesting detached officers and soldiers be returned to duty to the 1st Louisiana
Brigade commanded by Hays. In addition to Jackson, the verso bears two AESs by Jubal E. Early, the first dated
Dec. 25, 1862 and reading: "*This paper is respectfully forwarded with the request that such officers and men as
are not on extra duty in the division may be returned to the brigade.*" The second endorsement, dated "*HdQrs
Ewells Division January 12, 1863*" reads: "*Men on duty in the division can't be returned unless we under proposi-
tion* [unintelligible] *from this brigade.*" Integral sheets, each measuring 7.75" x 9.75", have been detached and
framed side by side in a gild frame measuring 27.5" x 17.5". Unfortunately Jackson's holograph and signature
have all but faded, and Early's endorsements fare only slightly better and rate a "4".

Estimate: $6,000-$7,000

Jefferson Davis Asks for Governor Brown's Cooperation in Transporting Arms by Rail in Georgia

72033   JEFFERSON DAVIS CIVIL WAR-DATED MANUSCRIPT LETTER SIGNED *"Jeffer. Davis".* 1½ pages, 7.75" x 9.75" lined paper, Richmond, Virginia, March 20, 1863, to Joseph E. Brown, the governor of Georgia, at Milledgeville. It reads, in full: *"In reply to my telegram of the 17th inst. in reference to the seizure of the State railroad, Genl. Bragg states, that the Ordnance officer at Atlanta asserted to him that the Road refused to transport arms and ammunition, and that then he (Genl. Bragg) directed the Quartermaster's Department to use force, if necessary, to get forward these supplies, and report the facts to Col. Hadly, Supt. The supplies were forwarded, and force was not used. Such action on the part of the officers of the Confederate Government is much to be regretted; although force, as I am glad to learn, was not used in this case. Genl. Bragg has been directed in the event of similar difficulties hereafter arising, to call upon you for assistance, with the assurance that you will be always ready to further, in any proper manner, the interests of our common cause."*

This is an excellent content letter as these two gentlemen were not the best of friends. Although Brown was an ardent secessionist, instrumental in Georgia following leaving the Union in January 1861, he did not care for the policies of Jefferson Davis and even referred to him as a tyrant. Brown's opposition to the power of the central Confederate government did much to hamper the general southern war effort though he was generally popular with his constituency. His continuing resistance to all Confederate attempts to seize the Western and Atlantic Railroad related to the situation discussed in this letter. Interestingly, a few years after the war, Brown became president of the aforementioned railroad. Stains along a repair in the lower right corner, else fine with a particularly bold signature.

Estimate: $2,000-$3,000

J.E.B. Stuart writes the Governor of Virginia: "Any one endowed with reason... and a common sense of justice, except Mr [Jefferson] Davis, must agree that such an outrageous distinction has no foundation whatever in either law, justice, or reason..."

72034   J.E.B. STUART AUTOGRAPH LETTER SIGNED TO HENRY A. WISE, GOVERNOR OF VIRGINIA, 3 pages, 7.75" x 9.75", Fort Leavenworth, Kansas Territory, March 23, 1857. With an ALS by Wise to fellow Virginian, John B. Floyd on the verso; and an endorsement signed by future Confederate General **Samuel Cooper.** Stuart writes, in large part: *"I have the honor to transmit herewith copies of testimonials this day furnished direct to the Comy General of Subsistence U.S.A. to be laid before the Hon. Secy of War. Availing myself of your kindness and the disposition expressed in your note of Decr 22d 1856, to Serve a Son of my lamented father, I send you certified copies of these papers for your assistance, premising that a vacancy may occur any day and be filled before you can hear it even at Richmond, which makes it necessary to urge an appointment for the first vacancy before it occurs. I have made it a simple application to the Hon. Sec Mr. Floyd through the proper channels, and have not gone out of my way for testimonials confining myself entirely to the officers of rank with whom I am now serving; but there are some remarks which I deem it not improper to make to you, in which I promise to be as brief as possible. The appointment which I seek, is the only way in which a Lieutenant of the line can anticipate the tardy progress of promotion as a kind of Brevet, retaining at the same time his lineal or Regimental rank as Lieutenant, but having the pay and emoluments of Captain. And in as much as his appointment as Captain in the Staff Dept. gives him no additional command or lineal rank, it can not be considered an encroachment upon the rights of Lieutenants Senior to him. In fact, the provisions of the Law making it entirely at the discretion of the presidents as, regards the selection, it would be quite reasonable to give such an appointment, other things equal, to the junior because the Senior will soon get his promotion in the regular way, entitling him to all the prerogatives of Captain. I understand (I have not seen them yet) that the Edition of the Army Regulations published just as Mr Davis made his exit from the War Dept, have the extraordinary [last word is underlined for emphasis] provision that no m[ounted]d officer shall be eligible to appointment in the Staff Departments. I can only account for such an absurdity by supposing that the unjust proscription [last word is underlined] of the Subalterns of the mounted Regt has been so long practically [last word is underlined] followed out, that it has passed unnoticed into the code. Any one endowed with reason common sense and, a common sense of Justice, except Mr Davis, must agree that such an outrageous distinction has no foundation whatever in either law, justice, or reason. From my limited acquaintance with Mr Floyd I cannot for a moment believe that he will allow himself to be trammeled by such a Regulation. The law expressly provides that the appointments shall be filled by the President by selection form the Subalterns (not of the Artillery & Infantry alone, but) of the line of the Army. And there have been appointments from mounted Regts. to the Staff - though I must say they are 'like angels visits few & far between'. You will find by the Army Register that in the entire Subsistence Dept three are from the Infantry and the remaining nine from the Artillery. It can not be denied that the Cavalry portion of our Army perform by far the most arduous duty belonging to the Service, ought it not then have a share of the immunities of the Service. I respectfully request that upon a full consideration of whatever claims, if any, I have you will if you feel justified in doing so, at your earliest convenience bring my appointment, to fill the first vacancy which occursin the Subsistence Dept U.S. Army, to the favorable consideration of the Hon[orab]le Sec. of War and the President."*

Gov. Wise writes on the verso: *"I enclose to you the within testimonials, well assured as I am that you will give to them all due consideration."* an endorsement signed by Samuel Cooper forwards the matter to the *"Commissary of Subsistence".* With the usual mail folds, and very clean save light soiling on the last page which would have served as the exterior; letter bears and excellent Stuart signature with rank as *"1st Lt 1st Cav."*.

Estimate: $10,000-$15,000

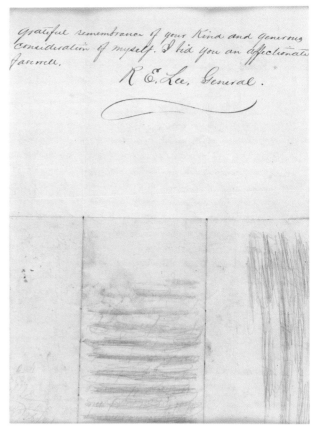

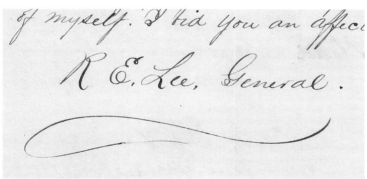

72035   1865 MANUSCRIPT "OFFICIAL" COPY OF ROBERT E. LEE'S FAREWELL ADDRESS, also known as "General Order No 9." 1¼ pages, 8" x 10" letterhead of the State of Virginia Executive Department at Richmond (1863 watermark), Head Quarters A.N.V., April 10, 1865. A war-date transcription on official State of Virginia letterhead of Lee's touching and heartfelt farewell to his troops in the Army of Northern Virginia. It reads, in full:

> *"After four years of arduous service marked by unsurpassed courage and fortitude, the Army of Northern Va has been compelled to yield to overwhelming numbers and resources.*
>
> *I need not tell the brave survivors of so many hard fought battles who have remained steadfast to the last, that I have consented to this result from no distrust of them. But feeling that valor and devotion could accomplish nothing that would compensate for the loss that must have attended the continuance of the contest, I determined to avoid the sacrifice of those whose past services have endeared them to their countrymen.*
>
> *By the terms of the agreement, Officers & men can return to their homes & remain until exchanged. You will take with you the satisfaction that proceeds from the consciousness of duty, faithfully performed; and I earnestly pray that a merciful God will extend to you his blessing & protection. With an unceasing admiration of your constancy and devotion to your Country, and a grateful remembrance of your kind and generous consideration of myself, I bid you all an affectionate farewell. R. E. Lee, General"*

This very well could be Virginia Governor William 'Extra Billy' Smith's personal copy of the Order since he fled the capital to Lynchburg and then to Danville taking government documents with him, directly responsible for the survival of documents such as these.

Provenance: *The Tharpe Collection of American Military History*

Exhibited: *The Liberty Heritage Society Museum*

Estimate: $8,000-$12,000

1851 University of Virginia Autograph Book Signed By John S. Mosby

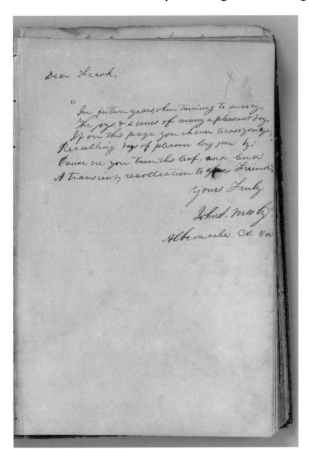

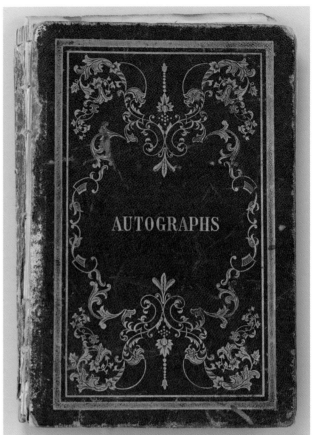

72036 **UNIVERSITY OF VIRGINIA AUTOGRAPH BOOK SIGNED BY MOSBY,** 174 pages, 8vo (5.5" x 8.5"), tooled gilt leather covers, 1851, published in Philadelphia by P. S. Duval. In addition to the blank pages typical of 19th century autograph books, this one carries several engravings specific to UVa. These include a likeness of Thomas Jefferson, a view of nearby Monticello, The Rotunda and portraits of several faculty members. The book belonged to student Frank P. Fulton of Portsmouth, Virginia and is inscribed with sentimental verse by 51 of his classmates, each naming his hometown and/or county and state. The most famous signatory here is none other than future Confederate partisan ranger John Singleton Mosby. He writes: "*Dear Frank, 'In future years, when turning to survey/ The joy & scenes of many a pleasant day / If on this page you chance to cast your gaze / Recalling days of pleasure long gone by / Pause ere you turn this leaf, and lend / A transient recollection to a friend'. Yours Truly John S. Mosby Albermarle Co. Va*".

A year after these lines were penned, the diminutive Mosby would be expelled from the university for shooting campus bully George Turpin. Mosby's actions, although of a defensive nature, earned him a certain notoriety and not a little jail time. It is highly probable that, like Mosby, many of the students named in this book would go on to serve the Confederacy some years hence. Further research will tell. Interestingly over 20% of the signers are from Alabama, making that state's presence at UVa second only to Virginia's natural dominance of the student body. The binding of this small book is loose with its worn front cover and several pages being separated from the spine. Internal foxing with moderate damp stains. Overall good condition.

Estimate: $4,000-$6,000

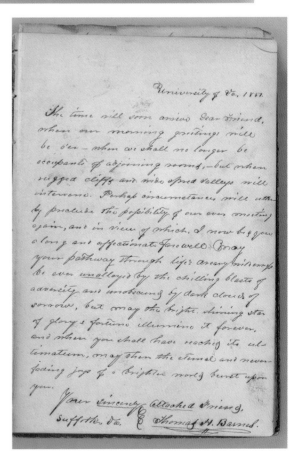

Mosby Reports Home: "The people threw open their doors to us... Mr. Palmer says ours is the finest Company that has come to Richmond, not in dress (for I can tell you we look like savages) but in fighting qualities..."

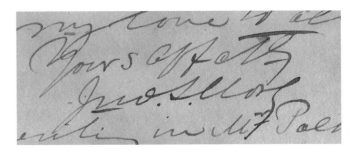

72037 JOHN SINGLETON MOSBY WRITES HOME TO HIS MOTHER DURING THE OPENING DAYS OF THE WAR – Early war-dated ALS *"Jno S. Mosby"*, 4 pages, 5" x 7.75", Richmond, June 18, 1861, to his mother recounting his march to Richmond. He writes, in part: *"Dear Ma — I reached this place yesterday evening. We had been 18 days on the road. We generally slept on the ground at night & I never before had such luxurious sleeping. I had no sign of a cold although it rained a good deal of the time. I fattened every day, our march was a perfect ovation. The people threw open their doors to us. I don't know how long we will stay here - about a week I think & from this place to Ashland 16 miles from here to Camp of Instruction. Virginia & McKendric Jefferies are there in a Co. The first person I met was Dick Wyatt - belongs to the Goodland Artillery - Willey Eppes treated the Company - he introduced me to his family & said he knows you very well - I sent all my clothes on here by railroad & have not been able to find them... I wish you would send me something to eat. the food here is very rough - nothing but fat salt meat & cold hard bread."* In postscripts he adds: *"I am writing in Mr. Palmer's store - he is very anxious for me to go home with him, but I have nothing but dirty clothes - a blue jeans hunting shirt over a blue flannel one...* [and on the fourth panel of the integral sheet] *always address me Capt. Jones Washington Mounted Rifles. Mr. Palmer says ours is the finest company that has come to Richmond, not in dress (for I can tell you we look like savages) but in fighting qualities..."* As he notes in his letter, Mosby was mustered into service as a private with the Washington Mounted Rifles. Prior to the First Battle of Manassas (Bull Run) on July 21, Mosby and his company were absorbed into J.E.B. Stuart's 1st Virginia Cavalry, portions of which accompanied Stuart to aid Beauregard at First Manassas. Mosby would soon gain the attention of his young commander and be appointed an adjutant of Stuart's staff before embarking on his illustrious career as a partisan ranger in 1863.

Letter has some wear and moderate toning, with professional restoration at folds, including minor replacement of some paper loss, However, ink remains bold and very legible. War-date letters by Mosby are extremely rare and the romance still evident in his impressions of the early days of the war make this letter particularly desirable and exciting.

Estimate: $6,000-$8,000

72038   FAMOUS *CARTE DE VISITE* SHOWING FIVE OF "MOSBY'S MEN",
Anderson & Co. backmark, Richmond, Virginia. Mosby's Rangers John Munson, Ben
Palmer, Thomas Becker, Walter Gosden and Alexander Babcock are posing here in
Confederate uniforms. This image is housed in a period wooden frame having a gilt inner
border. The overall framed size is 7.5" x 9". Very good condition. As the Confederacy's for-
tunes declined, the popularity of Colonel John Singleton Mosby and his command soared.
Consequently, the members of the 43rd Virginia Cavalry Battalion became favorite subjects
of various photographers.

Provenance: *The Tharpe Collection of American Military History*

Exhibited: *The Liberty Heritage Society Museum*

Estimate: $6,000-$8,000

72039   **THREE BROTHERS IN MOSBY RANGERS, CASED 1/6TH PLATE AMBROTYPE** − A slip of paper stored behind the image identifies the men in this portrait as James, Isham and Jerome Keith of Warrenton, Virginia, all of whom were serving in John S. Mosby's 43rd Virginia Cavalry Battalion at the time of this sitting. James and Isham wear civilian clothes whereas Jerome is in Confederate uniform. James and Isham previously served in the famous Black Horse Troop, Company "H", 4th Virginia Cavalry, whereas the younger Jerome's military career was entirely spent with Mosby. This poignant image is housed in a gutta-percha case with a chess-playing scene on both sides. A tiny bit of scattered spotting does not detract from the ambrotype's excellent surfaces and overall high state of preservation.

Provenance: *A. D. Payne Estate; The Tharpe Collection of American Military History*

Exhibited: *The Liberty Heritage Society Museum*

Estimate: $3,000-$5,000

Side Knife Belonging to Mosby's Sergeant Babcock

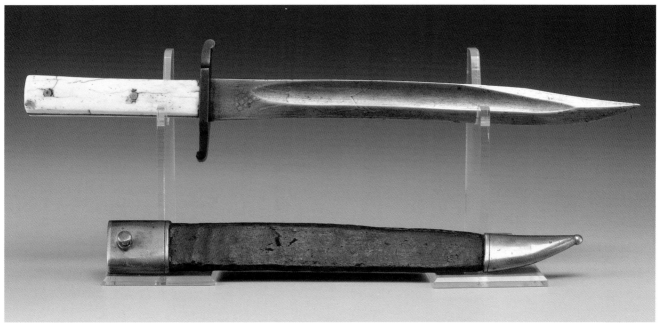

72040   MOSBY'S FIRST SERGEANT ALEXANDER G. BABCOCK'S BOYLE & GAMBLE SIDE KNIFE, 13.75" overall length with 9.5" blade, bone grips secured by brass pins, iron guard, etched foliate design on one side of the blade with crossed flags etched on the opposing side, leather sheath with brass throat and scabbard tip. Top mount engraved "*A. Babcock 43 batt'l*". The highly polished bone handle has minor age cracks and is pleasantly toned. The blade, although fresh and bright, is quite worn with the etching being largely reduced to an outline of the original. A split runs along the top seam of the sheath, otherwise it is intact and quite presentable. Overall fine condition.

Crafted by Richmond's premier edged weapon maker during the Civil War, this fine side knife was carried by First Sergeant Alexander G. Babcock of Mosby's 43rd Virginia Cavalry Battalion. Babcock, a New Yorker born in 1835, changed sides during the war and faithfully discharged his duties once becoming a Confederate partisan. He was attached to Mosby's artillery company as of 1864. Being a real bear of a man, the former Yankee features prominently in many of the late war photographs of Mosby and his men. Babcock, in spite of his Northern origins and unconventional enlistment, is buried in the hallowed ground of Richmond's Hollywood Cemetery.

Provenance: *The Tharpe Collection of American Military History*

Exhibited: *The Liberty Heritage Society Museum*

Estimate: $20,000-$25,000

72041   CAPTAIN FREDERICK WAUGH SMITH 2ND NATIONAL CONFEDERATE – MOSBY'S RANGER'S FLAG WITH ARCHIVE – Second National Confederate Flag, 31" fly, 17" leading edge, wool bunting, 10.5" x 10.25." The Canton consists of a St. Andrews cross with 13 stars on a white "Stainless banner'" field. The fly has a 1" hoist with three grommets. Intact with slight mothing and soiling as expected. It is professionally framed to an overall 38.5" x 23.5". This flag belonged to Frederick Waugh Smith, son of Confederate General and Virginia Governor "Extra Billy" Smith. The younger Smith, born in 1843, initially served with the 49th Virginia, was wounded at Fredericksburg and served as a lieutenant on his father's staff. On March 13, 1865, Frederick Smith obtained an appointment by President Jefferson Davis to Colonel John S. Mosby's command and served on Mosby's Staff until war's end. Smith brought this flag home with him from Mosby's command and, like many Confederate ex-patriots, after the Confederacy fell, moved to South Africa where he married and resided through the Boer War. The early 20th century found the former Confederate living in Washington, D.C. However, he returned to Cape Town in 1921 and stayed there until his death.

Included with Smith's flag are various biographical materials and the following personal items:

Carte de Visite Album, 10" x 6.25", heavily tooled gilt leather covers, contains photographs of Governor "Extra Billy" Smith and his wife. *Carte de Visite* of Confederate Captain Frederick Waugh Smith, Provost Marshal of Mosby's Rangers, Alexander Gardner, Washington, D.C. backmark.

Authentication: *The flag has been authenticated and treated by Textile Preservation Associates and comes with full documentation of its conservation. Fonda Thomsen Textile Preservation Sharpsburg, MD*

Provenance: *Virginia Governor William Smith (1861-1865);*
Captain Frederick Waugh Smith, provost marshal of Mosby's Rangers;
Gov. William "Extra Billy" Smith's family, Johannesburg, South Africa;
Dr John Lynn, Petersburg, Virginia, Old South Antiques;
The Tharpe Collection of American Military History

Exhibited: *The Liberty Heritage Museum, Warrenton, Virginia*

Estimate: $80,000-$120,000

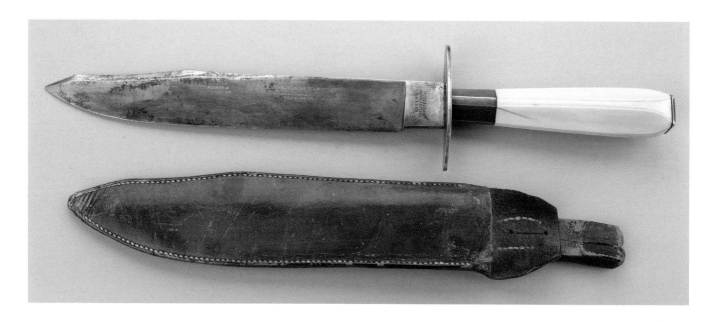

72042   CONFEDERATE BOWIE KNIFE CARRIED BY MOSBY RANGER JOHN HUME – 14" overall length, 9" blade, bone or ivory hilt, silver mount and guard, "Queen's / Cutlery Works / Sheffield" on ricasso, "Mapin / Brothers" and "The Hunter's Companion / Warranted Not To Be / Excelled In Quality" on blade, square, beveled silver pommel inset engraved "J.H. Va.", knife housed in stitched leather sheath. The engraved pommel serves to identify this fine Sheffield import as belonging to John Hume of Mosby's famous partisan command. Attractive patina on grip has three age cracks; sheath remains supple and enjoys tight stitching.

Provenance: *The Hume family; The Tharpe Collection of American Military History*

Exhibited: *The Liberty Heritage Society Museum*

Estimate: $8,000-$10,000

72043   A UNIQUE CONFEDERATE-ALTERED HARPER'S FERRY RIFLE – This 1855 U. S. Percussion Model .58 caliber rifle is stamped '1860' and 'Harper's Ferry' at the lock and the eagle motif stamped on the tape primer compartment. Originally fitted with a 33" round barrel, this rifle is unique in that it has been converted by a creative Confederate to use as a cavalry carbine. The barrel now measures just over 22" and the walnut stock has been checkered just behind the hammer and toward the patchbox for added grip o horseback. This is an interesting and attractive Confederate conversion.

Provenance: *The Tharpe Collection of Military History*

Exhibited: *The Liberty Heritage Society Museum*

Estimate: $5,000-$6,000

72044   MOSBY RANGER JOSHUA DEAR'S COLT ARMY MODEL 1860 AND RED SASH – His .44 caliber revolver, serial number 33582 marked "JLD" on the backstrap, features an 8" round barrel, 6 shot cylinder, loading lever and plunger, and back strap, all of iron. The trigger guard, front strap and blade front sight are brass. The serial number appears on barrel lug, frame in front of trigger guard, trigger guard flat, and butt strap (faintly). Wedge is unmarked. Cylinder is marked "Colt's Patent no. 3582" over "pat Sept 10th

1860" on circumference. Left side of frame marked "Colt's Patent" in 2 lines. Top of barrel marked "address Col. Samuel Colt, New York, U. S. America". Faint evidence of cylinder scene remains.

Wood grip exhibits some dings and scratches especially on left side near butt. "JLD" is scratched into butt strap. "S" stamped on front strap behind trigger guard, which will index.

Even, brown patina on barrel, cylinder and back strap. Traces of original finish on loading lever and frame. Brass has an even, mellow patina.

Provenance: *The Tharpe Collection of American Military History*

Exhibited: *The Liberty Heritage Society Museum*

Estimate: $4,000-$6,000

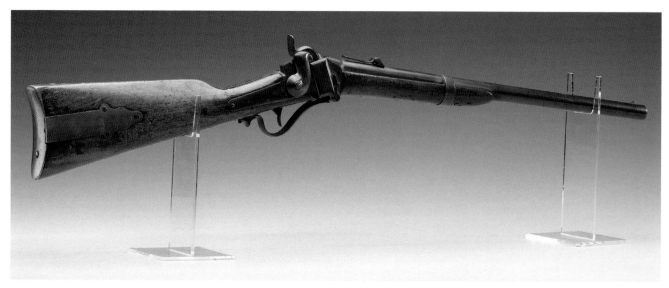

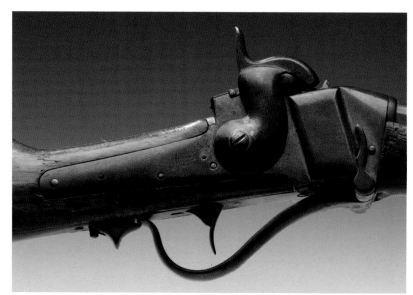

72045   A SHARPS CARBINE, PRIVATE WILLIAM A. KEYES, 'MOSBY'S RANGERS' – This Model 1852 Sharps .52 caliber percussion breechloader was carried by Private William A. Keyes of the famous Mosby's Partisan Rangers during the Civil War. Keyes was one of Mosby's original men and took part in the B&O Railroad 'Greenback Raid' on October 14, 1864 when Mosby and his men, including Keyes, liberated $168,000 in US greenbacks with each of the participants taking $2,000 each, while famously burning Union General Philip Sheridan's train. The raiders generally created havoc for the Union Army, effectively causing such diversion of Union resources that Mosby and his men like Keyes are generally credited for extending the war.

This Sharps cavalry carbine gives evidence of its use by Private Keyes. There is an even, rich patina of the 21½" barrel and many indentations of the wood at the forearm and buttstock. The 'Sharp's Patent 1852' is marked clearly at the lockplate with the serial number of 12726 below the 'Sharps Patent 1848' at the tang. Atop the barrel is the 'Sharps Rifle Manufg. Co. Hartford, Conn.' clearly stamped.

This Sharps carbine of Private William A Keyes is an historic and important weapon from the Mosby's Ranger unit in the Civil War.

Provenance: *The Tharpe Collection of American Military History*

Exhibited: *The Liberty Heritage Society Museum*

Estimate: $8,000-$10,000

72046   JOHN SINGLETON MOSBY SIGNED *CARTE DE VISITE* − Clearly signed *Jno S. Mosby* in pencil along lower margin, C. E. Jones & Vannerson, Richmond, Virginia Confederate backmark. This image would have been taken early in 1865 following Mosby's recovery from the December 21, 1864 wound that nearly killed him. His collar displays the three stars of a full Confederate colonel. Light stains on the back, some wear. Very good condition and very rare signed war-dated autograph.

Provenance: *The Tharpe Collection of American Military History*

Exhibited: *The Liberty Heritage Society Museum*

Estimate: $3,000-$5,000

Only Known John S. Mosby War Date Hard Image

72047   CASED 1/6TH PLATE AMBROTYPE OF JOHN SINGLETON MOSBY. This remarkable image was taken by a Winchester photographer in early 1865 while the Confederacy's celebrated "Gray Ghost" was recovering from a nearly fatal abdominal wound sustained shortly before Christmas, 1864. Mosby, looking decidedly ill, wears a coat and vest of military cut. His clothing, however, lacks any insignia and is dotted with civilian buttons. This outfit is typical of what he would wear when operating incognito in the field. The ambrotype is housed in the original gutta-percha Union case embossed on both sides with a fanciful agrarian scene. Minor emulsion loss does not detract in the least from the visual appeal of this unique historically important portrait of the Confederacy's "Grey Ghost."

On the evening of December 21, 1864 Lt. Colonel Mosby and partisan ranger Tom Love stopped for supper at the home of Ludwell Lake in Loudon County, Virginia. What should have been a pleasant repast among friends turned ugly with the unexpected arrival of a Federal force. A wild shot from the yard came through a window and struck Mosby just below his navel. Thinking quickly before the onset of debilitating pain, Mosby hid his fancy imported officer's coat and thus prevented an inquest that would have surely led to his capture. He also had the presence of mind to feign imminent death. The Federals took Love prisoner, but left the seemingly unimportant Mosby, who had given a false name, to die. Later, after the bullet was extracted, Mosby was sent to his father's home near Lynchburg to recover. He was promoted to full colonel during convalescence and returned to the field with the onset of the Confederacy's final spring. The rarest photograph of Mosby in existence.

Provenance: *J. Blackwell of Fauquier County, Virginia*
Wess Blackwell
The Tharpe Collection of American Military History

Exhibited: *The Liberty Heritage Society Museum*

Estimate: $40,000-$45,000

72048   JOHN SINGLETON MOSBY, A PLASTER BUST BY HERBERT BARBEE – John Singleton Mosby (1833-1916) was a Confederate cavalryman famous for his raiding behind enemy lines with his 'Partisan Rangers'. He is generally given credit for prolonging the life of the Confederacy, ruling in military superiority in eastern Virginia so much that the area became known as 'Mosby's Confederacy'.

This magnificent plaster bust of Colonel Mosby was completed by the master sculptor Herbert Barbee in 1920. Done in a bass-relief oval at 1" in depth and signed 'Herbert Barbee, 1920' under Mosby's left arm, the piece measures 18½" x 24½" and is in excellent condition. Mosby is depicted facing to his right in a serene pose dressed in his Confederate Colonel's uniform with the corresponding three stars at the collar. His highly-detailed Virginia frock coat buttons have been hand-gilded, the intricate lines of his facial features and hair well-defined, all giving the sense that this portrait could have been done from life, even though it was completed four years after his death as a commemoration of the great cavalry officer's life.

Herbert Barbee studied his craft in Italy and completed many pieces in the United States, but none as spectacular as this. He has captured the essence of Mosby and his stately demeanor. Fabulously framed in a a 5" highly-carved wooden frame with a beaded oval 26" opening, this portrait bust of Mosby is one of a kind.

Provenance: *The Tharpe Collection of American Military History*

Exhibited: *The Liberty Heritage Society Museum*

Estimate: $40,000-$50,000

MOSBYS MEN DESTROYING THE RAILROAD TRAIN AT CATLETTS STATION, MAY 28.

72049   A WATERCOLOR DRAWING OF GENERAL JOHN SINGLETON MOSBY'S RAID AT CATLETT'S STATION – This striking battle sketch was done by Alfred Von Erickson of Fredericksburg, Virginia, a wartime Confederate artist, Erickson followed the events of the Civil War documenting the battles and historical engagements near his home. In this 14" x 11" walnut-framed watercolor and pencil drawing titled Mosby's Men Destroying The Railroad Train at Catlett's Station, May 28, a band of Confederate Colonel John Singleton Mosby's raiders are seen atop a hill riding from the scene of railroad cars they have just burned in the background. Fellow raiders also are shown still at the scene but making their escape.

Alfred Von Erickson's paintings were such important accounts of Mosby's activities during the war that the sketches were used to make woodcuts to be used in Mosby Raider Lieutenant J. G. Beckham's book Life of Mosby published in 1866. This watercolor and pencil work is in very good condition with slight foxing at the right. The colors are still very strong and the work is protected by glass and is in a period walnut frame. It is signed 'A. E. Pencil sketch Fredericksburg, Va.' at bottom right.

Provenance: *The Tharpe Collection of American Military History*

Exhibited: *The Liberty Heritage Society Museum*

Estimate: $10,000-$15,000

MOSBY AMONG THE WAGON-TRAINS.

A.E. PENCIL SKETCH. Fredricksbg.V.

72050 **A WATERCOLOR OF MOSBY AMONG THE WAGON TRAINS** – This watercolor and pen sketch by noted Civil War artist Alfred Von Erickson portrays Confederate Raider Colonel John Singleton Mosby's men taking a Union wagon train. Von Erickson documented the war in and around his native Fredericksburg, compiling a series of drawings, sketches and watercolors during the war. This sketch is signed 'A. E. Pencil Sketch, Fredricksbg. Va.' at lower right. In vivid color Von Erickson depicts the raiders on horseback killing Union soldiers and burning the wagons while commandeering others. This is a beautiful wartime sketch, so important that it was used to make woodcuts for Lieutenant J. G. Beckham's book on Mosby just a year after war's end. It is in its beautiful walnut frame as well.*

Provenance: *The Tharpe Collection of American Military History*

Exhibited: *The Liberty Heritage Society Museum*

Estimate: $10,000-$15,000

MOSBY'S MEN DESTROYING THE RAILROAD IN GEN: GRANT'S REAR.

72051   MOSBY'S MEN DESTROYING THE RAILROAD IN GENERAL GRANT'S REAR -A WATERCOLOR BY NOTED CIVIL WAR ARTIST ALFRED VON ERICKSON – Alfred Von Erickson documented the exploits of famed Confederate raider Colonel John Singleton Mosby so well that his sketches and drawings were used in Mosby Raider Lieutenant J. G. Beckham's book Life of Mosby published just a year after the war was over.

This 13" x 11" watercolor and pencil work exemplifies how Mosby harassed General Ulysses S. Grant's forces causing Grant to divert precious resources from the overall war effort to combat Mosby's 'Partisan Rangers'. Erickson depicts the Mosby men destroying the railroad lines in Grant's Rear', emblematic of the type of actions that Mosby would orchestrate behind enemy lines, actions that prolonged the war. The colors are still vivid with only slight foxing of the paper at the top right.

This excellent example of Erickson's wartime work is in its period walnut frame and protected under glass. Signed 'A. E. Pencil Sketch, Fredericksburg, Va.' at the lower right, the work is in overall very good condition and is a historically important and contemporary account of Mosby's raiders.

Provenance: *The Tharpe Collection of American Military History*

Exhibited: *The Liberty Heritage Society Museum*

Estimate: $10,000-$15,000

TURNER'S HAND-TO-HAND FIGHT WITH CAPT: WORTHINGTON, 1ST VERMONT CAVALRY.
MOSBY AT MIDDLEBURG.

72052   A WATERCOLOR OF MOSBY'S MEN IN COMBAT BY CIVIL WAR ARTIST ALFRED VON ERICKSON – This vivid portrayal of combat was done in watercolor by noted Civil War artist Alfred Von Erickson of Fredericksburg. He documented many battles in and around Virginia, especially the exploits of Confederate raider Colonel John Singleton Mosby. In this watercolor and pencil Von Erickson depicts the close-quarters battle between Mosby's Lieutenant Thomas Turner and Captain Worthington of the 1st Vermont Cavalry. Measuring 16" x 11", the colors of this sketch are still vibrant with the Union blue and Confederate gray standing in sharp contrast in the center of the picture. In the background Von Erickson shows Mosby's men chasing Union cavalry. Signed 'A. E. Pencil sketch, Fredricksburg, Va.' in the lower right, it is matted and framed in a nice period walnut frame.

Provenance: *The Tharpe Collection of American Military History*

Exhibited: *The Liberty Heritage Society Museum*

Estimate: $10,000-$15,000

CAPTIVES of GEN: CUSTERS DIV: DRAWING LOTS.

72053   GENERAL CUSTER'S CAVALRYMEN DRAWING LOTS TO BE EXECUTED BY MOSBY – A WATERCOLOR AND PENCIL SKETCH OF GENERAL CUSTER'S MEN DRAWING LOTS TO BE EXECUTED – BY ALFRED VON ERICKSON – As Confederate Colonel John Singleton Mosby's raiders disrupted Union supply lines more and more in 1864, General Ulysses S. Grant reportedly told General Philip Sheridan that if any of Mosby's Rangers were captured, to line them up and execute them. That order was carried out by Brigadier General George Armstrong Custer's men and on September 22nd of that year Custer's troops executed seven of Mosby's men.

As this matted and framed 13½" x 11" drawing done in watercolor and pencil shows, Mosby swiftly retaliated. As he had captured seven Union troops of Custer's Division he ordered them executed. The Confederates proceeded to shoot, hang and do their best to exact revenge. Depicted here are seven of Custer's men drawing lots to determine who will be executed. Mosby sits at the left astride his horse as a Confederate passes a hat from which the unfortunates will draw their lot. This sketch of that historical event is titled *Captives of General Custer's Division Drawing Lots.*

This drawing was done during the Civil War and is signed 'A. E.' with the notation 'Fredericks bg. V.'. The artist, Alfred Von Erickson lived in Fredericksburg, Virginia and painted scenes during the war. He moved to Canada in 1866 but this watercolor and pencil sketch and others survived. They were important enough to have been given to John S. Mosby and used as a template for woodcuts that were used to reproduce images in Mosby Ranger J. G. Beckham's book of 1866, *The Life of Mosby*, thus dating these to the war years.

This sketch is titled *Captives of General Custer's Division Drawing Lots.* It has some slight foxing but the colors are very vivid. It come is a nicely matted, walnut frame.

Provenance: *John S. Mosby*
The Tharpe Collection of American Military History

Exhibited: *The Liberty Heritage Society Museum*

Estimate: $15,000-$25,000

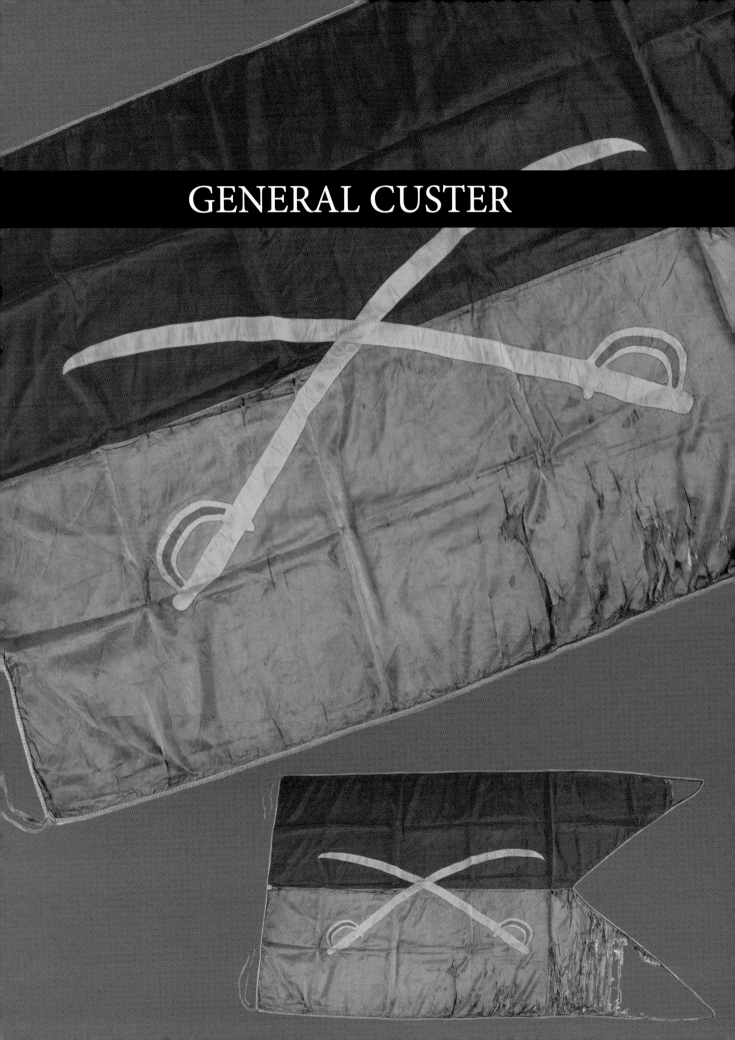

GENERAL CUSTER

72054   BRIGADIER GENERAL GEORGE A. CUSTER *CARTE DE VISITE,* by Matthew Brady & Co., New York, October 8, 1863. Framed with a custom brass nameplate to an overall size of 8" x 10". Light aging, very fine condition.

Estimate: $800-$1,200

72056   BRIGADIER GENERAL GEORGE A. CUSTER *CARTE DE VISITE,* by Matthew Brady & Co., New York, February, 1864. Framed with a custom brass nameplate to an overall size of 8" x 10". Light aging, very fine condition.

Estimate: $1,800-$2,000

72055   BRIGADIER GENERAL GEORGE A. CUSTER *CARTE DE VISITE,* by Matthew Brady & Co., New York, February 1864. Taken shortly after his wedding to Elizabeth Bacon, Custer seems here to be controlling his penchant for personal flair. Gone are the long locks and fancy custom-tailored uniform. Framed with a custom brass nameplate to an overall size of 8" x 10". Fine condition.

Estimate: $2,000-$3,000

72057   BRIGADIER GENERAL GEORGE A. CUSTER AND ELIZABETH "LIBBY" CUSTER *CARTE DE VISITE,* by Matthew Brady & Co., New York, February, 1864. Custer's attractive young bride would outlive him by almost 60 years. Framed with a custom brass nameplate to an overall size of 8" x 10". A small blemish in the upper field, very fine condition.

Estimate: $2,000-$3,000

72058   GENERAL PHILIP SHERIDAN AND STAFF *CARTE DE VISITE* **WITH UNPUBLISHED IMAGE OF CUSTER.** Possibly by Alexander Gardner, January 2, 1865. Shown left to right are Wesley Merritt, Philip Sheridan, George Cook, James Forsyth and George Custer. A rare and unpublished variant of Custer. Framed with a custom brass nameplate to an overall size of 8.25" x 12.25". Very fine condition and quite rare.

Estimate: $2,000-$3,000

72059   MAJOR GENERAL GEORGE A. CUSTER *CARTE DE VISITE,* by Matthew Brady & Co., New York, January 3, 1865. Framed with a custom brass nameplate to an overall size of 8" x 10". Inscription on lower portion of the image naming the subject. Very fine condition.

Estimate: $1,000-$1,500

72060   MAJOR GENERAL GEORGE A. CUSTER *CARTE DE VISITE,* by Matthew Brady & Co., New York, January 3, 1865. Framed with a custom brass nameplate to an overall size of 8" x 10". Period inscription - not Custer's autograph - in lower margin. Some loss to upper left corner where the print has peeled back from the matt and minor scuffing on lower margin. Fine condition..

Estimate: $900-$1,200

72061   MAJOR GENERAL GEORGE A. CUSTER *CARTE DE VISITE,* by John Goldin & Co., May 1865. Framed with a custom brass nameplate to an overall size of 8" x 10". Very fine condition.

Estimate: $900-$1,200

72062   MAJOR GENERAL GEORGE A. CUSTER *CARTE DE VISITE,* by Matthew Brady & Co., New York, January 3, 1865. One of the better known images of Custer. Framed with a custom brass nameplate to an overall size of 8" x 10". Very fine condition.

Estimate: $1,500-$1,800

72064   MAJOR GENERAL GEORGE A. CUSTER *CARTE DE VISITE,* by John Goldin & Co., May, 1865. Framed with a custom brass nameplate to an overall size of 8" x 10". Very fine condition.

Estimate: $1,800-$2,400

72063   MAJOR GENERAL GEORGE A. CUSTER *CARTE DE VISITE,* by John Goldin & Co., May, 1865. Framed with a custom brass nameplate to an overall size of 8" x 10". Very fine condition.

Estimate: $400-$600

72065   MAJOR GENERAL GEORGE A. CUSTER *CARTE DE VISITE,* after the original by John Goldin & Co., May, 1865. Framed with a custom brass nameplate to an overall size of 8" x 10". Light soiling, fine condition.

Estimate: $1,200-$1,800

72066   MAJOR GENERAL GEORGE A. CUSTER *CARTE DE VISITE,* by Matthew Brady & Co., Washington, D.C., May, 1865. Framed with a custom brass nameplate to an overall size of 8" x 10". Very fine condition.

Estimate: $1,800-$2,400

72067   MAJOR GENERAL GEORGE A. CUSTER *CARTE DE VISITE,* by Matthew Brady & Co., published by Beers & Mansfield, May, 1865. Framed with a custom brass nameplate to an overall size of 8" x 10". Very fine condition.

Estimate: $1,800-$2,400

**72068   GENERAL GEORGE ARMSTRONG CUSTER'S PERSONAL BATTLE FLAG
FROM LEE'S SURRENDER AT APPOMATTOX TO THE LITTLE BIGHORN**

The personal battle flag of General Custer, the most famous US Cavalry Officer in American history; this flag was handmade of silk by his wife Elizabeth during the final days of the Civil War and delivered to him on the battlefield in the midst of battle at Dinwiddie Court House near Petersburg, Virginia on March 31, 1865. Custer immediately took this flag as he charged his horse over the breastworks of Confederate General George Pickett winning the battle and bringing about Lee's surrender to Grant at Appomattox within a few days. Custer kept this flag by his side for the rest of his life as a symbol of the valor and patriotism shared by him and his beloved "Libbie." Fortunately for posterity, the flag was left at Custer's head quarters at Fort Abraham Lincoln, Dakota in 1876 as Custer and his men rode to their immortality at the battle of Little Bighorn.

General Custer's silk swallow-tailed cavalry battle flag measures 68" by 36". Centered between the red over blue bars are two hand cut white, crossed Cavalry Sabers making this flag instantly recognizable as a distinctive cavalry flag. Custer carried this flag throughout the remainder of the Civil War in battle at Five Forks, Namozine Church, Sayler's Creek, Dinwiddie Court House and Lee's surrender to Grant at Appomattox. Custer received the first Flag of Surrender from Lee's Confederate Army of Northern Virginia with this personal battle flag at his side, which brought about the end of the American Civil War.

Soon thereafter, Custer was promoted to major general and became the hero of the United States Army, victorious at Gettysburg as in all of his cavalry battles, he became the leading cavalry officer of the Civil War in 1865 - he achieved this destiny by the age of 25. But Custer had many battles left to fight, and he accepted a reduction in rank to stay in the US Army in command of all the cavalry in Texas in 1866 with headquarters in Austin. He soon became the commander of the legendary 7th Cavalry for service first in Kansas and across the Great Plains during America's westward expansion after the Civil War. This personal battle flag was with Custer as he made his way from the war-torn battlefields of Virginia to Texas and the West and finally to his destiny at Little Bighorn, Montana

where he and his entire command fought to their death against the Sioux and Cheyenne Indians of the Northern Plains.

This is one of the most important flags in American history, it remained in the Custer family, and was preserved by relatives from the Custer farmhouse in Monroe, Michigan. It was purchased directly from General Custer's nephew Lt. Col Charles Custer just 75 years after it last flew above General Custer, by the noted historian and Custer biographer Dr. Lawrence Frost who first published this flag in his book entitled *The Custer Album.* The Custer Flag has been authenticated by noted flag expert and historian Howard Michael Madaus; it is accompanied by a volume of historical research and authentication documents validating this as one of the greatest American icons in existence: Custer's Flag.

Provenance: *1. Elizabeth "Libby" Custer: Flag hand sewn in 1865, and delivered to Gen. Custer at Dinwiddie Cout House, VA on March 31, 1865
2. General George Armstrong Custer: 1865 - June 25, 1876 (his death)
3. The Custer Family: 1876-1956
4. Dr. Lawrence A. Frost: 1956-1990
5. Elizabeth Lawrence: 1990 - 2003
6. Thomas Minckler: 2003 - Present*

Estimate: $1,800,000-$2,200,000

GENERAL CUSTER'S APPOMATTOX CAMPAIGN CAVALRY FLAG

Throughout history, armies have carried flags. Flags provided a sense of identity and built pride and morale for the unit. Flags also provided a means of identifying unit locations and as a rallying point for soldiers in the confusion of combat. The U.S. Cavalry used swallowtail flag guidons in both the Civil War and Plains Indian Wars. In addition to regimental flags, various commanders adopted these as their own personal flags.

Custer's fourth Civil War personal flag was his pride and joy because it was hand sewn by his dear wife Libbie. It was made of a double layer of silk, red over blue bars, and adorned with white crossed sabers on both sides and bound with a coarse woven cord. Custer's Appomattox Campaign Guidon is the single most important and documented personal article from the Civil War period. Delivered on horseback by one of his staff and unfurled in the fury and fire at Dinwiddie Court House on March 31st, 1865, it was in Custer's hand as he leaped his horse over Pickett's breastworks the next day at Five Forks. A personal inspiration to Custer, this Guidon was with him until the end came at Appomattox. Custer's constant hammering of the rebel forces played a major part in the final phases of the war. This Guidon was present at the following Civil War battles: Dinwiddie Court House, Five Forks, Namozine Church, Saylor Creek, and Appomattox Station.

The final Campaign of the Army of Northern Virginia began March 25, 1865 when General Robert E. Lee sought to break General Ulysses Grant's stranglehold at Petersburg, Virginia by attacking Fort Stedman. Lee failed and Granted counterattacked at Five Forks, which led tothe Confederate retreat that eventually resulted in the Confederate surrender at Appomattox on April 9th, 1865. On March 29th General Phillip Sheridan undertook a flank march to attack Lee's Petersburg defenses. A steady downpour turned roads into mud, slowing his advance. Major General Fitzhugh Lee's Cavalry and Major General George Pickett's infantry division met the Union vanguard north and northwest of Dinwiddie Court House and drove it back, temporarily stalling Sheridan's movement. When the Union infantry approached from the east, General Pickett withdrew to the vital road junction at Five Forks. General Robert E. Lee ordered Pickett to hold this vital intersection at all cost. The battle at Dinwiddie Court House on March 31 involved 65,277 troops and both sides suffered a total of 821 casualties.

Prior to this time, General Custer had sent Lieutenant Peter Boehm to Washington with letters to the War Department. In addition, he carried a personal letter to his wife, Libbie. She received the letter and, in turn, entrusted Lieutenant Boehm with this magnificent silk flag hand made by her and embroidered with her name on one of the swallowtail points. Libbie had promised Custer she would make him a new personal flag to be carried in the Appomattox campaign and had spent every moment to complete it in time.

Lieutenant Boehm wrapped this flag around his body underneath his uniform for fear he might be captured en route to the battlefront in Virginia. Boehm arrived safely after riding through Mosby's Confederacy alone and unscathed.

Late the next day, Private Huff, the Color Bearer of Custer's Cavalry, was carrying it during an engagement at Five Forks. He was mortally wounded, along with Custer's Bugler and Orderly and Libbie's name was shot off the Guidon. Custer was untouched by the fusillade and swung down from his saddle to grab this flag without dismounting, swirled this flag over his head and leapt over the breastworks of Major General George Pickett.

George Custer wrote to his wife Elizabeth 6 miles from Dinwiddie, Virginia on March, 31, 1865:

"Owing to the impassible state of the roads, we are still at the point from which I wrote yesterday. Last Night Lt. Boehm arrived, with what all pronounced 'the handsomest flag I have ever seen.' What renders it infinitely dear to me is that it is the work of my darling's hands. It could not have arrived at a more opportune moment. It was attached to the staff when battle was raging all along our lines. Cannon and musketry saluted it as its folds opened to the breeze. I regarded it as a happy omen. We have planned to procure a new staff for our beauty. Lt. Boehm had to pass through enemy country for a considerable distance without an escort. He is extremely venturesome, and was determined to join us. Fearing capture he wrapped the flag about his person under his clothes, and in this way brought it to your Boy."

On April 1st the final Union Army offensive of the civil War occurred at Five Forks. The Union forces were commanded by Sheridan and the confederate forces were led by Pickett. Five Forks was to be the Waterloo of the Confederacy. The confederate loss at Five Forks threatened Lee's last supply line, the South Side Railroad. Pickett's total casualties most likely exceeded 6,000.

In a letter dated April 2, 1865 from Washington, Libbie wrote to her parents, Mr. And Mrs. Bacon, about the same guidon:

"…Then, too, I have been making a flag for Autie to take on this last raid. It really is beautiful, like the old one, only larger - red and blue silk with white crossed sabers on both sides, and edged with heavy white cord. Lt. Boehm took it to him." At Saylor's Creek on April 6, Custer's horse was killed from under him on

one foray, and in another, one of his color bearers was killed instantly. Later Custer seized his Guidon and led a successful charge at Appomattox Station on a Confederate battery.

Albert Barnitz was an officer in the 2nd Ohio Volunteer Cavalry and was present with General Custer at Appomattox. As a published poet, he wrote years later to immortalize this large charge in verse:

"Custer led! - with his flag unfurled!
His breeze-blown standard of scarlet and blue,
Far seen at the front, when the fight waxed hot,
And the shells crashed loud, and the bullets flew!
Blithely he rode and with dauntless air,
Girl-like but resolute into the fray,
With a luster of Gold on his wind-tossed hair,
And jacket resplendent with bullion gay!
Over his shoulders his scarlet scarf
Floated and flamed as he held his course;
Never a leader so buoyant as he
Fell on the foe with such measureless force!"

Lieutenant Boehm recollected the following in a letter to Mrs. Custer on September 15, 1910 from Chicago:

"My Dear Mrs. Custer,

I am highly honored to be still in your remembrance. I do indeed remember taking your flag to the General. The flag was the incentive, which gave me strength to carry out my mission, which resulted in my most highly prized honor.

The General had dispatched me with letters to the War Department, also with one to you. You entrusted me with Cavalry Guidon on one of the points of which you had embroidered your name.

The command to which I had formerly belonged was now General Grant's bodyguard, and knowing the old men pretty well, I appealed to their sergeant who procured me a horse - a splendid animal. Pass and countersign enabled me to pass the pickets - the two lines were very close to each other - having wrapped your Guidon around my body. And so I reached the General.

Being extremely tired I lay down to sleep, but shortly the General received orders to push forward to reinforce Merritt and Crook who were being driven back from Five Forks… March 31st.

The General rode ahead of the command with a few men, including myself, reaching Dinwiddie Court House about 4 in the afternoon. We found our lines in considerable confusion, being driven back. I took your Guidon from the color bearer, and with and orderly, Huff, rode with the General along the lines. We succeeded in rallying the men and re-informing the line, checking Pickett's advance. This enabled the General to place his command in position that evening.

It was during this engagement your name must have been shot off the Guidon, as we were under very heavy fire. Huff was mortally wounded while riding alongside of me, and died that evening. My arm was almost shattered at Five Forks next day and does not trouble me to speak of, except when occasional pains make me a judge of weather."

Years later, after the Guidon's illustrious career along side General George Custer during the Appomattox campaign, it was found in the attic of the Custer farmhouse on the north side of North Custer Road in Monroe, Michigan by Lt. Col. Charles Custer, a grandson of General Custer's brother Nevin. It was purchased by Dr. Lawrence Frost on May 31st, 1956. The Guidon is item #22 on page 2 of Dr. Frost's sale list of General Custer's possessions. Also, a document signed by Lawrence Frost describing the Guidon states it is unquestionably the same one referred to in Merrington's The Custer Story on page 147. On the reverse of the document Frost drew a diagram of the Guidon with measurements of 36" high and 5½" long. All of the three documents accompany the Guidon. On page 57 of Frost's book, The Custer Album, is a sketch by Civil War artist and Harper's Weekly correspondent and Harper's Weekly Correspondent

A.R. Waud, entitled "Receiving the Flag of Truce." It depicts Custer and his troops receiving the Flag of Truce (a white towel tied to a branch) from a Confederate officer near the Appomattox Court House. The flag of truce came just in time to prevent a charge Custer was preparing to lodge and procured an exchange of notes between Grant and Lee agreeing to meet the village of Appomattox Court House. Clearly visible in the sketch of the Confederates surrendering to General Custer by Waud is Custer's flag with its distinctively designed crossed sabers sewn by his wife Libbie.

Provenance: *Elizabeth Custer*
George A. Custer
Charles A. Custer Family Collection
Dr. Lawrence Frost Collection
Private Collection
Thomas Minckler Collection.

Literature: Whittaker, Frederick. *A Complete Life of Gen. George A. Custer.* New York, 1876, pp. 302, 306.
Barnitz, Albert. *With Custer at Appomattox.* Cleveland, 1903, p. 37.
Merington, Marguerite, ed. *The Custer Story: the Life and Intimate Letters of General George A. Custer and his Wife Elizabeth.* New York, 1959, pp. 147-148.
Graham, Col. W.A. *Custer's Battle Flags.* 1952.
Frost, Lawrence. *The Custer Album.* Seattle, 1964, p. 61.
Madaus, Howard Michael. *The Personal And Designating Flags of General George A. Custer, 1863-1865.* Washington, 1968, p. 13.
Frost, Lawrence. *General Custer's Libbie.* Seattle, 1976, pp. 126-127.
Reedstrom, Ernest Lisle. *Bugles, Banners and War Bonnets,* pp. 126-127.
Urwin, Gregory J.W. *Custer Victorious: The Civil War Battles of General George Armstrong Custer.* Edison, N.J., 1983, pp. 233-260.
Leckie, Shirley A. *Elizabeth Bacon Custer and the Making of a Myth.* Norman, 1993, p. 65.

HISTORICAL PERSPECTIVE OF MAJOR-GENERAL GEORGE A. CUSTER'S FOURTH PERSONAL HEADQUARTERS FLAG DURING THE CIVIL WAR

by Howard Michael Madaus

Major-General George Armstrong Custer's fourth personal headquarters flag dates from March of 1865, but its basic design is the same as the three other personal headquarters flags that had been made for him in 1863 and 1864. This design was wrought on a swallowtail field, that is an otherwise rectangular flag with a triangular wedge cut out of the flying edge so that the design would be readily identifiable even in the lightest movement of the wind or motion of the flag. The design that appeared on the four personal headquarters flags flown near Custer was otherwise simple: the field was divided horizontally into two bars of equal width, the upper red and the lower blue. Appliquéd in the center of this field were two white crossed sabers, unsheathed and displayed crossing with their cutting edges up. In the years before the Civil War such crossed sabers served as the distinctive insignia of the cavalry regiments serving on the western frontier. Custer's flag bearers during the War carried four successive flags of this basic design. Fortunately a combination of production idiosyncrasies conjoin with surviving documents and references to permit a reasonably accurate sequence of usage.

The first personal headquarters flag carried to mark his presence on the battlefield and in camp was made shortly after the Gettysburg campaign. The use of a coarse woolen material for its field, its crude quality, and the non-symmetry of its crossed sabers suggests that it was improvised in the field. The flag bears two battle honors, "BOONESBORO" over "FALLING- WATER", first penciled in outline and later finished in silver thread embroidery. Since the former honor commemorates an action fought on 7 July and the latter one on 14 July, it is thought that the making of this flag took place during the second week of July, 1863.while Custer and his brigade were in the field. By contrast, Custer's second personal headquarters flag evidences the professional workmanship of a commercial flag maker. Of the same basic design as the first personal flag, the second flag is made of silk, edged on its exterior sides with a gold fringe. The crossed sabers are painted to each side of the field in their natural colors— silver blades, golden hilt, and brown grips, and are perfectly symmetrical. Also painted to the field in shadowed gilt letters in a single

column between the sabers and what had been the pole sleeve is a list of eleven battle honors starting with "HANOVER" (fought on June 30th 1863) and ending with "CULPEPPER" (fought on September 13th 1863). Since all the honors (save one) are applied in the same artistic style and in the same paint, it seems likely that they were all applied simultaneously by the same artist that applied the crossed sabers to the field of the flag, in the case of the second personal flag, sometime after the engagement at Culpeper on September 13th 1863. Supplementing the probability of a September-October date of manufacture, in a letter written by Custer on October 12th 1863 by he refers to "my new battle-flag, so soon to receive its baptism in blood." Custer concludes his account of the battle of by commenting that: "My color-bearer had his horse shot." Eight months later, Custer's color-bearer would suffer a more grievous calamity , as would the flag he carried.

At the battle of Trevilian Station (June 11th and 12th 1864) Custer's Michigan Cavalry Brigade was all but surrounded by two divisions of Confederate cavalry. Nine days later (June 21st 1864), Custer related an incident of the battle: "Sergeant Mashon was struck while gallantly carrying his flag at the head of the charge. He lived until morning. When shot he remained in his saddle till our lines began to waver., when he made his way to me, saying, 'Gencral, they have killed me. Take the flag'. To save it I was compelled to tear it from its staff and place it in my bosom." The editor of this letter evidently misread the flag bearer's name. In his official report of the May- July 1864 campaign, Custer correctly identifies his personal flag bearer's name: "I am called upon to record the death of one of the 'bravest of the brave', Sergt. Mitchell Beloir, of the First Michigan Cavalry, who has been my color bearer since the organization of this brigade. Sergt. Mitchell Beloir received his death-wound while nobly discharging his duty to his flag and to his country. He was killed in the advance while gallantly cheering the men forward to victory." Since the leading edge of Custer's second personal flag is tattered and torn, as would be expected if it was torn from its staff, Custer's letter of June 21st 1864 serves to indicate the date of the last usage of that flag. This same data at the same time it also suggests when his third personal flag approximately came into use.

Because its field is well made and composed of high quality scarlet and dark blue wool bunting with white appliquéd cotton sabers, Custer's third personal flag is thought to have been commercially produced. After two months of intense campaigning in May and June of 1864, the cavalry of the Army of the Potomac was granted a respite and was permitted to refit. It is likely that Custer may have ordered a new personal flag at that time. Shortly afterward two of the three cavalry divisions of the Army of the Potomac were sent to the Shenandoah Valley. The Army of the Potomac's 1st Cavalry Division (which contained Custer's Michigan Brigade) left on August 8th 1864, followed by the 3rd Cavalry Division on the 16th of August. Custer continued to lead his Michigan Brigade to the Valley in August. However, on September 26th 1864 to assume command the 2nd Cavalry Division, Department of West Virginia, whose commander (Brigadier-General W.W. Averill) had proven less than satisfactory as a division commander. However, before Custer could take command of 2nd Cavalry Division, Custer received a "gift" from the War Department. Brigadier-General James H. Wilson , a staff officer without any prior field experience, who General Grant had brought with him to the east in the Spring of 1864 (and whom Custer considered to be an "imbecile"), was relieved of the command of the 3rd Cavalry Division and ordered back to the "western theater". On the same day that Wilson was sent back "west" (September 30th 1864), Custer's orders to take command of the 2nd Cavalry Division were revoked, and he was reassigned, instead, to the command of the 3rd Cavalry Division.

A week later (October 7th 1864), Harpers Weekly sketch artist, Alfred Waud, executed a drawing of Custer's division near Mount Jackson, Virginia. Near Custer an orderly holds a flag, divided into two horizontal bars and bearing crossed sabers. This is thought to be the earliest representation of Custer's third personal flag. The same flag (as well as the 3rd Cavalry Division designating flag heretofore flown with General Wilson) appears draped on its staff in a photograph of Custer's headquarters on Christmas Day, 1864. The much worn designating flag seems to have been retired shortly after the photograph was taken, and only the third personal flag was carried in the first three months of 1865. Confirming the use of but a single headquarters flag in the weeks prior to the receipt of

his fourth personal flag, on March 11th 1865, Custer informed his wife: "I wish you could see your boy's headquarters now. My flag is floating over the gate, and near it, ranged along the fences, are 16 battle-flags captured by the 3rd Division." These battle-flags had been captured by Custer's division at Waynesboro, Virginia on March 2nd 1865. Shortly afterwards the 3rd Cavalry Division (as well as the 1st) was ordered to return to the Army of the Potomac for operations against the flank of General Lee's over-extended lines. It was here, near Dinwiddie Court House, Virginia that Custer received his fourth personal headquarters flag.

Custer's fourth personal headquarters flag measured essentially three feet on its hoist (staff edge) by five and a half on its fly (to the points of the swallowtail— but only four feet from the hoist to the cut of the swallow-tail.) Like its three predecessors, thee design consists of a red horizontal bar over a medium blue horizontal bar, with white, unsheathed crossed sabers (edges up) appliquéd in the center of each side. Like the second personal flag, the fourth is made from silk, but in two thicknesses for durability in the field. Despite the flag's high quality ingredients, it was not commercially made, but rather was hand sewn by Mrs. Elizabeth Custer, who commented about the project she had recently completed in a letter to her parents, dated April 2nd 1865: "Then too, I have been making a flag for Autie to take on his last raid. It really is beautiful, like the old one, only larger— red and blue silk with white crossed sabers on both sides, and edged with heavy white cord. Lt. Boehm took it to him." This "heavy white cord", a nearly ¼ of an inch in diameter and made of hemp or twisted wool, extends around the full flag, including the leading edge where it secures three pairs of ties for securing the flag to a staff. Importantly, its presence serves to confirm the identity of the fourth personal flag. One other identifying feature distinguished Custer's fourth personal headquarters flag, but that element is now missing from the flag.

Evidently Elizabeth Custer signed her name in embroidery stitches to identify the source of the flag she sent in March of 1865. The portion of the flag with this embroidery, probably the upper tail of the swallowtail, is now missing, it having been shot away in one of the engagements between the 31st of March and the 8th of April 1865. Newly appointed Second

Lieutenant (later Brevet Captain) Peter Martin Boehm of the 15th New York Cavalry, who had brought the flag from Mrs. Custer to the general, carried Custer's new flag for most of March 31st 1865. With it he (Lt. Boehm) rallied the retreating Union forces, and he remembered the original presence of Mrs. Custer's name on the flag. In his letter to Elizabeth Custer under the date of September 15th 1910, Lieutenant Boehm recollected:

> "The General had dispatched me with letters to the War Department, also with one to you. You entrusted me with the Cavalry guidon on one of the points of which you had embroidered your name."

HISTORICAL PERSPECTIVE OF GENERAL CUSTER'S FLAG IN TEXAS AND THE WEST 1865-1876

by Howard Michael Madaus

It is well known that the " Personal Flag" of Major General George Armstrong Custer made for him by his wife Libbie was hand-delivered to him during the last days Civil War, in the midst of battle where it was immediately put into use during the battle at Dinwiddie Court House, Virginia in March of 1865. These events set into play Lee's surrender to Grant less than two weeks latter. But due to the battle wear on this cavalry guidon it is obvious that Custer used this flag well beyond the Civil War.

The history of Custer's flag in the post-civil war period. Custer's fourth personal flag and the only flag ever made for him by his wife "Libbie" is detailed here. The flag is mentioned twice and that peripherally during the period Custer served in Texas and the "American West."

While the evidence is suggestive, it is known that there was a gradual diminishing role for high-ranking officers "personal flags" in the post- war U. S. Army. However, it is also known that General Philip Sheridan carried one of his "Personal Flags" in Texas, which is now preserved in the Smithsonian Institution, as did General Wesley Merritt who also carried his "Personal Flag" in Texas while serving with Custer as the other cavalry

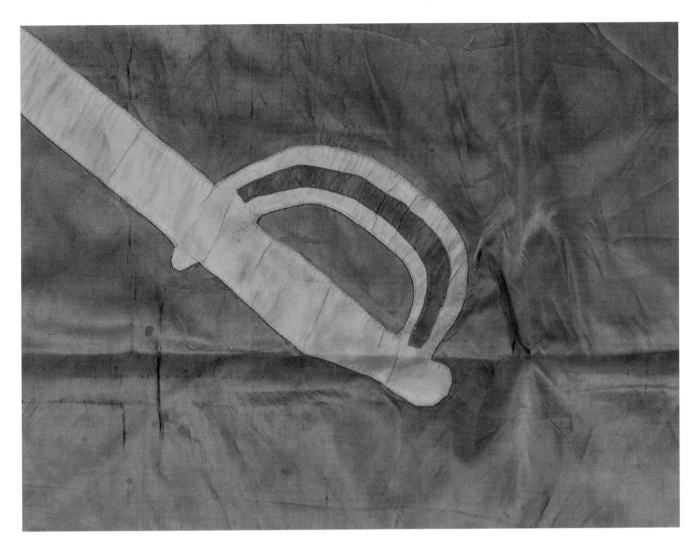

division commander. Merritt's flag now occupies a prominent place in the West Point Museum at the United States Military Academy.

Personal Headquarters flags were devised to permit staff officers and couriers to locate an officer in the field. Generically, these flags fall into two types. "Designating flags" identified the location of a specific level within a command structure, regardless of the officer in command. "Personal flags", on the other hand, indicated the presence of a high-ranking officer, notably a "general" whether on the battlefield or at his headquarters.

On 22 May 1865, just one day before the two day long celebratory parade in Washington DC, honoring the victorious Union hero's of the Civil War, Lieutenant General U. S. Grant commanded the Adjutant General's office in Washington to issue orders that detached the two most aggressive cavalry commanders in the Union Army to the West - Major General George Armstrong Custer and General Wesley Merritt, with their staff officers, to report to Major General Philip Sheridan in New Orleans for duty in Texas to command Sheridan's cavalry in his newly created "Military Division of the Southwest". Ostensibly the cavalry divisions of these two officers' commands were to engage the last Confederate forces under General Edmund Kirby Smith's still operating in Texas, which would not formally surrender until 26 June 1865. But there was also a hidden agenda for this "Army of Observation" that Custer served in; they were to carefully monitor the Confederate forces that refused to surrender and had crossed the Rio Grande, aiding Maximilian in his conquest of Mexico. To insure that these rebels would not reorganize and begin the rebellion all over again General Grant ordered two columns of about 5,000 cavalrymen to patrol the Texas border with Mexico and maintain Law & Order during the Federal occupation of Texas.

While Custer would proudly led his cavalry men in the "Grand Review-Victory Parade" in the nations capitol on 23 May 1865, he and his entourage with his wife "Libbie" and "Eliza" (the Custers' domestic cook) in

tow began their trek to Texas and eventually the West. The trip involved a rail ride from Washington DC after the Victory parade to the Ohio River, followed by a steamboat journey down the Ohio and Mississippi Rivers to Sheridan's headquarters in New Orleans. On 18 June 1865, Custer was provided with more detailed instructions through Special Orders No. 13 from the headquarters of the Military Division of the Southwest.

> *"Major General George A. Custer, U. S. Volunteers, will assume command of the following number regiments, and the commanding officers of the said regiments will report their respective commands to him on their arrival at Alexandria, La. ; Seventh Indiana Cavalry; First Iowa Cavalry; Fifth Illinois Cavalry; Twelfth Illinois Cavalry; Second Wisconsin Cavalry."*

E. P. Parsons
Assistant-Adjutant General

Sheridan had supposedly selected these five regiments from among the three brigades, which formed the Cavalry Division, Department of West Tennessee, stationed at Memphis after a review to demonstrate the division's proficiency.

A cavalry division of only five regiments was quite a contrast to the divisional structure of the 3rd Cavalry Division, Army of the Potomac which Custer had commanded only a month earlier. When Custer's 3rd Division returned from the Shenandoah in January of 1865, his command consisted of sixteen regiments organized in three brigades. Despite the diminished numbers, Custer further divided his command into two brigades, even before his limited force had gathered at Alexandria. Emmet C. West of the 2nd Wisconsin Cavalry (and no admirer of Custer) wrote in the post-war period:

> *"…after so long service, the five regiments were so reduced in members that probably there were engaged in the force for two*

Please visit <u>HA.com</u> to view other collectibles auctions.   *A 19.5% Buyer's Premium ($9 min.) Applies To All Lots*

small regiments, but Custer, being a Major-General, must command a division, therefore he divided the small brigade and made two of it. The first, composed of the 5th and 12th Illinois and 7th Indiana , was commanded by Col. (sic) [Brigadier-General] James W. Forsyth. The second, composed of the 1st (sic) [2nd] Wisconsin and 1st Iowa was commanded by Colonel Thompson."

Custer's ego was not the only consideration in the dividing of the five regiments into two brigades. James William Forsyth's military career paralleled Custer's in many respects, including service as a staff officer before graduating to Brigadier, received his commission as Brigadier-General of Volunteers on 19 May 1865, only a few days before Custer was ordered to Sheridan's command in Louisiana. This suggests that his assignment to command a brigade of Custer's new division was anything but accidental.

The official creation of the 2nd Brigade, 2nd (Custer's) Cavalry Division was not made until 5 August 1865, with General Orders No. 14:

"Hereafter this command will be known as the Second Division Cavalry, Military Division of the Gulf and will be composed as follows:

I The First Brigade is organized by Special Order No. 14; from this headquarters.
II The Second Brigade comprising the following regiments; First Iowa Cavalry, Lieutenant-Colonel A. G. McQueen commanding; Second Wisconsin Cavalry' Lieutenant Colonel N. H. Dale commanding
III Colonel Wm. Thompson, first Iowa Cavalry will assume command of the Second Brigade

By Command of Major General Custer
J L Green, A.A.G.

Under this organizational structure, Custer's 2nd Cavalry Division finally departed Alexandria, Louisiana on 8 August 1865 for Hempstead, Texas. The close column march from Alexandria to Hempstead lasted until 26 August 1865, under abominable 120-degree heat. Their stay at Hempstead was a little over two months in length. Edmund Kirby Smith having surrendered in late June, the Union forces in Texas devolved into "occupation duty" maintaining Law & Order. Reflecting their new role, on 29 October 1865, Custer's Division departed Hempstead for the state capitol in Austin, arriving there on 4 November 1865

Before the Custer division's departure to the Texas state capitol on 27 October 1865, the 5th Illinois Cavalry was mustered out of federal service, reducing the division to four regiments. On 15 November 1865 the 2nd Wisconsin Cavalry was also mustered out and sent home. Over the next six months, the balance of the division fulfilled their terms of enlistment and were phased north - the 7th Indiana on 18 February 1866; the 1st Iowa on 16 March 1866, and finally the 12th Illinois on 29 May 1866. In the interim, the War Department took measures to reduce the expenses of the army in the upkeep of the surfeit of high-ranking officers by decommissioning them from volunteer service. Forsyth was the first general officer to lose his commission, being honorably discharged on 15 January 1866. Custer would feel the next "blow". On 1 February 1866, Custer was honorably discharged from the U. S. volunteer service.

George Armstrong Custer and "Libbie" would remain in Austin only a few days longer to close their financial affairs. Custer would revert to his Regular Army commission as captain, as the Grand Army of the Republic dissolved into history.

It was during this nine-month period from May of 1865 to February of 1866, while Custer commanded a two-brigade division, that Custer continued the field use of this "Personal Flag " just as Gen. Sheridan and Gen. Merritt who brought their flags to Texas. General Sheridan never devised a system of designating flags for the forces he commanded in Texas, although some of the eastern commands transferred to Texas during its occupation, continued to fly their old designating flags. Sheridan preferred to fly his own personal headquarters flag - a swallowtail flag divided horizontally, red over white into two equal width bars, and having a five-pointed star of contrasting color on each bar, which is now in the Smithsonian.

Custer would have carried this flag with him while he put down the law-

lessness; even the slave trading that was still taking place in south Texas. On many occasions he prevented the destruction of private property, endearing him to many Texans. This flag made for him by his wife Libby, would have also been used at the home he and his wife shared at Austin, the building the included the Asylum for the Blind, a structure that still stands today. Libbie was the only US Army officer's wife to travel and live with her husband throughout the west. She was always by his side making their home, at his Headquarters from 1865 to his death in 1876, from Texas to the northern plains of the West. Custer was one of the few military officers in the West that actually had a home to come back to at the various western forts where his was stationed.

On 28 July 1866, Congress authorized the creation of four new regiments of cavalry - the 7th and the 8th Cavalry for white troops and the 9th and 10th Cavalry for African American troops who became famous, known as the, "Buffalo Soldiers". When formed, George Armstrong Custer was appointed the 7th Cavalry's Lieutenant Colonel, with immediate field command of the regiment. These four new regular cavalry regiments supplanted the volunteer forces that had served on the plains in 1865 and 1866. Operating on smaller scale when the great volunteer forces gathered during the Civil War, brigades and divisions seldom were called into service, the battalion or the regiment being the prime operational combat unit. As such, the regimental standard became the latter day "headquarters' flag".

The regimental standard of mounted forces from 1833 through 1877 consisted of a fringed dark blue silk field, 27 inches on the pike by 29 inches on the fly, bearing a painted rendition of the "Arms of the United States" surmounting a three-piece scroll bearing the regimental designation, also painted. Six photographs are known to survive from the Custer era that depict the regimental standards of the 7th Cavalry. Of note is one photograph credited to November 1868, depicting Custer's Osage scouts and the 7th's regimental standard, wherein both the eagle's wing from the cavalry's arms and a section of the scroll are visible. Significantly, a penciled notation on the right margin of the photograph identifies this standard as "hdqrs. flag", giving credence to the concept that the "personal" headquarters flags used during the Civil War were retired by that date, being replaced by new flags issued in the field.

An important newspaper account gives us evidence of Custer's "Personal Flag " being displayed in his study at Fort Abraham Lincoln, Dakota Territory in 1876. It comes from the Detroit Free Press in a July 31, 1879 article relating to the unveiling of the Custer monument at West Point. After reviewing the upcoming ceremonies, the article shifts to Monroe, Michigan and to Custer's former home where his parents and sister still lived. His study had been reproduced exactly the same as when he was living at Fort Lincoln before his Last Stand. Open to visitors by the then, three years after his death at The Little Bighorn, the newspaper notes that:

"Here the visitor may find reproduced with the most minute fidelity of detail the General's study or private office exactly as it appeared at his headquarters at Fort Abraham Lincoln when he left it for the last time to engage in the fatal expedition."

The newspaper spares no detail in describing the office - the books, pictures, revolvers with pearl handles - and more:

"His headquarters flags, with captured colors hang upon the walls…"

We are fortunate that this personal flag of General Custer, his most prized military possession, made for him by his beloved wife Libbie, is still existent, and privately held. The most important Custer Icon that exists, it was carried by Custer from Lee's Surrender to Texas and the West.

72069   THREE RIMFIRE .32 CALIBER CARTRIDGES BELONGING TO GENERAL GEORGE ARMSTRONG CUSTER, from a pair of pearl-handled revolvers, intact with original brass shell casings. The bullets' lead has oxidized to an even patina while the casings enjoy a deep, old toning. The cartridges come in a small white envelope imprinted by the office of the late Dr. Lawrence Frost, noted Custer historian and collector from Monroe, Michigan. The front of the envelope carries a signed note in Frost's hand, reading: "*12-11-53 From Gen. Custer's Pearl Handled revolvers small bullets are for pair / larger bullets were mixed with them / Smith & Wesson .38 R.F.*"

Estimate: $4,500-$6,500

72070   CAVALRY BUTTON FROM GENERAL GEORGE ARMSTRONG CUSTER'S UNIFORM AS SAVED BY HIS FAMILY – 23 mm, heavily gilt two-piece brass construction, the face is dominated by a Federal eagle with spread wings holding an olive branch and arrows in its talons, a shield emblazoned with a large "C" (for "Cavalry") is centered on the eagle's chest, the button's underside carries the R & W Robinson Extra Rich depressed backmark (Tice 28). The shank has been removed with a hinged attachment pin affixed in its place so that the button can function as a brooch. The holes resulting from the shank's removal have been filled with solder that matches the brass of the button back. In pristine condition.

A 5" x 3" typed note gives the button's provenance as follows: "Cavalry Buttons From The Uniform of General George Armstrong Custer. 3- 23 - 57. From Miriam Custer." Miriam was the daughter of Nevin Custer, one of General Custer's brothers. As such, the famous cavalryman was her great-uncle. A seemingly unrelated signature, ". *Frost*", is inscribed over the date on the note. This would have been penned by Dr. Lawrence Frost, noted expert on Custer and a collector. The button temporarily resided in his esteemed collection with Custer's wife Libbie wearing his buttons often.

Estimate: $4,500-$6,500

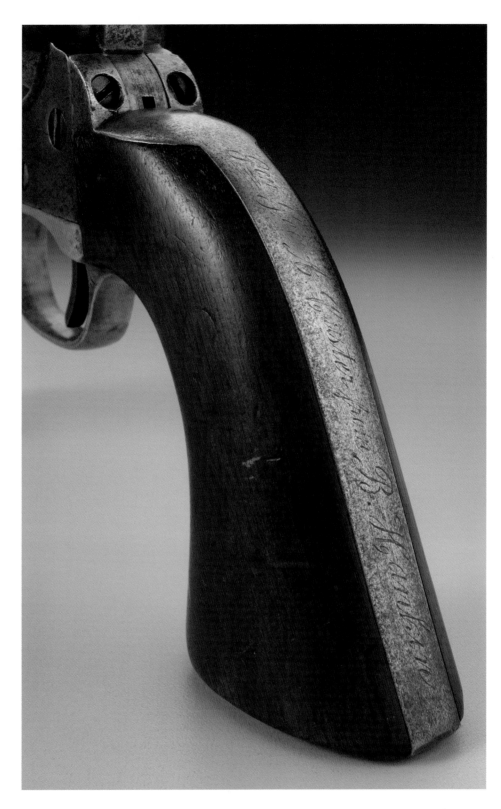

72071   AN 1860 COLT ARMY REVOLVER PRESENTED TO GENERAL GEORGE ARMSTRONG CUSTER - The major revolver used by US troops during the Civil War, this .44 caliber revolver bears an inscription presenting it to General George Armstrong Custer from a 'B. Hankin'. Bearing the serial number 140014 and featuring an 8" round barrel, 6 shot cylinder, back strap, loading lever and plunger and butt strap, all iron, this 1860 Colt has been published extensively indicating its presentation to Custer. The trigger guard, front strap and blade front sight are brass. The serial number 140014 appears on the barrel lug, on the frame in front of the trigger guard, trigger guard flat, and butt strap. "6535" is stamped on the bottom of the wedge. The grip is walnut.

The top of the barrel is stamped "Address Col. Sam L Colt, New York, U.S. America" with the cylinder circumference stamped "Colt Patent No. 0014" over "Pat. Sept. 10,1850". "Colt's Patent" is stamped on the left side of the frame in two lines.

The back strap is engraved "Gen. Geo. A. Custer from B. Hankin", faintly, but legible. Descending from a family collection, this weapon has been known to exist in Kansas for many decades, but, as yet, the identity of Mr. Hankin is unknown. Custer spent much time in Kansas and it is possible that this Colt was given to him by an English sportsman who had hunted buffalo with him and was an admirer of his Civil War deeds.

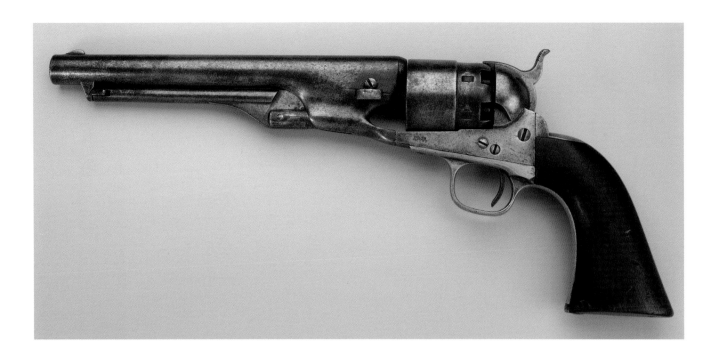

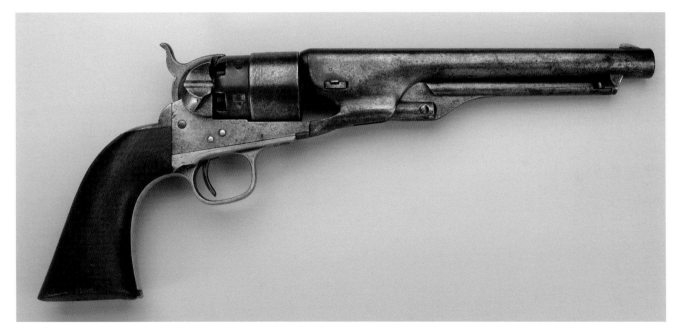

This 1860 Colt is in good mechanical condition with a dark, rich patina on all iron parts except the last 3" of the barrel near the muzzle end which is darker. There are some minor dings and light pitting throughout. The grip has a few dings along the edge of the butt and minor scratches on the right side. The brass parts have a mellow patina which match the overall wear of the gun.

There is extensive provenance with this 1860 Colt. A two-page " Statement", undated, by John S. duMont states that he purchased this revolver in 1952. Mr. duMont believed that 'B. Hankin' was probably an English sportsman who hunted with Custer and purchased a pair of Colt Army Model revolvers, had them engraved, and then presented them to Custer. The pair were split up at some unknown point. The accompanying file contains evidence of another Army Model with the same presentation on the back strap. A 1952 letter from Chas W. Fritz to John duMont states that he (Fritz) had owned the pair and "had an affidavit from a son of B. Hankin certifying that his father had given Custer these guns". He goes on to say that "these guns became separated and I sold the remaining one and the affidavit some years ago"

Published: *Samuel Colt Presents,* pg. 190
Life Magazine, March 2, 1962
Frontier Guns pg 34
Amon Carter Museum of Western Art, Ft Worth, TX, 1964
Gun Report, December 1963
Firearms in the Custer Battle by Parsons and duMont (pictured but serial number not mentioned)

Estimate: $45,000-$65,000

 A 19.5% Buyer's Premium ($9 min.) Applies To All Lots

72072   *GEN'L CUSTER LEADING THE WOLVERINES* AT GETTYSBURG – A PAINTING BY FRANKLIN DULLIN BRISCOE, 1889. July 3, 1863 - Gettysburg, Pennsylvania, the turning point of the Civil War. Newly minted Brigadier General George Armstrong Custer is leading his Michigan Wolverine Brigade of cavalry against Confederate General J.E.B. Stuart at the same time General George Pickett is making his fateful charge at Cemetery Ridge. Custer's dashing figure in battle is showcased in this oil on canvas masterwork of artist Franklin Dullin Briscoe. Dated 1889 and signed 'F. D. Briscoe', this 36" x 22" masterpiece depicts the exact moment at which General Custer orders his momentous charge that drove JEB Stuart's cavalry, led by Genera Wadel Hampton, into the forests at Gettysburg. Hampton himself would suffer saber blows to the head as he tried to regroup his men and repulse Custer's assault.

With Custer as the centerpiece of the picture, at the forefront with his long golden hair flowing and saber drawn, the battlefield smoke and confusion are broken only by the bright colors of the Union and Confederate flags that break through the maelstrom of battle. War horses are depicted dying as are the men of both sides - but Custer is clearly the focus here. A Brigadier for only two weeks prior to Gettysburg, George Armstrong Custer was eager to prove he was worthy of command. Racing in front of his troops to lead the charge, one contemporary account notes of Custer's cavalry charge, "the two columns (one led by Custer and one by Hampton) had come together with a crash…" Custer's fame would only grow throughout the war and thereafter.

Franklin Dullin Briscoe (1844-1903) was known for his battlefield scenes of Gettysburg including a historical mural over 230 feet long in ten panels that toured the United States after the war. Handwritten on the verso of this canvas are the words 'Gettysburg, July 3rd, 1863 - Gen'l Custer leading the Wolverines - F. D. Briscoe 1889'. Briscoe's paintings are rare with most examples being held in museum collections. This oil on canvas depicting General Custer at Gettysburg has only recently come onto the market from a private collection in Philadelphia and has never been offered before. Its original stretcher is labeled 'McClees Galleries, 1897 Walnut, Philadelphia, Est. 1845'. This is a singular opportunity to own a magnificent work of a major Civil War artist depicting General Custer leading his cavalry charge at the Battle of Gettysburg, less than a mile from our auction today!

Provenance: *The Tharpe Collection of American Military History*

Exhibited: *The Liberty Heritage Society Museum*

Estimate: $80,000-$120,000

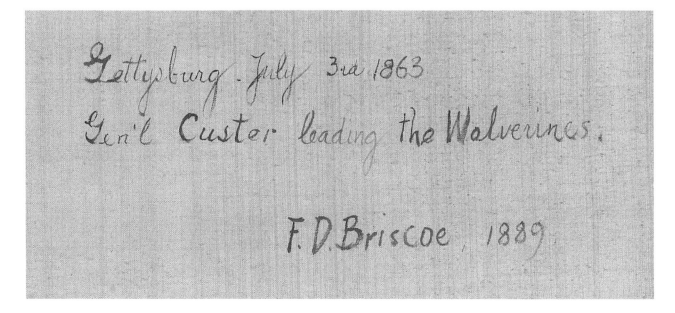

72073   GENERAL GEORGE ARMSTRONG CUSTER HIS MANUSCRIPT "FAIR READING" COPY OF HIS FAREWELL ORDER DELIVERED TO HIS TROOPS AT LEE'S SURRENDER, 3.5 pages, 5" x 8", front and verso. Original spelling. Headed: *"Copy of Order/ Head Qrs 3d Cavalry Division/Appomattox Court House April 9-1865/Soldiers of the 3d Cavalry Division."* In part, *"With profound grattitud towards the god of battles by whose blessings our enemies have been humbled and our armis rendered triumphant Your commanding Genral avails himself of this his first opportunity to express to you his admiration of the heroic manner in which you have passed through the Series of battles which to day resulted in the surrender of the enemys entire army - the record established by your indomitabl courage is unparralelled in the annals of war. your prowess has won for you the respect and admiration of your enemies during the past six months althoug in most instances cnfronted by superior numbers **you have Captured from the enemy in open battle (111) one hundred and Eleven pieces of field artillery (65) Sixty five Battle flags and upward of (10,000) Ten thousand prisoners of war including (7) Seven Genral officers** - within the past ten days and included within the above you have captured (46) forty Six pieces of field artillery and (37) Thirty seven battle flags - you have never lost a gun nor lost a color - and never have been defeated…let us hope that our work is done and that blessed with the comforts of peace we may soon be permitted to enjoy the pleasures of home and friends - for our comrades who has fallen let us cherish a greatfull remembrance - to the wounded and to those who languish in Suthron prisons let our heart felt sympathies be tendered. And now speaking for myself alone - when the war is ended and the task of the historian begins when those deeds of daring which has rendered the name and fame of the Third cavalry Division imperishable and incribed upon the bright pages of our countrys history. **I only ask that my name may be written as that of the commander of the 3d Cavalry Division.**"* An ironic last line from the General whose name is remembered in his country's history as being associated with the 7th, not the 3rd Cavalry, and with the Battle of the Little Bighorn, not the Civil War. Strengthened with tape between pages two and three. In fine condition.

Estimate: $8,000-$12,000

72074   A STRIKING PASTEL PORTRAIT OF BREVET MAJOR GENERAL GEORGE ARMSTRONG CUSTER – Major General George Armstrong Custer has been the subject of many historical debates, and fortunately for us, many artistic renderings of his strong personae and presence. This vivid pastel measures 11" x 14" and is done in the oval, matted and spectacularly framed in a heavily gilded wooden frame.

Covered by glass, the portrait portrays Custer in one his most famous poses, the one dated May 1865 that was captured in a photograph by John Goldin and Company. But the unnamed artist here captures what Goldin could not - the vivid colors of Custer's golden hair, his major general's shoulder straps and gold buttons. Even at the close of the war, Custer still wears his cavalier's hat with one side turned up, but with a more peaceful expression, perhaps, because the war has ended.

This is a beautiful rendering of Custer in the pastel medium which lends itself to maximizing expression, color and contrast as in this striking portrait of the famous cavalryman who went on to Indian fighting on the Plains. Wardate portraits of Custer are very rare.

Provenance: *The Tharpe Collection of American Military History*

Exhibited: *The Liberty Heritage Society Museum*

Estimate: $20,000-$25,000

72075 ONE OF THE LAST PORTRAITS EVER TAKEN OF GEORGE ARMSTRONG CUSTER, professionally matted and framed to 11.25" x 17.5" overall. This cabinet card is imprinted on the lower front margin by New York photographer Jose M. Mora and dates to March, 1876. Custer is shown in the full dress uniform of a U. S. Cavalry Lieutenant Colonel as commander of the 7th U. S. Cavalry, just a few months before his Last Stand at Little Big Horn. In excellent condition.

Estimate: $2,000-$3,000

72076 BRVT. MAJOR GENERAL GEORGE ARMSTRONG CUSTER AUTOGRAPH ENDORSEMENT SIGNED "*G. A. Custer*". One page, 3" x 5", Headquarters Nov. 26, [1864]. Custer requests an application be granted in full: "Headquarters, 3rd Div. Cav. M.M.D. Nov.26, This case being an urgent one, I earnestly recommend that this application be granted. G.A. Custer Bvt. Maj, General Com. 3 Div. & A C of Cav".

Estimate: $2,000-$3,000

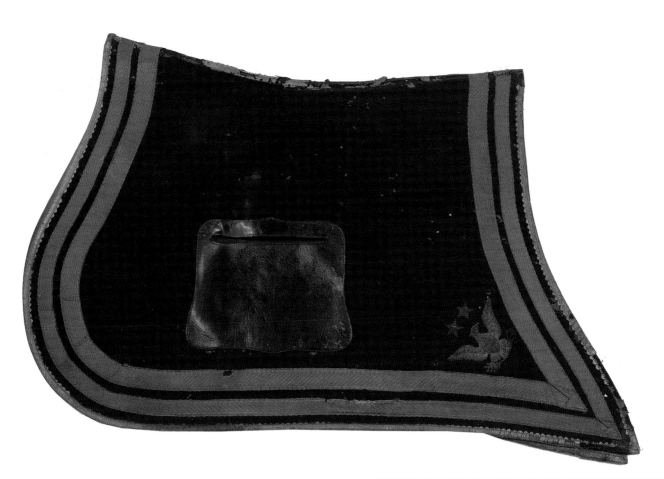

72077　MAJOR GENERAL PHILIP SHERIDAN'S ORNATE SADDLE

CLOTH – Major General Philip Sheridan was one of General Ulysses S. Grant's favorite commanders. A West Point graduate, Class of 1853, Sheridan was promoted to captain after the attack on Fort Sumter. He later fought at the Battle of Pea Ridge and at Corinth where he met Brigadier General William T. Sherman who was influential in seeing that Sheridan was given his own regiment, the 2nd Michigan Cavalry. Sheridan would become fast friends with General Grant and go on to become one of the most famous cavalrymen of the Union Army.

This ornate saddlecloth was owned and used by General Sheridan in the Civil War. Measuring 46" across and 39" from front to back, the blanket graced the back of General Sheridan's famous mount Rienzi, a horse he later named Winchester after he made is famous ride (see prints next lot) in October 1864 to rally his troops and defeat Confederate Lieutenant General Jubal Early. It was for that action that President Abraham Lincoln promoted Sheridan to major general, the two-star designation which appears on this elaborate saddle blanket. After Sheridan's famous horse on which this blanket was used died, he was stuffed and is now in the Smithsonian Institution.

The dark blue felt of the blanket is trimmed by two 1¼" gold bands. The entire blanket is trimmed in a gold-colored leather trim as well. At the rear bottom corners of the blanket are two heavy gold bullion federal eagles with two five-pointed bullion stars above signifying Sheridan's rank of major general. The entire cloth and bullion along with the trim is laid down on heavy black saddle leather on the underside of the blanket. There are two leather slits in the blanket for the cinch strap to be threaded through, each heavily lined inside and out with black leather. There is some cloth loss on each side from saddle wear and natural cracking at the top of the blanket, however the blanket is in overall good condition.

Major General Sheridan would go on to completely defeat Confederate General Early's army in the Appomattox Campaign and was instrumental in forcing General Robert E. Lee's surrender. He was not promoted to lieutenant general until 1869 thus making this saddle blanket being used by him through the remainder of the Civil War and the West, in Texas and on the Great Plains in Indian fighting with Custer serving along side him.

This is a beautiful and remarkable saddle blanket owned by one of the most famous and effective generals of the Civil War.

Provenance: *Francis Lord, General Philip Sheridan's granddaughter*
The Tharpe Collection of American Military History

Exhibited: *The Liberty Heritage Society Museum*

Estimate: $80,000-$120,000

Please visit *HA.com* to view other collectibles auctions. *A 19.5% Buyer's Premium ($9 min.) Applies To All Lots*

72078 **THE FAMOUS PAINTING OF MAJOR GENERAL PHILIP SHERIDAN BY THOMAS BUCHANAN READ (1822-1872)** *SHERIDAN'S RIDE FROM WINCHESTER* – Thomas Buchanan Read was a celebrated artist even before the Civil War when he worked as a Major on the staff of General Lew Wallace giving talks and creating propaganda art for the war effort. Also a poet and a sculptor, he was known as early as 1840 for his portraiture art having completed a very celebrated commission for a portrait of William Henry Harrison. But he favored historical pictures with a poetic flair. In this painting of a hard-charging Major General Philip Sheridan on horseback mounted on his general's saddle cloth (see previous lot) in the midst of the Battle of Winchester, Read created his most magnificent work. Born in Chester County, Pennsylvania in 1822, Thomas Buchanan Read exhibited his art at the Pennsylvania Academy and the National Academy of Design. After his service with General Wallace he briefly set up a studio in New Orleans with the express purpose of completing a portrait of General Sheridan. He would later return to Europe and Rome, Italy to complete this exquisite picture of Sheridan in battle. This 54" x 38" striking oil on canvas depicts Sheridan at the highest point of his Civil War career at the Battle of Winchester. Sheridan is charging into battle astride his famous horse Rienzi, his courageous mount that he renamed 'Winchester' after this battle. Considered a hero of the war himself, Winchester was preserved after his death at the Smithsonian Institution. Sheridan has his saber in hand, rallying his troops who have started to retreat until they see their valiant General rushing to the battlefield from twenty miles away upon hearing of their dismay. While his horse is straining at the bit, Sheridan is shown with his hat turned up at front by the rushing wind, racing through scattered cannon balls, shattered canteens and broken rifles giving evidence of the battle that is raging about him. Signed and dated 'T. Buchanan Read, Rome, 1870', the colors of this painting and the dynamism of Read's characterization of Sheridan's ride give evidence of Read's poetic work. Indeed, Read composed a famous poem to coincide with the picture. Titled Sheridan's Ride, Read describes the General's gallop to the battlefield in eloquent prose that he translates into art in this picture. Sheridan's horse "with his wild eye full of fire" and of Sheridan, "Hurrah! Hurrah for Sheridan! Hurrah! hurrah for horse and man!" This striking painting is superbly framed in a 4½" carved ornate wood and gilt frame decorated with stars at the upper corners, laurel at the sides with a rosette and an elaborate stand of arms and flags at each of the lower corners. There is a medallion at the center bottom and a plaque denoting the painting and the artist. There are small flecks at the top right of the frame, but the painting is in excellent condition, bright and vivid in color, a true masterpiece capturing the essence of this Civil War hero.

Provenance: *The Tharpe Collection of American Military History*

Exhibited: *The Liberty Heritage Society Museum*

Estimate: $200,000-$300,000

72079 MAJOR GENERAL PHILIP SHERIDAN'S GOLD MEDAL PRESENTED BY GENERAL ULYSSES S. GRANT – A favorite of General Ulysses S. Grant, Philip Sheridan was promoted swiftly through the ranks during the Civil War. An 1853 graduate of West Point, he had distinguished himself on the frontier and in the Pacific Northwest. He was promoted to captain just after Fort Sumter.

Making influential friends quickly at the start of the war, Sheridan was appointed as colonel of the 2nd Michigan Cavalry. Within six months he would be a major general.

Union commander General Ulysses S. Grant was so impressed with his actions that he brought Sheridan to the east and made him commander of his cavalry of the Army of the Potomac.

Later, General Grant presented this ornate gold cavalry medal to Philip Sheridan as a token of his esteem and admiration for his great cavalry leadership. The medal measures 2" x 2" at its widest and highest points and is hinged at the top. A cavalry saber hilt protrudes from the top of the medal above a bar below which is a pair of crossed cavalry sabers. Immediately below the sabers is a wreath encircling a calligraphied 'S' attached to a blue lapis medallion.

Below the medal there is a flagstaff that slides through four rings for the attachment of a ribbon which survives, but is not attached to the medal. The red and white ribbon is in the form of Sheridan's major general's cavalry guidon with the white and now-purplish stars situated on the red and white bars of the swallow-tailed ribbon.

This is truly a remarkable medal awarded to the Union cavalry legend Major General Philip Sheridan by General Ulysses S. Grant. It is featured prominently on Sheridan's uniform in the famous post-war photographs captured by photographer C. D. Mosher's images of Sheridan in dress uniform as he continued to serve in the United States Army, ultimately rising to the rank of four-star general. A copy of the photograph accompanies this medal. While the gold is in excellent condition, the ribbon is somewhat soiled and is detached from the medal.

Provenance: *The Norm Flayderman Collection; The Tharpe Collection of American Military History*

Exhibited: *The Liberty Heritage Society Museum*

Estimate: $80,000-$120,000

72080   PHILIP SHERIDAN SIGNED CABINET CARD PRESENTED TO U.S.GRANT – "*P. H. Sheridan Lieut General*" below image in margin, H. Rocher, Chicago, Illinois backmark. An aging Sheridan appears here in a full dress uniform decked out with service medals, including the gold medal presented to him by General Grant, and having three stars on its epaulettes. This image dates from between the late 1870s and Sheridan's 1883 appointment to full General. Slight wear to edges with hairline water stains along the lower margin and through the left field. Overall fine condition. Philip Sheridan (1831 - 1888) is best remembered as Grant's cavalry chief during the latter part of the Civil War. His scorched earth policy in the Shenandoah Valley set the tone for modern warfare.

Provenance: *U.S. Grant II; Christie's; The Tharpe Collection of American Military History*

Exhibited: *The Liberty Heritage Society Museum*

Estimate: $25,000-$35,000

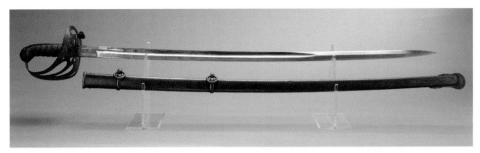

72081   THE SWORD OF GENERAL PHILIP SHERIDAN PRESENTED TO THOMAS DONALDSON, OF THE SMITHSONIAN INSTITUTION

– General Philip Henry Sheridan was one of the most famous commanders of the Civil War. This presentation sword was presented to Thomas Donaldson in 1887, a good friend of Sheridan's who was an collector of American historical artifacts.

An 1853 graduate of the United States Military Academy at West Point, Sheridan served in the 1st United States Infantry Regiment and took part in Indian fighting receiving a minor wound near Portland, Oregon. At the out-break of the Civil War he was already a seasoned warrior who quickly rose through the ranks to lead the Cavalry Corps of the Army of the Potomac un-der his friend General Ulysses S. Grant. Sheridan was instrumental in blocking General Robert E. Lee's escape and forcing his surrender at Appomattox Court House.

This imported sword owned by General Sheridan early in his career was man-ufactured by David Wilhelm Walscheid of Germany, a popular maker of this ornate version of the 1850 regulation foot officer's sword which were widely imported during the early days of the Civil War (*Echoes of Glory,* Time-Life, pg. 74). Sheridan would be active in the United States Army after the Civil War including fighting in the Indian Wars where he was promoted to Lieutenant General. President Grant sent Sheridan to observe the Franco-Prussian War where Sheridan toured Europe, returning to report to Grant. In 1886 Sheridan was named as president of the Military Order of the Loyal Legion of the United States, a military order that dated back to the Civil War composed of almost every military officer of note. Modeled on the Society of the Cincinnati, membership was later opened up to descendants of such officers.

It was on that ceremonial occasion that we learn that Sheridan was a close friend of Thomas Corwin Donaldson, a former Civil War officer and personal friend of President Rutherford B. Hayes. Donaldson writes extensively in his memoirs of the induction of Sheridan as Commander of the Loyal Legion at the Historical Society of Pennsylvania in Philadelphia. As Donaldson wit-nessed the event, former President Hayes was present and handed the ivory gavel of Commander to Sheridan. Afterwards, the group walked to the local chapter of the Loyal Legion where they viewed a copy of the famous painting *Sheridan's Ride to Winchester* whereupon Hayes remarked, "Get me a copy of this lithograph; I am one of the few men that saw this ride."

It was shortly after this event that Sheridan presented this sword to Thomas Donaldson. Engraved at the ornate spread-eagle guard, *Philip H. Sheridan, Lieut. Genl. to Thomas Donaldson. Feb. 24th 1887* In his memoirs, Donaldson later writes of how Sheridan gave him a full recollection of the ride at Winchester on a later occasion, most certainly the date of this presentation.

Thomas Donaldson was a major collector for the Smithsonian Institution but also amassed an enormous personal collection of historical objects ranging from President Abraham Lincoln's furniture, an original copy of the 13th Amendment signed by President Lincoln, General Grant's 'unconditional sur-render' letter and this sword given to him personally by Lieutenant General Philip Sheridan. It is listed in the *Memoirs of Thomas Donaldson* as edited by Watt P. Marchman which is housed at the Rutherford B. Hayes Presidential Center in Fremont, Ohio.

The 1850 Regulation foot officer's sword is an ornate version made and imported by Walscheid for the U. S market at the beginning of the Civil War with a 33" Solingen blade. Along the 19½" fuller there appears foliate engraving with the federal eagle clutching a ribbon bearing the inscription 'E. Pluribus Unum'. At the ricasso is the brass round insert with the word 'proved'. On the reverse is the maker's mark at the ricasso with foliate engraving extending up the fuller interspersed by the engraved 'U. S.' The brass guard has openwork in the form a spread-winged eagle over a 'US' and is surmounted by the inscription 'E. Pluribus'. A ribbon at the top of the guard bears the engraved dedication from Sheridan to Donaldson. The rayskin grip is bound by twisted brass wire and overall the sword is in very good condition with a nice dark patina throughout.

This is an early Civil War sword owned and used by General Philip Henry Sheridan, one the greatest military men America has had to offer, perhaps during his famous ride. It was received by a prominent soldier, historian and collector who helped amass the extensive collection at the Smithsonian Institution..

Provenance: *Philip Sheridan to Thomas Donaldson; The Tharpe Collection Of American Military History*

Exhibited: *The Liberty Heritage Society Museum*

Estimate: $80,000-$120,000

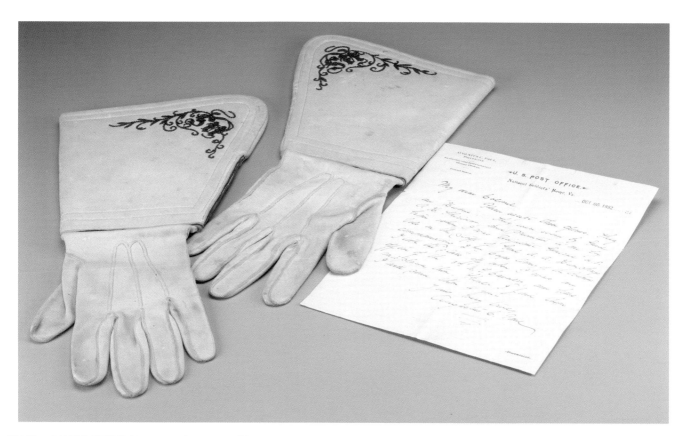

72082   MAJOR GENERAL PHILIP SHERIDAN'S CAVALRY GAUNTLETS, GIVEN TO CAPTAIN AUGUSTUS C. PAUL   Union Major
General Philip Sheridan was one of the most famous cavalry generals in the United States Army during the Civil War. These gauntlets were used by him
during the Civil War and given to an acquaintance, Captain Augustus C. Paul.

After graduating from West Point in 1853, Sheridan served in Texas and in the Pacific Northwest where he engaged in Indian fighting. It was in Oregon
that he was slightly wounded and began to hone his negotiating skills with Indians that he would use after the Civil War.

A career army officer by the time of Fort Sumter, Sheridan was promoted to captain at the outbreak of the war. After a stint of duty in Missouri, Sheridan
made it into battle at Pea Ridge, Arkansas. In May of 1862 he received an appointment as colonel of the 2nd Michigan Cavalry and was promoted to
Brigadier General only months later. He would lead his cavaliers at Perryville, Stones River and Chickamauga. But it was during the Overland Campaign
in May of 1864 that General Sheridan would have encountered the young Captain Augustus C. Paul, then serving as Assistant Adjutant General of US
Volunteers to General A. A. Humphreys of the Union's 2nd Corps.

The son and grandson of career army officers, Augustus Chouteau Paul was appointed as Assistant Adjutant General to General Humphreys after his
service at the Battle of Stones River and after being captured at the Battle of Spottsylvania. A handwritten, signed letter dated October 25, 1892 from
Augustus C. Paul which accompanies these gauntlets states that Paul was given them by General Sheridan during Paul's service with 2nd Corps under
General Humphreys. Further, in the letter Paul mentions that he took the stars off the gauntlets when he served as an officer of the 3rd US Cavalry. Paul's
reference in the letter is to his post-Civil War service in the New Mexico and Arizona Territories when he reenlisted in the US Army as a 2nd lieutenant
with 3rd US Cavalry after the war.

The gauntlets, made by Schuyler, Hartley & Graham, are of fine buff leather and measure approximately 16" from the tip on the middle finger to the longest point of the gauntlet that would reach to the upper forearm. There is elaborate gold-threaded embroidery in a foliate pattern at the upper corner of
the gauntlet with the 'US' initials being especially heavily threaded. The remaining impressions are still visible where the single stars on each gauntlet have
been removed as mentioned by Captain Paul in his accompanying letter written by him in 1892 while he served as Postmaster of the National Soldiers'
Home in Virginia. The gauntlets are in otherwise very good condition.

Augustus C. Paul's service later in Wyoming and Western Nebraska from 1872 to 1876 culminated in his brush with history. The 3rd US Cavalry was part
of the Big Horn and Yellowstone Expedition commanded by Brigadier General George Crook. Leaving for the Bighorn Mountains with General Crook,
Paul was to meet with two other columns, including the one led by Lieutenant Colonel George Armstrong Custer. Due to not only the massacre at Little
Big Horn, but also because of their own near-disastrous fight with a large contingent of Sioux and Cheyenne at the Rosebud River, neither Paul nor Crook
were ever able to join their forces with Custer.

These cavalry gauntlets, presented to fellow US Army officer Augustus C. Paul by General Philip Sheridan, were obviously treasured (and used) by
Captain Paul as he made his way through the Civil War and into the Indian Wars and are a remarkable showpiece.

Provenance: *Gen. Philip Sheridan, Augustus Paul, The Tharpe Collection of American Military History*

Exhibited: *The Liberty Heritage Society Museum*

Estimate: $45,000-$65,000

72083   A COMPASS INSCRIBED FROM GENERAL PHILIP SHERIDAN TO H. C. KOCH – This compass was a gift from Union General Philip Sheridan to his topographical engineer H. C. Koch. Koch, an architect from Milwaukee noted the presentation by having it engraved on the reverse as follows:

This compass
Was given me
By
Gen. P. H. Sheridan on Jan. 3rd 1863
After the Battle
Of Stone River.
H. C. Koch

Henry C. Koch was born in Germany and came to the United States to work as an architect. He enlisted with the 24th Wisconsin Volunteers and served as General Sheridan's topographical engineer making sketches and maps throughout the war. He lived at Milwaukee after the war, designed over 700 buildings including Milwaukee City Hall.

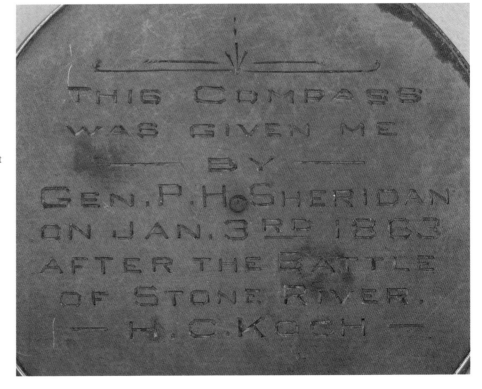

This compass given to him by General Sheridan is made of brass and is missing the case cover. The glass is also broken giving evidence that this compass was used extensively during the war.

Provenance: *P. Koch family; The Tharpe Collection of American Military History*

Exhibited: *The Liberty Heritage Society Museum*

Estimate: $45,000-$65,000

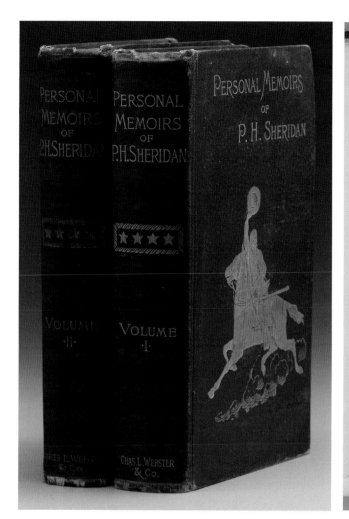

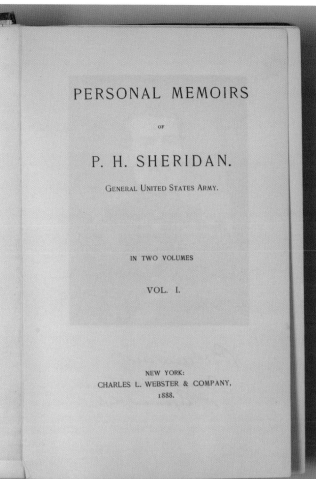

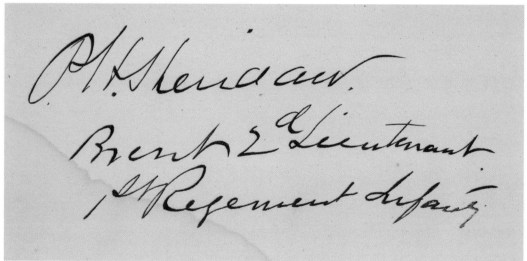

72084 **THE *PERSONAL MEMOIRS OF P. H. SHERIDAN* AND SIGNATURE BY SHERIDAN – TWO VOLUMES OF THE AUTOBIOGRAPHY OF THE CIVIL WAR GENERAL** – This two-volume set of the famed Union cavalryman's memoirs are 500 pages each in length, octavo with their original dark green cloth covers. With attractive gold stamping on the spine, each volume has a large gold stamp on the cover of General Philip Sheridan on horseback, depicting his famous ride from Winchester. While the binding of volume one has separated, it may be easily repaired. There is some light foxing as well. Overall the volumes are in good condition.

Provenance: *The Norm Flayderman Collection; The Tharpe Collection of American Military History*

Exhibited: *The Liberty Heritage Society Museum*

Estimate: $100-$200

72085   THE SPURS OF MAJOR GENERAL GEORGE THOMAS, A *CARTE DE VISITE* OF THE GENERAL
− George Henry Thomas, an 1840 graduate of West Point fought in the Mexican War before becoming one of the most famous Union general of the Civil War, particularly known for his victory at Nashville.

These silver spurs are from early in his career, perhaps, due to the style of the spurs, the large 13-point star rowels and long curved shanks, the Mexican War where he distinguished himself at the Battle of Monterrey and then at Buena Vista. After teaching at West Point, Thomas was torn over the choice he had to make at the outbreak of the Civil War. A career Army officer but a native of Virginia, he chose to stay in the US Army.

Rising to the rank of Major General, Thomas undoubtedly had the spurs with him as he commanded the Army of the Cumberland and at the occupation of Nashville, Tennessee. Still sturdy with the rowels soundly in place, these spurs measure 8" from the tip of the rowel to the front of the spur where the leather buckles would be attached.

These spurs come with a *carte de visite* of Thomas as a major general. The photograph bears the back stamp of *"E. & H.T. Anthony, 50 Broadway, New York, From Photographic Negative in Brady's National Portrait Gallery."*

Provenance: *The Norm Flayderman Collection; The Tharpe Collection of American Military History*

Exhibited: *The Liberty Heritage Society Museum*

Estimate: $10,000-$15,000

AMERICAN FLAGS

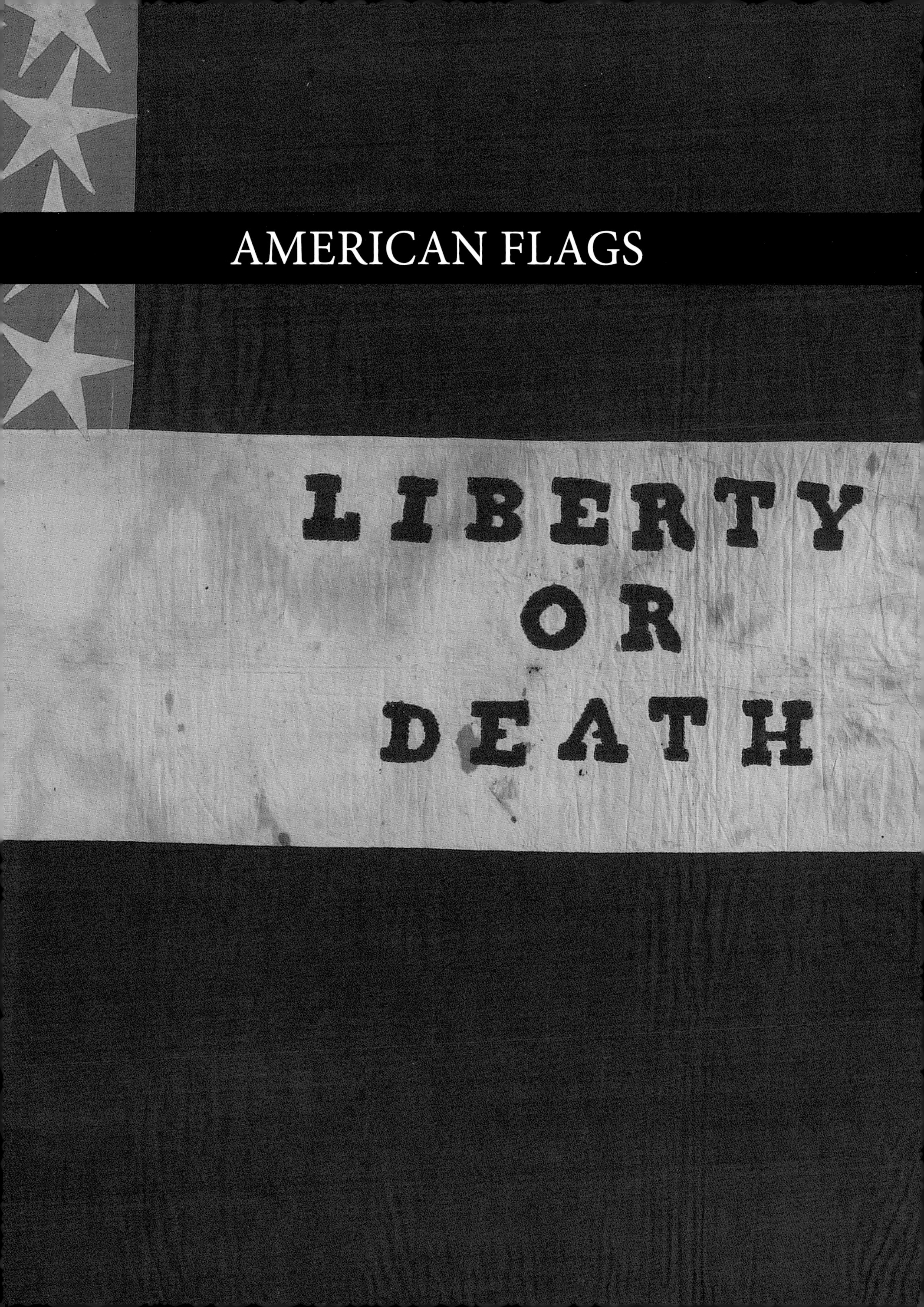

**72086   EARLY 18TH CENTURY
U. S. NATIONAL FLAG, CA. 1790**
– One of the earliest documented
American flags in existence. Just 2
years after the government was formed
and the Constitution was adopted,
this flag would have flown during
George Washington's first Term as the
first President of the United States of
America, which was still comprised of
the original thirteen colonies. 13 stars,
wool bunting, 44" x 75", twelve stars
in three rows of four with one larger
center star, purportedly from the Old
Sandy Point Light House, New York in
1790.

The lighthouse was built in 1764 at the
southern end of New York harbor in
New Jersey but was dismantled during the Revolutionary War to keep the
British navigators from using it. They
promptly rebuilt it and the lighthouse
has stood at the harbor ever since, the
oldest working lighthouse in the United
States.

Authentication: *Letters of authenticity
and research from renowned Civil War
flag expert and author Howard Madaus.*

Provenance: *The Crow Art Partnership Collection (Dallas, Texas)*

Estimate: $18,000-$24,000

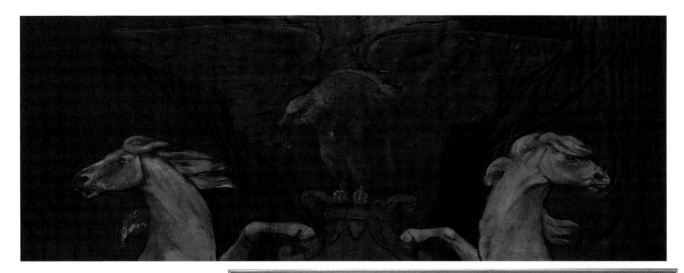

72087 PENNSYLVANIA STATE FENCIBLES BANNER, PAINTED BY GULLAGER CA. 1798 – Magnificent and early banner of the Pennsylvania Fencibles of Philadelphia as well as one of the earliest American flags in existence. The state seal is beautifully hand painted by Christian Gullager, active in Philadelphia from 1798-1826. Born in Copenhagen, Denmark, he studied at the Royal Academy of Fine Arts in Copenhagen where he was awarded a silver medal in 1780. He came to the newly founded America and married Mary Selman in Newburyport, MA in 1786. He painted numerous portraits of Newburyport citizens and moved to Boston in 1789 and advertised as a portrait painter located at Hanover Street. This particular flag was painted by him in 1805. Made of dark navy blue silk and measuring 35" x 57½". Gold fringe at the bottom only.

Authentication: *Letters of authenticity and research from renowned Civil War flag expert and author Howard Madaus.*

Exhibited: *Nannos Collections*

Provenance: *The Crow Art Partnership Collection (Dallas, Texas)*

Estimate: $60,000-$80,000

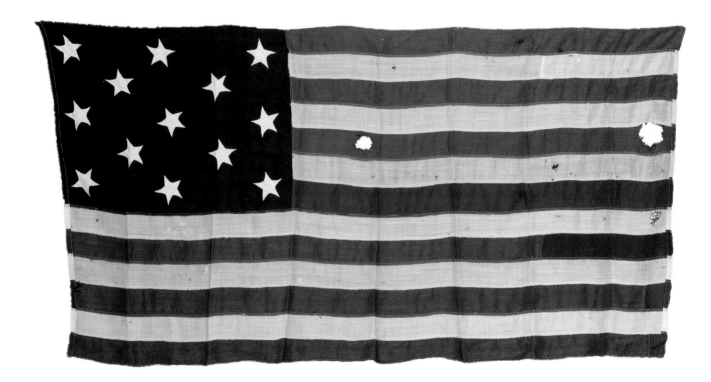

72088   EARLY 18TH CENTURY U. S. NATIONAL FLAG - CA.1795 - One of the earliest documented Stars and Stripes in existence, consisting of 13 stars in a 3-2-3 configuration, wool bunting, 48" x 92". Purportedly belonged to Parker Brown of Salem, Massachusetts in 1795.

Authentication: *Letters of authenticity and research from renowned Civil War flag expert and author Howard Madaus.*

Provenance: *The Crow Art Partnership Collection (Dallas, Texas)*

Estimate: $8,000-$12,000

72089   MICHIGAN NAVAL MILITIA FLAG, CA. 1840 – The most beautiful flag in the collection, with a hand painted American eagle on the open seas, with flags and streamers, surrounded by 26 hand painted gold stars. On a beautiful gold silk field, 55" high on the staff by 67" wide on the fly exclusive of 2¾" deep worsted gold fringe on three sides, bearing in its center on the reverse side a scalloped panel 34" high by 44½" wide depicting in its center a seascape with its central device, an eagle perched on a scallop sea shell holding in its talons four arrows and an olive branch. On its breast is a shield of red and white vertical stripes under a red (not blue) "chief," all with gold border. A scroll of white shaded light blue edged red emanates from the eagle's beak with nation motto E PLURIBUS UNUM in black Roman letters ½" high; also with U.S. national and plain white colors aft. All surrounded by an arc of 26 gold eight pointed stars, the 26th star representing Michigan, dates the flag to the period 1837 - 1845.

Authentication: *Letters of authenticity and research from renowned Civil War flag expert and author Howard Madaus.*

Provenance: *The Crow Art Partnership Collection (Dallas, Texas)*

Estimate: $30,000-$40,000

72090   MASSACHUSETTS STATE MILITIA FLAG, CIRCA 1850 – A magnificent silk flag with gold fringe measuring 66" on the fly and 55" at the hoist, this is a beautifully painted Massachusetts State Seal, which contains a full standing portrait of an Indian Chief in native attire with a tomahawk in his belt. This same image is on a bronze Revolutionary War cannon barrel from Massachusetts. On the reverse is the Massachusetts Pine Tree Emblem, complete with Liberty Cap, perched on the top of the tree. This same image of a Pine tree image appears on Massachusetts's coinage of the period as well as on their Revolutionary flags. A remarkable flag with original gold silk ties, this flag certainly would have flown during the first years of the Civil War, carried by militia volunteers from Massachusetts.

Authentication: *Letters of authenticity and research from renowned Civil War flag expert and author Howard Madaus.*

Provenance: *The Crow Art Partnership Collection (Dallas, Texas)*

Estimate: $30,000-$40,000

72091 CAVALRY FLAG OF 3RD NEW YORK "HUSSARS" – This exquisite and quite rare style of embroidered flag belonged to Capt. George W. Sauer's Company C of the 3rd Cavalry, known as the "German Hussars" from New York City. They volunteered for federal service and left the state on July 23, 1861. The company was composed of one hundred volunteers from other companies upon the request of the General Government for some cavalry, for three months' service, and left the state July 23, 1861.

The officers of the company were as follows: Capt. Sauer, age 33, enrolled at New York City, to serve three months, and mustered as Captain, July 23, 1861; mustered out with company, November 2, 1861, at New York; Charles Lambert, First lieutenant, mustered out with company, November 2, 1861, at New York City.

Side A: Blue silk field, Gilt thread star in all four corners. Center panel is composed of a floss silk portrait of the Hussar's commanding officer mounted on a white horse, sword drawn and raised in his right hand with gilt epaulets. Wearing a medium blue triple breasted Hussar pelisse and a black leather shako. Trousers matching the jacket in color with a gold stripe on the outer seam. All set against blue sky with white clouds interspersed. Stars are 1¼" across points. The fringe measures 2/14".

Side B: Hand embroidered using gold gilt thread. Double sprigged wreath surmounted at junction by U.S. eagle. Two U.S. flags with 13 stars suspended from brown velvet lances with halberd heads with a Union shield at bottom. Blue silk field, yellow silk fringe on 3 sides. 21" on the hoist by 24½" on the fly. 1¾ " sleeve. The script reads "3d Regt., 1st Troop, NY, German Hussars".

Authentication: *Letters of authenticity and research from renowned Civil War flag expert and author Howard Madaus.*

Estimate: $16,000-$20,000

Kill Cavalry's Personal Banner From His Wife

72092   UNION CAVALRY GENERAL JUDSON KILPATRICK'S PERSONAL BANNER, 90" x 2.5", double swallow-tail form, of gold silk throughout with red border enclosing a hand-stitched blue silk legend reading "KILPATRICK'S CAVALRY…ALICE." Minimal soiling and in excellent condition. This unique streamer carries the Christian name of Kilpatrick's first wife, Alice Nailer, whom he wed upon graduating with West Point's Class of 1861. It is highly likely that the young Mrs. Kilpatrick personally stitched the banner for her rising star of a husband. In fact, a *New York Times* story from November 23, 1863 recounts Kilpatrick's receipt of a Third Division battle flag made by Tiffany and mentions the banner as follows: "From the top of the flag, besides the tassels pendant are two yellow streamers bordered with red - one bearing the name of 'Alice'…". The banner is accompanied by a field photograph of Kilpatrick that is matted to a 10" x 12" board. A verso inscription states that it was taken in September, 1863. The general is shown standing before his tent and smiling directly at the photographer. Printed on glossy stock with a few light scratches. The mount is moderately aged and has some light chipping to its finish.

The young and reckless Hugh Judson Kilpatrick (1836 - 1881) was tolerated by his superiors, urged on by his ego, corrupted by greed and loathed by many who crossed his ambitious path. Kilpatrick was a divisional cavalry commander who rose to the rank of brevet major-general during the Civil War. His casual disregard for the safety of his men led to his nickname of "Kill Cavalry". Because he was a fighter, though, Kilpatrick was given increasing responsibility during the course of the war. A veteran of Brandy Station and Gettysburg, Kilpatrick transferred to the Western Theater and served as Sherman's cavalry commander.

Provenance: *The Tharpe Collection of American Military History*

Exhibited: *The Liberty Heritage Society Museum*

Estimate: $25,000-$35,000

”If any one attempts to haul down the American flag, shoot him on the spot.”

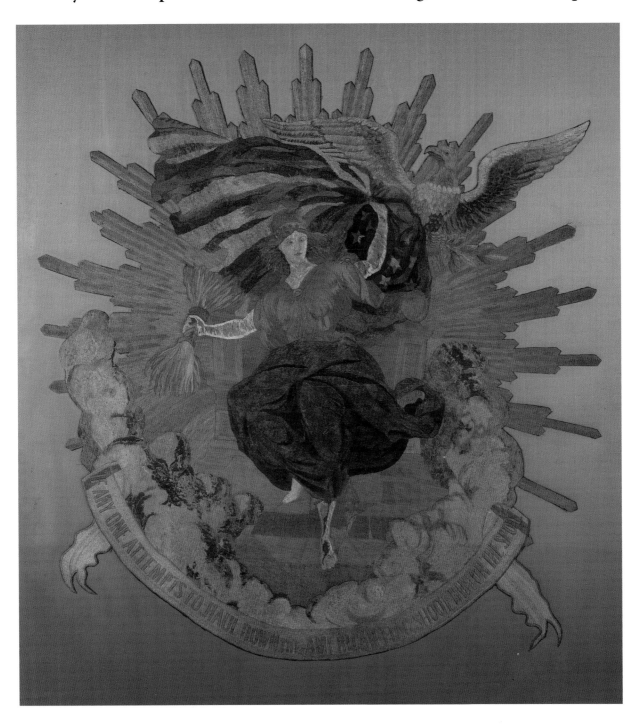

72093   EMANUEL LEUTZE-DESIGNED FLAG PRESENTED TO UNION MAJOR GENERAL JOHN A. DIX ‒ commemorating one of the most famous quotes to have come out of the Civil War. This historically significant flag was presented to Dix in a public ceremony on the evening of April 23, 1864, at the close of the New York Sanitary Fair. Mrs. William T. Blodgett, wife of a prominent New York businessman, active participant in the Sanitary Commission, and promoter of the arts, had commissioned the manufacture of the flag by the legendary Tiffany & Co. (which, by the way, supplied the Union with swords, flags, and surgical instruments during the Civil War). At the time of this presentation, Dix was president of the United States Sanitary Commission. The design is a striking scene of Liberty rising from her seat, grasping the American flag in one hand and the thunderbolts of war in the other. The display further incorporates along the bottom the famous slogan assigned to Dix: "If anyone attempts to haul down the American flag, shoot him on the spot." Elegantly framed by the original intricately designed standard, the needlework retains much of its color and graphic appeal. Although removed from the original silk backing in 1970, the focal point of the piece has been maintained and displays in very fine condition. Complete at 47.25" x 49.50" with the central feature measuring 38.5" x 41".

Born in 1798 in New Hampshire, John Adams Dix started his military career early, joining the Artillery as a military cadet at the tender age of 14. After moving to New York with his wife to manage some of her family's land holdings, he entered the practice of law, later serving not only in various New York state offices but also as a U.S. senator (1845-1849). James Buchanan appointed him secretary of the treasury in January of 1861. One of Dix's immediate concerns was the fact that local authorities in southern states were seizing U.S. forts, arsenals, and revenue cutters. He sent a special messenger, W. Hemphill Jones, to New Orleans to provision the cutters there and move them to New York. Jones sent Dix a dispatch saying that southern-born Captain Breshwood of the revenue cutter *Robert McClelland* had refused to obey the order at which point, on January 29th, Dix sent the famous telegram with his strong comments about the flag:

Treasury Department, January 29,1861

Tell Lieutenant Caldwell to arrest Captain Breshwood, assume command of the cutter, and obey the order I gave you. If Captain Breshwood, after arrest, undertakes to interfere with the command of the cutter, tell Lieutenant Caldwell to consider him as a mutineer, and treat him accordingly. If anyone attempts to haul down the American flag, shoot him on the spot.

John A. Dix
Secretary of the Treasury

Although the telegram was prevented by the Confederates from arriving at its intended destination, the press discovered and printed the text. Dix immediately became one of the first Union heroes of the Civil War. He later said of the telegram, "…the order was not the result of any premeditation- scarcely of any thought. A conviction of the right course to be taken was as instantaneous as a flash of light; and I did not think, when I… wrote the order in as little time as it would take to read it, that I was doing anything particularly worthy of remembrance…" Millions of patriotic northerners certainly saw it differently! Here we offer the flag that became a testimonial to the service of John A. Dix and the motto that was emblazoned in the minds of every Northern recruit. Dix was quite touched and honored to receive this flag and, in a letter to Mrs. Blodgett, he said of this flag and the presentation ceremony, "…I can never forget that I owe to your kindness the most valuable testimonial of my public services that I have ever received. The obligation is the more grateful to me, because you seem of all others to be the least conscious of the value of what you have conferred."

Emanuel Leutze, the designer, was a German-born painter who specialized in American patriotic images. One of his greatest works is the iconic *Washington Crossing the Delaware.* He was commissioned in 1860 to decorate a stairway in the Capitol Building in Washington which produced another very familiar and famous work, *Westward the Course of Empire takes its Way.* One of Leutze's students at the National Academy of Design, Augustus St. Gaudens, would later become famous for his eerily similar interpretation of Lady Liberty on the beloved United States $20 gold piece in 1907.

This is an important and stunningly beautiful center emblem from General Dix's flag, commissioned, designed, and manufactured to pay honor and respect to a great and inspirational man who served his country faithfully and selflessly for 63 years. It is worthy of inclusion in the finest collections and should remain a symbol of the very best of American patriotism for generations to come.

Provenance: *Handwritten letter dated October 16, 1970, signed by the owner of Forge Antiques, Patricia S. Sullivan, of Katonah, New York . The flag was purchased at an auction of items stored in outbuildings at the Dix estate on Orange Rd. Mt. Kisco, New York.*

Estimate: $25,000-$30,000

72094   23RD ARMY CORPS FLAG MADE FROM CAPTURED CONFEDERATE FLAGS IN MACON GEORGIA CONVERTED INTO A U.S. STARS & STRIPES U. S. FLAG – A very unusual Civil War flag, consisting of captured Confederate flags from the arsenal in Macon, Georgia during Sherman's March to the Sea. The 35-star configuration in the form of a shield represents the 23rd Army Corps, a large regimental corps flag of wool bunting, 108" x 228." The obverse hoist marked "H. Kitchell," the commander of the 98th Illinois. The reverse hoist is also marked "E. Kitchell" and "EK." Accompanied by a large file of Kitchell newspapers and documents, including the original label for the history of the flag written by Kitchell documenting that this was made from captured Confederate flags at Macon, Georgia at the end of the Civil War on April 20,1865 by the 98th Illinois Regiment.

Provenance: *The Crow Art Partnership Collection (Dallas, Texas)**

Estimate: $8,000-$12,000

72095   34 STAR U. S. BUILDING/CAPITOL FLAG MADE BY FOSTER OF NEW YORK CA. 1863 – A monumental size 34-star Civil War flag, made to fly over a government building or state capitol. Made of wool bunting, 114" x 156". Non-regulation in size, thus most certainly made for a large building. The hoist is stenciled by the flag maker "F .T. Foster, NY".

Provenance: *The Crow Art Partnership Collection (Dallas, Texas)*

Estimate: $2,000-$3,000

72096   A 35-STAR FLAG WITH HAND-APPLIQUED STARS − This 35-star flag is hand-sewn and measures approximately 50" on the hoist and 100" on the fly. Made of red, white and blue bunting, this 35-star pattern was used from 1863-1865 and was the type most seen during the war.

The hand-appliqued stars of this flag are unique and have a twinkling appearance, with blue borders and white thread used to stitch them into the 45" x 26" blue bunting canton. There have been approximately 4" of the end of the fly sewn back onto itself in an apparent effort to make the flag shorter for display purposes. The flag has general fading of the colors.

On the hoist there is a tag with bears the words 'B. F. Almy'. The flag is in good condition overall and makes a fine display piece of a wartime flag.

Estimate: $2,000-$3,000

72097   13 STAR U. S. NAVY BOAT FLAG, CA 1863 – A US Navy "Boat" flag depicting 13 stars in a 4-5-4 configuration, made of wool bunting, 32" x 58" inches. This flag has only 7 stripes, which is unusual. The hoist has the flag maker's name: "H. Korn, Philadelphia".

Provenance: *The Crow Art Partnership Collection (Dallas, Texas)*

Estimate: $3,000-$4,000

72098   A UNION GUNBOAT FLAG FROM THE USS KENESAW – The *USS Kenesaw* was a Union gunboat that operated up and down the Tennessee River during the campaign of 1863-1864. Pressed into service from its former use a steam cargo ship at the start of the war, the Kenesaw flew this swallowtail flag made of bunting, measuring 48" at the hoist and approximately 168" at the fly and approximately 133" at the swallowtail.

Noted flag historian and author Howard Michael Madaus in his report of authentication on this rare flag stated that this flag was the only one of its kind he had examined. Visually attractive, the flag is composed of three horizontal bars; red at the top, dark blue at the middle and white at the bottom. The word 'Kenesaw' is appliquéd on both sides, each letter being 11¾" high in cotton.

There has been a repair to the bottom white bar done with a bunting patch about 9" wide and 15" high. The flag has excellent provenance dating to the Civil War, first brought home after the war by a Major C. E. Bliven it was donated to the Toledo Soldiers Memorial and thence to a private collector.

Authentication: *Letters of authenticity and research from renowned Civil War flag expert and author Howard Madaus.*

Estimate: $8,000-$12,000

72099 **13 STAR U. S. NAVAL "BATTLE FLAG"** – A U.S. Navy Boat flag that saw extensive battle use, with bullet holes and cannon shot. This flag illustrates the ferocity of battles it flew in and tells the story of the Civil War. Interestingly enough, its lanyard is still in its hoist. 13 stars in a 4-5-4 configuration, made of wool bunting, 43" x 81", with extensive battle damage.

Provenance: *The Crow Art Partnership Collection (Dallas, Texas)*

Estimate: $3,000-$6,000

72100   RARE CIVIL WAR UNION FLAG – REGIMENTAL MARKER FLAG – Approximately 10% of the Union regiments raised for service during the American Civil War were presented with non-regulation "general guide" or flank marker flags by their benefactors. These small flags were carried by the "general guide sergeants" posted at each flank of the regiment in line to assist the field officers in maintaining a straight line of battle. These "marking flags" took a number of forms and were made in a variety of designs; many, however, followed the basic pattern on the regulation bunting camp colors, with fringe added. Such is the case for those presented to the 2nd New York Volunteer Infantry, the "Troy Regiment," before it departed to defend the nation's capital.

The Second Regiment New York State Volunteer Infantry was organized at Troy, New York and accepted for service by the state on the 14th of May 1867 and during this time participated in the following engagements: New Market Bridge, Va., Big Bethel, Action between the Monitor and Merrimac at Hampton Roads, Va., Oak Grove, Peach Orchard and Savage Station, White Oak Swamp and Glendale, Malvern Hill, Groveton, Bull Run, Fredericksburg, and Chancellorsville.

The flag consists of a white silk field, 15½ " to 16" high on its staff by 18⅜" to 18⅝" wide on its fly, both dimensions exclusive of the 1⅜" deep twisted silk yellow fringe that decorates three of the four sides of the flag. The regimental numeral "2," in a medium to dark blue silk is appliquéd to the field, slightly off-center. This figure is 8¾" high by 5¼" wide. Three pairs of dark blue silk ties decorate the staff edge the flag for securing it to its staff.

In addition to being framed, the flag is netted with a nylon honeycomb pattern translucent overcovering of the style initially used by Elizabeth Roser to conserve the New York State flag collection.

Authentication: *Letters of authenticity and research from renowned Civil War flag expert and author Howard Madaus.*

Provenance: *The Crow Art Partnership Collection (Dallas, Texas)*
Chicago Historical Society (deaccessioned in 1974)
Formerly in the Charles Gunther Collection (1893-1920)

Estimate: $6,000-$8,000

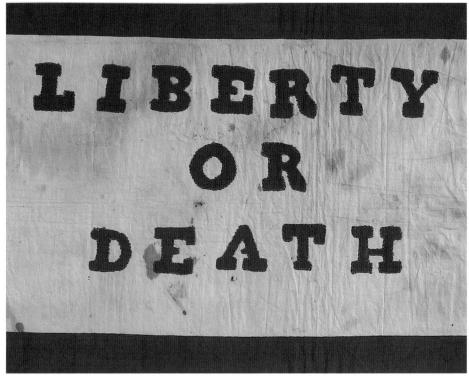

 A 19.5% Buyer's Premium ($9 min.) Applies To All Lots

72101   CONFEDERATE "LIBERTY OR DEATH" FLAG CAPTURED BY CUSTER'S CAVALRY FROM STUART'S CAVALRY DURING THE RETREAT AFTER THE BATTLE OF GETTYSBURG IN 1863. Confederate 1st national flag; believed to have been taken from the baggage train at Jack's Shop, Virginia during the Confederate retreat after the Battle of Gettysburg when Stuart's cavalry was protecting Lee's retreat. It was captured by William Goodman, Company I, Fifth Michigan Cavalry (Custer's Cavalry). He enlisted from Salem, Michigan August 19, 1862 and was taken prisoner at James City, Virginia on October 11, 1863. Goodman remained a prisoner of war and died at the infamous Andersonville, Georgia prison on July 24, 1864. Accompanied by Private Goodman's family photograph album, which includes a 1/6th plate tintype of him standing with a cavalry saber. Also his kerchief with other personal and family effects, including a GAR medal.

Authentication: Flag is a variation of the 1st national flag of the confederacy, the "Stars and Bars." Measuring overall 34⅜" on the hoist (staff edge) by 53" wide on the fly. The field is composed entirely of cotton and consists of three horizontal bars - red uppermost, 11 inches wide but with a gap at the top of an inch. The center bar is 9¾" wide and the lowest red bar is 12¼" wide. Inset into the upper staff corner but extending only through the top red bar is a medium blue canton 12¼" high on the hoist by 12½" wide bearing 13 white cotton 5-pointed stars each 3¾ " across their points appliquéd by hand to the obverse side, possibly cut away on the reverse. The leading edge of the flag is hemmed to a depth of ⅜" and once bore 4 hand sewn buttonhole eyelets. The lower and fly edges are decorated with a dark blue silk curtain 1¼" wide secured by floral decorated tape ¼" wide. In the center of the white bar is 16½" from the hoist edge is a 3 line motto, **LIBERTY/ OR/ DEATH"** in red cotton large block letters with serifs 1⅜" tall.

The 'Liberty or Death' motto was a common declaration during the Civil War, a demand made by the Virginian and Revolutionary War hero Patrick Henry in 1775 at St. John's Church in Richmond. Many Confederates believed the Civil War to be the second American Revolution in which many of their ancestors had fought and died. Indeed Patrick Henry's grandson was William Roane, the former United States Senator from Virginia. Henry' sister's grandson was Confederate General Joseph E. Johnston. 'Liberty or Death' was still very much a mindset during the Civil War.

Authentication: *Letters of authenticity and research from renowned Civil War flag expert and author Howard Madaus.*

Provenance: *Captured by William Goodman, 5th Michigan Cavalry*
The Don Tharpe Collection of American Military History

Exhibited: *The Liberty Heritage Society Museum*

Estimate: $80,000-$120,000

72102   A RARE CONFEDERATE EIGHT-STAR FIRST NATIONAL FLAG
− This Eight-Star Confederate First National flag still retains its vibrant colors and is beautifully hand sewn on polished cotton. At 140"on its fly and 75" at the hoist, this flag is a rare configuration of seven stars arranged in a 36" circle around a central star in the middle of the polished cotton blue canton. The two red bars divided by one white bar make this a classic First National Confederate design, but this particular pattern with eight stars makes up only 10% of the known First National designs.

As Virginia was the eighth state to secede from the Union on April 17, 1861 followed by Arkansas as the ninth only 30 days later, this flag was only authorized during that 30-day interval. Most of those known to exist in museums are from the Western Theater of the war, mostly from Louisiana or Mississippi regiments. Units of the famous New Orleans Washington Artillery and the Charles Clark Rifles of the 12th Mississippi are just a few of the units that flew this sort of flag. Indeed this flag was possibly made in New Orleans due to its early dating and construction. A stenciled number '25', 1" in height appears in black ink on the obverse of the flag on the fly edge.

Noted flag conservator Fonda Thomsen examined the flag and there were no alterations or repairs found during the examination. Significantly, the noted author and flag expert Howard Michael Madaus examined this flag as well. His authentication, research and analysis are included with this rare Confederate First National flag adding to its historical importance.

Provenance: *The Gary Hendershott Collection*

Estimate: $30,000-$40,000

72103   CONFEDERATE 1ST NATIONAL PATTERN FLAG – The original seven star Confederate flag was the first flag of the Confederate states in 1861. A very fine, company-sized flag made of dark blue, white, and bright red wool bunting with hand-sewn, 5 pointed stars in the dark blue canton and a coarse linen hoist with 3 hand-sewn grommets. The flag measures 17¼" on the hoist and 37" on the fly exclusive of a 1" wide hoist. The canton measures 12" wide and 11 /12" high and contains a circle of 7 white, 5-pointed stars 2" wide at the points. The field is composed of 3 horizontal stripes, the white stripe lying between the 2 red stripes. The first two stripes are 25" on the fly and 5⅞" wide; the third stripe is 37"on the fly.

Provenance: *The Crow Art Partnership Collection (Dallas, Texas)*

Estimate: $12,000-$16,000

**72104 CONFEDERATE LIGHT ARTILLERY (OR CAVALRY) GUIDON –
CAPTURED AT FORT HINDMAN –** A very rare swallowtail Confederate artillery guidon of a large size with its original blue lanyard. It was originally discovered furled around
its staff with its red painted tin "halberd head" finial - now missing - in the attic of Corp.
James L. Sheehan, a former member of the 127th Illinois Volunteer Infantry. Captured
and taken home by him as a battlefield trophy from Fort Hindman, Arkansas (Arkansas
Post on the Mississippi River during Grant's siege of Vicksburg in January 1863). This
flag is very similar to the guidon of "Hill's Cavalry" (7th Tennessee Cavalry), captured at
Island No. 10 in April 1862.

Authentication: This flag is swallowtail in configuration, measuring 30" on its staff by 39"
on the fly (29¼" from staff to cut of swallowtail), and is composed of two horizontal wool
bunting bars, white over red, with a dark blue wool bunting canton (14½" high by 10½"
wide) inset into the upper staff corner, bearing thirteen white cotton (machine sewn ap-
pliqué) stars, the center 3¾" across its points, and the twelve in an ellipse surrounding it,
each 2¼" across their points. Finished on the hoist edge by a white canvas duck sleeve 2½"
wide where flat for the staff. The flag was secured to its staff with a blue silk cord extending from the top and bottom of the sleeve.

Authentication: *Letters of authenticity and research from renowned Civil War flag expert
and author Howard Madaus.*

Provenance: *Captured by Corp. Sheehan, 127th Illinois Volunteers, acquired by Daniel
Potochniak of Hanover Park, Illinois from a descendant of 127th Illinois Volunteers; Crow
Art Partnership Collection (Dallas, Texas)*

Estimate: $25,000-$35,000

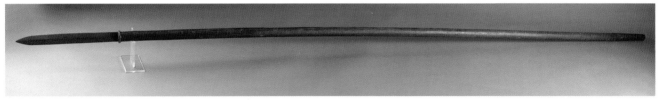

72105   A CONFEDERATE CAVALRY GUIDON AND FLAGSTAFF – A Confederate cavalry guidon is a very rare find. This example measures 17" on the fly and 12" at the hoist and has seen much use. Designed in the First National pattern, this swallowtail cavalry flag has eleven stars on its blue field and two red bars divided by one white bar. At the time of manufacture of this type of guidon the stars were only applied on one side. The colors have faded and there is damage at the upper end of the swallowtail and at the field and along the hoist.

Confederate troops used these type flags throughout the ranks, especially when trying to maintain formation or a straight line when in battle. In that sense, with the battle flag at the center of the cavalry, the guidons would serve as marker flags.

Typically attached to a lance, it is fortunate that this guidon's lance accompanies this flag as well. Contemporary accounts note that these guidons flew from these 8-foot long lances that were commonly referred to as 'Richmond Pikes'. Securing at three places along the pike, the guidon here was at one time attached to this pike since there are traces of cloth at the points where it was secured with tacks.

This is a very unique and rare Confederate battle flag, made even more historically important since it has its original flagstaff lance.

Estimate: $14,000-$18,000

72106   A VERY RARE CONFEDERATE SECESSION FLAG – 1861 – This is an extremely rare Confederate secession flag, one of only two known to exist. A six-star variant of the Confederate First National flag, this flag was made prior to the adoption of the First National design on March 4, 1861.

This flag has eleven stripes and most likely dates to January or February 1861. It is both hand and machine sewn on dark red, white and blue bunting with the central five-pointed star surrounded by an additional five stars design in white cotton.

Noted author and flag expert Howard Michael Madaus authenticated this flag and a copy of his research accompanies this flag. In that report he explains attempts by the people of secessionist states to incorporate the 'stars and stripes' design into the early flags of the new Confederacy.

This flag measures 126" on the fly and 91¼" at the hoist. The blue canton measures 40½" at the staff and 39½" on the fly. The central five-pointed star measures 35½" in diameter while the smaller surrounding stars are 7½" in diameter. There are three whipped eyelets that pierce the white and blue canvas heading for attachment to a staff.

This is a beautiful flag that dates to the earliest days of the war. With only minor moth holes, it is in excellent condition making it a superb display piece.

Authentication: *Letters of authenticity and research from renowned Civil War flag expert and author Howard Madaus.*

Provenance: *The Crow Art Partnership Collection (Dallas, Texas)*

Estimate: $18,000-$24,000

72107 RARE TEXAS CONFEDERATE "BONNIE BLUE" FLAG OF THE 3RD TEXAS STATE CAVALRY – One of the rarest Confederate flags in existence, this "Bonnie Blue" Flag is one of only six known to exist in private hands as well as in museum collections. During the Civil War, patriotic songs were written about the "Bonnie Blue" flag of Texas that led Texans into battle. A once in a lifetime opportunity to own one of the rarest Confederate flags in existence.

History ascribed to the flag at that time stated that it was "picked up on one of the Texas battlefields during of the War of the 60's by Private 1st Class S.A. Buffum, Co. A. 3rd Regt. Cavalry Texas State Troops." The flag is 36" square with a dark blue field. It is made of a bunting or wool mix, and its method of attachment is missing. The white 5-pointed star is 17½" inches across its point in the center of the field cotton.

Exhibit History: This flag was part of the centerpiece display at the Texas Historical Exhibit in the Texas Building during the 1936 Texas Centennial Exposition.

Authentication: *Letters of authenticity and research from renowned Civil War flag expert and author Howard Madaus.*

Provenance: *The Crow Art Partnership Collection (Dallas, Texas). Originally acquired by Mr. George W. Wray, Jr., Atlanta, Georgia in 1970s.*

Estimate: $80,000-$120,000

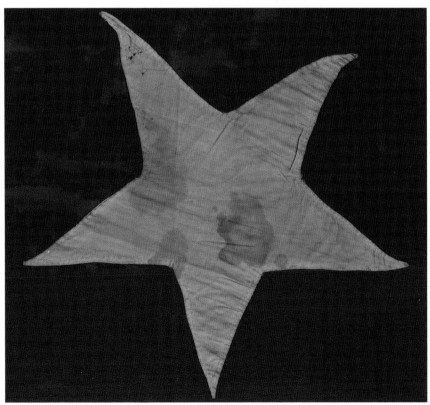

72108   CONFEDERATE TEXAS STATE "LONE STAR" CAVALRY GUIDON – This rare "lone star" pattern state flag was "captured" (confiscated) at Milam, Texas by Union occupation forces from the 48th Ohio Battalion, which had been formed in 1865 from the consolidated regiments of the 48th, 83rd, and 114th Ohio Infantry who were stationed in Texas under the command of General Sheridan. General Custer was also stationed in Texas in command of the Cavalry, and some of his men could have participated in the capture of this Cavalry flag. This is one of only five known and verified Confederate Texas State flags of the 1839 "Lone Star" pattern of Texas Independence fame. The flag was discovered in a Grand Army of the Republic collection in Findlay, Ohio. It is among the rarest Confederate flags in existence.

This flag is swallowtail in configuration, measuring 11½" from the staff to the cut of the swallowtail. The field follows the directive of the state's 1839 flag design and is composed of a dark blue polished cotton vertical bar 6⅛" wide, bearing a single white cotton, five-pointed star, 4¼" across its points, along the hoist, and two horizontal bars of wool bunting, white over red, for the balance of the field. The three exterior edges are finished with remnants of a gold metallic fringe, 1¾" deep, while the hoist edge is composed of a 1" wide twill weave cotton canvas heading, pierced at each end with a hand sewn button hole eyelet.

Note: The flag is of a size that could also be used as a lance pennon, and, since several Texas Cavalry units were armed with the lance in 1861, this is a possible usage of this rare flag.

Authentication: *Letters of authenticity and research from renowned Civil War flag expert and author Howard Madaus.*

Provenance: *The Crow Art Partnership Collection (Dallas, Texas)*

Estimate: $40,000-$60,000

72109   THE CONFEDERATE BATTLE FLAG OF THE 18TH VIRGINIA CAVALRY – CAPTAIN G. JULIAN PRATT – BATTLE OF GETTYSBURG – The vibrantly blue Saint Andrew's Cross highlights this Confederate battle flag belonging to Captain G. Julian Pratt who had an outstanding career with the Confederate Cavalry in Lee's Army of Northern Virginia. As a young student at the University of Virginia he left his studies to join one of the three student companies known as "The Sons of Liberty" to come from that esteemed Jeffersonian institution. Soon after that, Pratt reported to General Henry A. Wise and was given the task of organizing a company of marine artillery to defend the marshes of Roanoke Island. While in the process of recruiting his marines he was captured by Union soldiers there. After his exchange, Pratt enlisted in General John D. Imboden's 1st Regiment of Partisan Rangers. From this time on he was in command of the cavalry. Soon after this, he took it upon himself to enlist a company of cavalry inside the enemy's lines and equipped them from the enemy stores. This company became the Company H, 18th Virginia Cavalry and in December of 1862 Julian Pratt was its first Lieutenant. At the Battle of Piedmont Capt. Frank Imboden, General Imboden's brother, was captured and Lt. Pratt soon was promoted to the rank of captain. It was from that point in 1862 that he was in command of the cavalry.

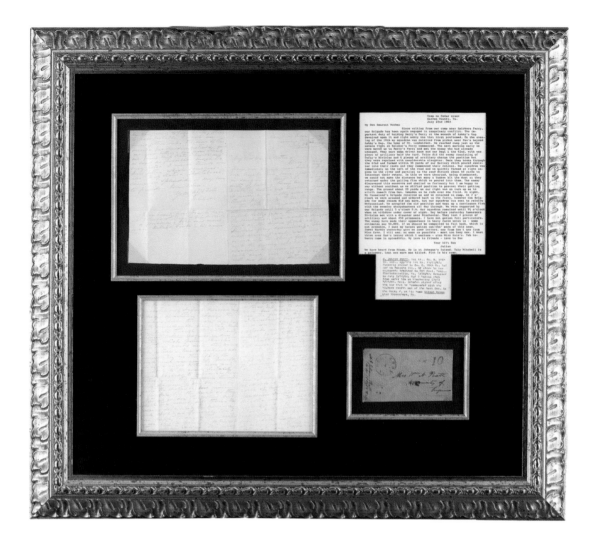

Julian Pratt led his men in many battles under this battle flag as they met with great victory as well as showing extraordinary courage in the Battle of Winchester in 1864, where he had three horses shot out from under him (Pratt lost two horses under the same circumstances in other battles). He was himself twice wounded participating in the Battles of Gettysburg, Front Royal, Fisher's Hill, and New Market among many others. General Imboden constantly praised him for his gallant style that reminded many of General J.E.B. Stuart. In July of 1863 Captain Pratt's men were moved up the Chambersburg Pike to a point just west of the Confederate line on Seminary Ridge where they fought the engagement at Gettysburg. When the last of Pickett's men straggled back after their infamous charge, Captain Pratt as a member of Imboden's Cavalry was given the task of protecting the Confederate retreat south. The Federals also attacked this wagon train on several occasions only to meet with Captain Pratt's anger and call of duty to defend the valiant men who had been wounded in the Battle of Gettysburg. During the Battle of Gettysburg, the 18th Virginia Cavalry lost 87 men killed and wounded.

This battle flag of the 18th Virginia Cavalry was fought under from Gettysburg to New Market. The cavalry flag measures 36" on its hoist by 32" on its fly. The field is made of a red wool cotton dress cloth with a dark blue St. Andrew's cross made of cotton. Applied to each side of the cross were eleven white polished cotton five-pointed stars with one in the center. This battle flag was homemade and is one of only five Confederate Army of Northern Virginia homemade cavalry size battle flags known to exist. It is truly an incredible example as bullet holes are still very evident in its field. Pratt had an esteemed career in the Confederate Cavalry and this battle flag was his most prized possession.

Accompanied by Captain Pratt's battlefield letter as well as Captain Pratt's Southern Cross of Honor with his name engraved in period script.

Authentication: *Howard Michael Madaus, distinguished flag expert and author, letter of authentication and lengthy research.*

Estimate: $140,000-$160,000

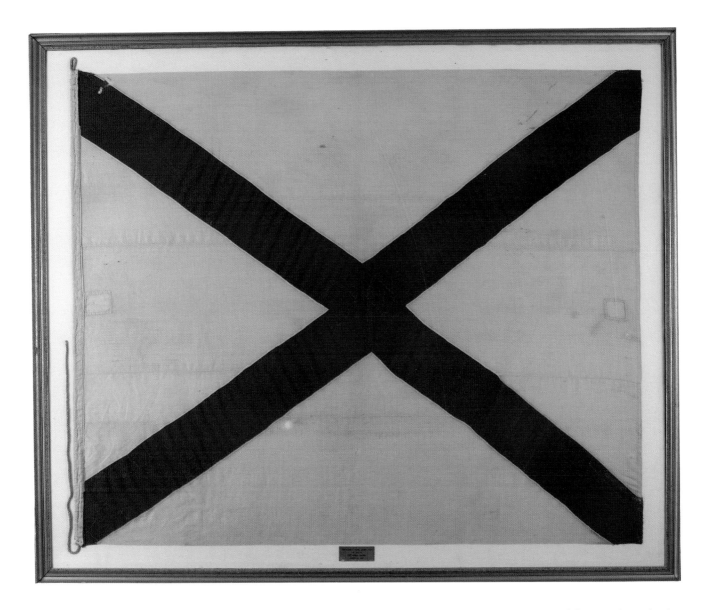

72110   CONFEDERATE NAVAL SIGNAL FLAG – CAPTURED AT FORT MORGAN, ALABAMA, IN 1864 – A Confederate made naval style signed flag signifying "guard." Captured with the surrender of Fort Morgan in Mobile Bay near Mobile, Alabama, August 23, 1864.

Under the early light of dawn on August 5, 1864, Union Admiral David Farragut led a flotilla of 14 wooden ships, four ironclads, and numerous gunboats into Mobile Bay to seal off the city of Mobile, one of the two remaining Confederate ports. While entering the bay, the Union monitor *USS Tecumseh* struck a submerged torpedo and sank. Under fire from both the Confederate fleet and Fort Morgan, Farragut had to choose between retreating or risking the minefield. He then issued his famous order, "Damn the torpedoes! Full speed ahead!"

Passing the minefield safely, Union ships defeated the Southern flotilla, while Union ground forces captured the forts. Although the city of Mobile remained in Confederate hands, the last blockade-running port on the Gulf Coast east of the Mississippi was closed.

Flag consists of a white wool and bunting field, pieced horizontally in each quadrant formed by the red wool bunting St. Andrew's cross 7½" to 8" wide, inset into the field. Flag measures 65" on its hoist by 81" on its fly, including the 1¼" wide white (turned tan) heading that serves as a sleeve for a single halyard rope attachment, lopped into an eyelet at the top and extended 30" at the bottom. Flag shows service and bears at least five patches to cover previous damage.

Authentication: *Letters of authenticity and research from renowned Civil War flag expert and author Howard Madaus.*

Provenance: *The Crow Art Partnership Collection (Dallas, Texas)*
Formerly in the collection of George Wray of Atlanta, Georgia

Estimate: $12,000-$16,000

72111   POST CIVIL WAR LIGHT ARTILLERY GUIDON, BATTERY A, MASSACHUSETTS VOLUNTEER MILITIA – Guidon of Independent Battery A, Massachusetts Volunteer Militia, agreeing with the 1879 Regulations for Massachusetts Volunteer Militia. Possibly in unofficial use (un-plushed) format prior to 1879. This guidon measures 16½" on its staff (hoist) edge by 18¼" on its fly (and 14" from the staff to the cut of the swallowtail), exclusive of the yellow gold, 2" deep, silk fringe on its fly and lower sides. The field is composed of two silk, horizontal bars, red over white, sewn together by hand. Painted over the center of the junction of the bars is a brown disc, 5⅞" in diameter bearing a pair of crossed bronze cannon barrels 5¾" long each, circumvented by a gold edge blue belt 1⅞" wide (inclusive of the gold edges) bearing the inscription "BATTERY A" arched over "M.V.M" painted in ⅞" high gold black lettering (with serifs).

Authentication: *Letters of authenticity and research from renowned Civil War flag expert and author Howard Madaus.*

Provenance: *The Crow Art Partnership Collection (Dallas, Texas)*

Estimate: $4,000-$6,000

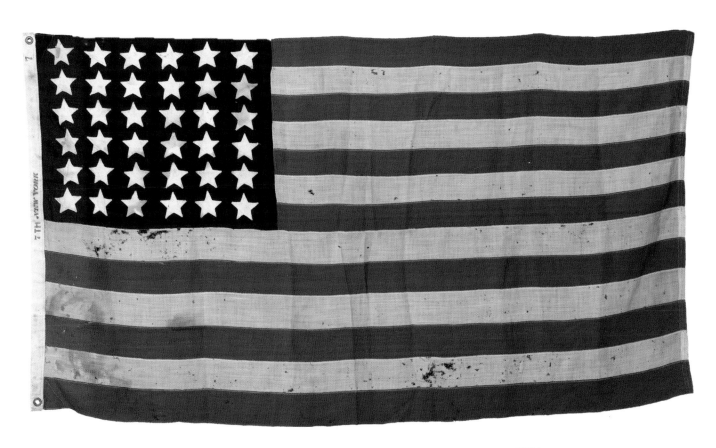

72112   A FLAG OF THE 7TH NEW YORK INFANTRY – This is a hand-sewn 36-star, 13 stripe Union flag of the 7th New York Infantry which mustered into service about the time that Nevada, the 36th state was added to the Union. They took part in the Siege of Petersburg and fought at Deep Bottom and Hatcher's Run. They mustered out of service at Hart's Island, New York in August 1865, this being their last national flag.

This 36-star pattern was not the officially adopted pattern which came into use only in July 1865. This pattern consists of 6 rows of 6 stars hand-appliqued on a blue 30" x 22" canton. They are applied only on one side with the opposite blue canton cut out to reveal the star. The flag measures 81" at the fly and 45" at the hoist which is stenciled '7th New York' in period ink. The material is wool bunting and cotton stars with brass loops at each end of the hoist for attachment to a staff. The flag is in overall good condition with two holes at the bottom center.

Provenance: *The Crow Art Partnership Collection (Dallas, Texas)*

Estimate: $4,000-$6,000

72113   THE FLAG OF THE 2ND NORTH CAROLINA UNITED STATES COLORED TROOPS – This is an extraordinarily rare flag from the North Carolina Colored Troops of the Union Army. The 2nd US North Carolina USCT, who fought with the 36th US Regiment served as guards for prisoners at Point Lookout, Maryland until seeing action at the Siege of Petersburg. They took part in the Battle of Chaffin's Farm, New Market Heights and the Battle of Fair Oaks. Involved in the Appomattox Campaign they also saw duty at the occupation of Richmond on April 3, 1865. They were moved to Texas along the Rio Grande for service until they mustered out of service the next year.

This white and green distinctive flag measures 70" on the fly and 60" at the hoist. At the center of the wool bunting cloth is a 21" x 28" evergreen tree hand-sewn on both sides into the patchwork design of this flag. There are single eyelets at the hoist through which the flag was at one time attached to a staff. Since it has seen much action, the flag has been conserved by placing it between a fine transparent mesh on either side. There are holes at the top and bottom and several stains that appear to be from blood. The tree device has faded to a light green, however the flag is stable and is very distinctive, historically important as it is the only hand-sewn United States Colored Troops flag from North Carolina known to exist.

Provenance: *The Crow Art Partnership Collection (Dallas, Texas)*

Estimate: $4,000-$6,000

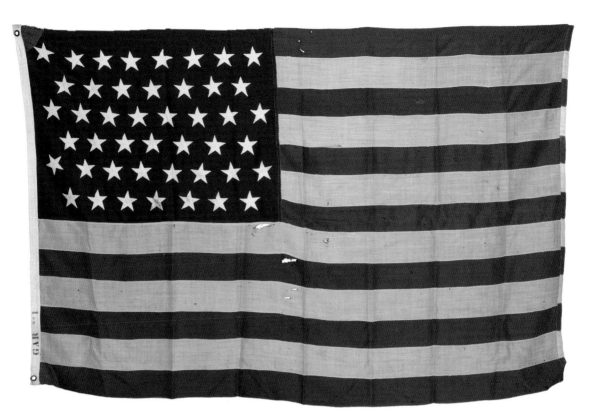

72114   38 STAR U. S. " GRAND ARMY OF THE REPUBLIC" FLAG – Grand Army of the Republic flag made by Macy's, 38 stars wool bunting, 60" x 96", canvas hoist is stenciled "GAR 1" and the famous flag maker, "R.H. Macy Co." New York.

Authentication: *Letters of authenticity and research from renowned Civil War flag expert and author Howard Madaus.*

Provenance: *The Crow Art Partnership Collection (Dallas, Texas)*

Estimate: $1,000-$2,000

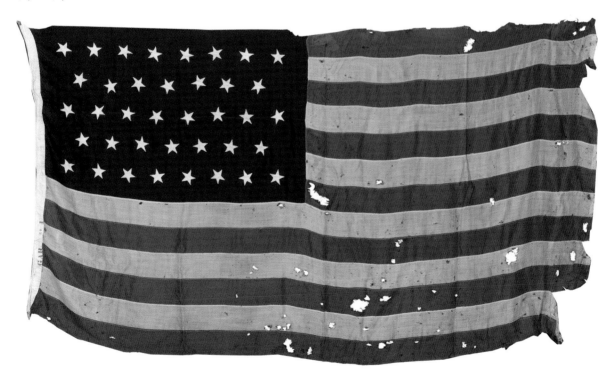

72115   38 STAR U. S. "GRAND ARMY OF THE REPUBLIC" FLAG – Grand Army of the Republic 38 star flag, wool bunting 60" x 124", canvas hoist stenciled "GAR 1," purportedly used by the very first Grand Army of the Republic Post chartered in Philadelphia, PA.

Authentication: *Letters of authenticity and research from renowned Civil War flag expert and author Howard Madaus.*

Provenance: *The Crow Art Partnership Collection (Dallas, Texas)*

Estimate: $1,000-$2,000

72116   A BEAUTIFUL 46-STAR INFANTRY FLAG – A rare and historical flag, this 46-star staggered pattern of 7 and 8 stars in the canton was used after the admission of Oklahoma into the Union on July 4, 1908. Used for only four years during the administrations of Theodore Roosevelt and William H. Taft, it is machine-sewn of heavy wool cloth, this distinctive and attractive flag has a 2" gold fringe and was used as an infantry flag. Measuring 74" at the fly and 70" at the hoist, the hoist has a loop through which a staff was passed to carry the flag. The 30" x 38" canton with the 46 stars has a reinforcement patch at the top at the hoist, another appearing at the bottom of the flag at the last red stripe at the hoist. This is an attractive and rare flag, historically important.

Provenance: *The Crow Art Partnership Collection (Dallas, Texas)*

Estimate: $1,000-$2,000

72117   21ST U.S. INFANTRY REGIMENTAL FLAG – HAND PAINTED IN GOLD CA. 1890s – A rare Spanish American War regimentally marked flag, with 45 stars, wool bunting, 50" x 68" with gold fringe. The center stripe bears a unit designation painted in gold, "21ST REGIMENT U. S. INFANTRY." Originally formed during the War of 1812 this flag flew over U.S. Forces during the Spanish American War in Cuba at the battle of Santiago (Roosevelt's famous charge up San Juan Hill).

Authentication: *Letters of authenticity and research from renowned Civil War flag expert and author Howard Madaus.*

Provenance: *The Crow Art Partnership Collection (Dallas, Texas)*

Estimate: $8,000-$12,000

72118   21ST U. S. INFANTRY REGIMENTAL FLAG – EMBROIDERED US EAGLE, CA. 1890 – A superb and beautiful regulation US Army Regimental flag, 52" x 84", with gold fringe, a blue field and a magnificent large embroidered federal eagle over riband bearing unit designation boldly painted in gold, "TWENTY-FIRST U.S. INFANTRY." This regimental flag would have accompanied the Stars & Stripes of the 21st US Infantry during the Spanish American War when they fought in Cuba during the battles of Santiago Heights (Roosevelt's famous charge up San Juan Hill).

Authentication: *Letters of authenticity and research from renowned Civil War flag expert and author Howard Madaus.*

Provenance: *The Crow Art Partnership Collection (Dallas, Texas)*

Estimate: $8,000-$12,000

72119   U. S. INFANTRY REGIMENTAL FLAG – CA 1890

– A magnificent regimental silk flag of the famous 1st Washington Infantry U.S. Volunteers. This flag measures 71" on the fly and 50" on the hoist with a blue field with a beautiful hand painted eagle under a gilt sunburst with red riband bearing the designation "1st Washington Infantry U.S. Volunteers". A rare flag from the Northwest, Washington had just become a state in 1889. Their volunteers would have carried this flag during the Spanish American War in the Philippines.

Authentication: *Letters of authenticity and research from renowned Civil War flag expert and author Howard Madaus.*

Provenance: *The Crow Art Partnership Collection (Dallas, Texas)*

Estimate: $18,000-$24,000

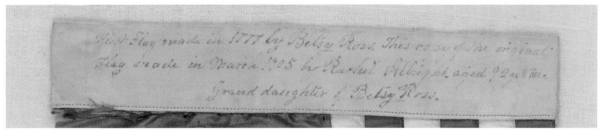

72120 **A COPY OF THE BETSY ROSS FLAG MADE BY HER GRANDDAUGHTER** − This is a remarkable miniature flag, a copy of the 'Betsy Ross' design that was actually made by her granddaughter Rachel Albright in 1905. Albright was 92 years and 8 months old when she crafted this meticulously done fine silk red, white and blue classic. Measuring 12" on the fly and 7" at the hoist, the thirteen red and white stripes are hand-sewn as are the thirteen white five-pointed stars in the blue canton. At the hoist there is a handwritten inscription in ink as follows: *First flag made in 1777 by Betsy Ross. This copy of the original flag made in 1905 by Rachel Albright aged 92 yr. 8m. Granddaughter of Betsy Ross.* There is some loss at the top right of the canton, otherwise this one-of-a-kind flag made by the granddaughter of Betsy Ross is intact and vivid in color, making it an impressive presentation flag. It is framed in a wooden gilt 2" frame and is set down on a fine linen cloth covered by glass.

Provenance: *The Crow Art Partnership Collection (Dallas, Texas)*

Estimate: $4,000-$6,000

72121   A GETTYSBURG DRUM OF THE 140TH PENNSYLVANIA – This drum of the 140th Pennsylvania Infantry originally belonged to Private Isaac Golden as noted on the drum's side. Painted into a ribbon held in an eagle's beak are the words 'E. Pluribus Unum,' along with Private Golden's name. In front of the eagle is the Federal shield and the eagle holds an olive branch in one claw and a quiver of arrows in the other. This drum has seen much use as the unit saw action at Gettysburg and Chancellorsville among other battles.

The heads of the drum are in need of restoration and the varnish has crackled, as the drum has been stored for many years. The tension ropes are missing and the top drumhead is loose from the drum itself, which measures 12" in height. Both drum heads measure 16" in diameter and have been repaired with tape. The A. Rogers Company of Flushing, New York manufactured this drum and their label is still inside the shell of the drum.

While this drum could benefit from restoration, due to its identification with a soldier and its battle history, it is an important historical piece even in this condition.

Provenance: *The Norm Flayderman Collection*

Estimate: $3,500-$4,500

72122   CONFEDERATE CARTRIDGE BOX PICKED UP FROM THE BATTLEFIELD AT GETTYSBURG. The handsome cartridge box presented here was most often used by Union infantrymen, though this example was surely used by a Confederate soldier. The "U.S." embossed seal inside an oval normally seen on the outer flap of these cartridge boxes has been ground down and tarred over. Following the bloodiest battle of the Civil War, a local Gettysburg family picked the box up from the battlefield, and it remained with the family until the late twentieth century. The maker's initials are blind-stamped on the inner flap, "S.H. Young & Co. Newark N.J." Closing strap is intact. Overall, the leather on the box is dried, cracked, and flaking in a few areas, to be expected from such a battle-worn piece of Civil War history.

Estimate: $1,200-$1,800

72123   A GETTYSBURG BASS DRUM FROM THE OLD SHIELDS MUSEUM − This bass drum was de-accessed from the Shields Museum at a Gettysburg auction in 1985 and sold to a private collector. The museum was started in 1918 and consisted primarily of Gettysburg family collections, people who had collected artifacts from the battlefield, fresh after the conflict or 'battlefield pickups' as they were known.

This bass drum measures two feet in height and has a two feet in diameter drumhead. It still has its faded spread eagle design on the side of the drum measuring 16" x 10". The drum's wood shell has a dark varnish with 10 hoop eyelets. The ropes date from the 1880's.

This drum has no maker's mark and is in overall good condition and makes a very nice display piece with a Gettysburg connection.

Estimate: $8,000-$10,000

72124   CONFEDERATE HOME-MADE CARTRIDGE BOX FOUND ON GETTYSBURG BATTLEFIELD. Wooden body with tacked on leather closure flap and belt loops, metal closure stud, 6" x 2.25" x 2.5", with brass dove and star inlay on reverse, crazing and light wear to the leather, else very good condition. A provenance letter from the North Missouri Historical Society accompanying this cartridge box indicates that it was picked up on the Gettysburg battlefield immediately after the battle by a local family. The letter further indicates that the cartridge box belonged to a Confederate sharpshooter dressed in civilian clothing who hid his rifle and this cartridge box in a tree and sauntered away from the Union troops to avoid capture. The significance of the inlayed dove and star is unknown.

Estimate: $800-$1,200

72125   CAPTURED AT GETTYSBURG U. S. ARMY CAP BOX DECORATED BY A REBEL SOLDIER – 3.75" x 4", marked "Jewell / Maker / Hartford" on inside flap. This standard Union Army cap box has a brass finial on the underside and retains a handful of unused copper percussion caps. What makes this item special is that a Southerner has carved a Confederate First National flag and the letters "CSA" into the leather on the outside flap. A very old and now illegible paper label above the flag could no doubt enlighten us as to this item's provenance. Considerable wear and crazing to leather, one belt loop missing and a split on the top flap rendering attachment to the finial impossible. Quite rare and desirable, with original "caps" just as it was found on a Gettysburg battlefield 140 years ago.

Provenance: *Lee Walker, The Tharpe Collection of American Military History, feature article in 1970s by Company of Military Historians.*

Exhibited: *The Liberty Heritage Society Museum.*

Estimate: $8,000-$12,000

72126   A FIELD DRUM OF THE 41ST US INFANTRY – RICE'S STATION AGAINST LONGSTREET – This wonderful field drum of the 41st US Infantry has a spectacular spread-winged eagle with the federal shield and ribbon painted on its shell. While it has seen much use in the field, the drum is rugged and striking in the image that remains with the ribbon bearing the designation '41 Reg. US Infantry' in the eagle's beak.

At 16½" in diameter, the drum's upper head is in good condition with no tears. While the bottom head snares are present, the head skin is torn across the diameter of the drum. On the opposite side of the regimental eagle is an elaborate design of brass tacking where the snare tension brass is still present. The ropes are present as are the seven leather tighteners. Made of highly-grained maple, this drum is very distinctive in appearance with some flaking of the painted image and tension wear at the rims. The drum comes with a pair of period mahogany drumsticks.

The 41st US Infantry under Colonel Llewellyn Haskell fought admirably at Rice's Station where they engaged Confederate General James Longstreet forcing his withdrawal.

Estimate: $12,000-$16,000

72127   UNION CARTRIDGE POUCH, PARTIAL BAYONET SHEATH AND BELT. These items were allegedly picked up on the Gettysburg battlefield and were part of the Shield's Museum collection. The set includes a general-purpose cartridge pouch, unmarked, with belt straps, both buckles, missing the closure strap, dry and crazed but in good condition; the remnants of a bayonet frog and sheath, all suspended on a 2" wide leather belt missing the buckle, most of the black finish worn off but in serviceable condition.

Estimate: $1,000-$2,000

72128   A FIELD DRUM OF THE 100TH NEW YORK VOLUNTEERS, BATTERY WAGNER – This field drum was used by the 100th New York Volunteer Infantry, a unit that fought at the famous assault on Battery Wagner on Morris Island, South Carolina. Having already seen action at Williamsburg and Malvern Hill, the unit was witness to the slaughter at Battery Wagner in July 1863. They were present at General Robert E. Lee's surrender at Appomattox Court House as well.

This 11½" tall 16½" diameter field drum is made of maple and still has its snares intact. Both the upper and lower drum heads are present with only a slight buckle of the lower rim. The ropes and leather rope tighteners are present as well, the tighteners having two stars on each of the pulls. Painted in red on the side of the drum is '100 N. Y. S.' Included with this drum are two discharge papers from a soldier in the 100th New York, private Charles D. Ford. They both measure 8" x 10" and have been repaired at the folds with tape, but are a good connection to the drum and otherwise in good condition. The overall condition of the drum is very good making it a nice piece from a historic Civil War unit.

Estimate: $3,000-$4,000

72129   A CONFEDERATE DRUM CAPTURED AT BEAUFORT, SOUTH CAROLINA – This Confederate wood drum was captured at Beaufort, South Carolina during the winter of 1861-1862 by Private Daniel M. Reed of Company G, the 50th Pennsylvania Infantry. The family provenance states that Reed was a part of a force camped at Beaufort and that Reed found the drum in an abandoned fort. Reed was killed later that year at Chantilly, Virginia and his personal effects along with this drum were sent back to his family in Pennsylvania

This rough-hewn drum is obviously not Union issue. Confederate drums are exceedingly rare and most were hand made as is this example liberated by Private Reed. The wood is actually a single wide strip that has been wrapped around and tacked with rows of tacks to secure the piece making the shell of the drum. At 15" in height and 17" in diameter, the drumheads are made of calfskin and are intact with no holes. The tension ropes are of a later date but the leather tighteners appear to be original to the drum. There is a notation that can be seen inside the vent hole of the drum that indicates the drum was "restored and repaired Feb, 1983."

The most striking aspect of the drum besides its quality craftsmanship and construction is the eagle and seven stars painted on the side of the drum. Although somewhat crudely done, the eagle is typical of the Confederate representation with seven stars. The seven stars represent the states, including South Carolina, which seceded from the Union within the first three months before the fall of Fort Sumter. While the image of the eagle and stars are faded and show considerable wear, the fading of the eagle and stars appear to be mostly from age as this drum was removed from service after only several months of use.

This drum is accompanied by an archive of copies of Private Reed's letters he wrote home before he was killed at Chantilly. Also, there are copies of notarized statements from the former owners of the drum stating that it came from the Reed family before being sold in 1982. The drum also has two rough-hewn drumsticks.

Estimate: $3,000-$4,000

72130   A 19TH CENTURY PAINTED MAPLE DRUM – This maple drum dates to the mid to late 19th century and has a beautiful painted eagle on the side of the drum. The rims have separated from the edges of the drum and the strings are loose at the bottom. The tension ropes are new and the drum measures 15½" in height and is 16½" in diameter.

Estimate: $800-$1,200

     A 19.5% Buyer's Premium ($9 min.) Applies To All Lots

72131   A VERY RARE CONFEDERATE COLONEL'S FROCK COAT – COLONEL JOHN THOMPSON BROWN, 1ST VIRGINIA ARTILLERY, KILLED AT THE BATTLE OF THE WILDERNESS – Confederate Colonel's uniforms are more rare than those of Confederate generals. This frock coat was worn by Colonel John Thompson Brown of the 1st Virginia Artillery, the 'Richmond Howitzers'.

This beautiful frock coat has been superbly preserved since Colonel Brown's death on May 5, 1864 at the Battle of the Wilderness. A Union non-commissioned officer, Sergeant Watson from Michigan, removed the coat from Brown's body and took it back home where it had been held in his family until just ten years ago. It was then that a descendant returned the coat to Virginia.

This Confederate frock coat, one of the most rare in existence not only because of the rank signified but also due to its historical significance, is being offered here for the first time at auction.

This Confederate Colonel's artillery frock coat is in cadet gray with a standing collar which has three gilt stars hand-sewn into the red cloth backing and attached to the collar. It has magnificent, unusually large triple-gold braids of quatrefoil that run up each of the sleeves which also indicate Brown's rank as a Colonel. The sleeves are in the Confederate officer's pattern. The double-breasted uniform has eagle staff buttons as well. There are three smaller cuff buttons on each sleeve as well as eagle staff buttons on the coattail. It is trimmed with distinctive artillery red piping on the double-breasted part of the coat, piping that extends to the top of the collar and at the coattails, even at the cuffs.

John Thompson Brown was named captain of the 1st Virginia Artillery, the 'Richmond Howitzers' on July 12, 1861. His Colonel's uniform is an extreme rarity. It is in overall superb condition and is a highly attractive Confederate uniform.

Provenance: *The Watson Family*
The Tharpe Collection of American Military History

Exhibited: *The Liberty Heritage Society Museum*

Estimate: $90,000-$120,000

CONFEDERATE TIN CANTEEN

Carried by Pvt. Benjamin B. Pendleton during the war between the states. The canteen is of the typical "drum" type design, manufactured in the south for issue to the Confederate forces.

Please visit *HA.com* to view other collectibles auctions. *A 19.5% Buyer's Premium ($9 min.) Applies To All Lots*

72132   "STONEWALL" JACKSON'S COURIER, THE "TAIT" SHELL JACKET OF PRIVATE BENJAMIN S. PENDLETON – WORN AT THE SURRENDER AT APPOMATTOX – This is an extremely rare artillery shell jacket made by Tait of Ireland that made its way to the Confederacy through the Union blockade. It was worn by Private Benjamin S. Pendleton who had the distinction not only of serving as a courier for Confederate General Stonewall Jackson, but also wore this uniform at the surrender of the Confederate forces with General Robert E. Lee at Appomattox on April 9, 1865.

Private Pendleton wore this artillery shell jacket during the last year of the war, at the close of which he would be listed in the Appomattox parole book as one of only 35 surviving members of the famous 'Stonewall Brigade'.

Constructed of wool cloth by the Peter Tait and Company of Limerick, Ireland, this is the only Tait uniform known to have run the blockade that is still in existence. In fact, it is the only foreign-made Confederate shell jacket known to be in private hands. Heavily worn by Private Pendleton, the shortages of buttons at the close of the war are exhibited in this uniform which has a combination of five 'CS' staff buttons, one Old English script 'I' button and two eagle buttons. They are held in place by square-cut nails that run through the shank of the button inside the fabric of the coat. Inside the jacket there is a small card written and signed by Pendleton that reads as follows:

> *This jacket worn by B. S. Pendleton, Co. B, 2nd Virginia Infantry, Stonewall Brigade, Army Northern Virginia, worn at the surrender of General Lee*
> *April 9, 1865 -*
> *B. S. Pendleton*

The facts of the make, ownership and use of this jacket make it an extreme rarity, not to mention the fact that it made it through the Union blockade to the Confederacy. The jacket is in overall good condition with some moth holes to the right sleeve, a small hole at the left bottom and at the left top. The red artillery collar and the buttons serve to make this an excellent presentation piece with an even greater historical value attached. The shell jacket has been authenticated by the historian and expert Les Jensen and comes with an archive of Pendleton family provenance and research.

Provenance: *The William Turner Collection*

Estimate: $80,000-$100,000

72133   CONFEDERATE GENERAL THOMAS ROSSER'S COLLAR INSIGNIA, each approximately 4.5" x 2.5". These two strips of buff cloth are heavily embroidered in gold with the laurel wreath and three stars prescribed for general officers by Confederate regulations. The bullion composing wreath and stars is only lightly tarnished. The set comes from the uniform of Major General Thomas Rosser (1836-1910), a key player in the Army of Northern Virginia's cavalry operations. Rosser, a Virginia native and West Point graduate, joined the famed Washington Artillery of New Orleans when the war started. A favorite of J.E.B. Stuart's, he was made colonel of the 5th Virginia Cavalry. From Second Manassas through Appomattox, Thomas Rosser was in the saddle. In fact, his men made a final charge at Appomattox on April 9, 1865 and managed to cut their way through Federal lines without surrendering to Custer.

Provenance: *Rosser Family, Charlottesville, VA*
The Tharpe Collection of American Military History

Exhibited: *The Liberty Heritage Society Museum*

Estimate: $20,000-$30,000

72134   ENGRAVED SILVER "PRESENTATION SWORD" PLATE FROM J.E.B. STUART TO THOMAS ROSSER, 4" x 1.5". A schematic American eagle has been cut from a piece of sheet silver and forms the top border of this plate. The face is engraved, "Lewinsville / Sept. 11th, 1861 / Presented to Capt. T. L. Rosser by Brigadier General J. E. B. Stuart". The verso has seven applied attachment pins and is stamped "Lewis" by its maker, a reference to the Richmond silversmith Ian Lewis, who was also a button maker. Light scratches as expected. Virginia-born West Pointer Thomas L. Rosser commanded a battery in New Orleans's famed Washington Artillery during the opening months of the Civil War. He was present in support of Stuart's First Virginia Cavalry when they opposed a Federal force operating in Fairfax County, Virginia. The Yankees were driven away with casualties while the Confederates emerged victorious and unscathed. Stuart acknowledged Rosser's pivitol role with the hatpin offered here and with this statement in his official report of the incident: "...The officers and men behaved in a manner worthy of the General's highest commendation, and the firing done by the section under the direction of Captain Rosser and Lieut. Slocum (all the time under fire from the enemy's battery) certainly, for accuracy and effect, challenges comparison with any every made." Rosser had gotten J. E. B. Stuart's favorable attention and went on to become a Confederate Major General of cavalry.

Provenance: *The Tharpe Collection of American Military History*

Exhibited: *The Liberty Heritage Society Museum*

Estimate: $20,000-$30,000

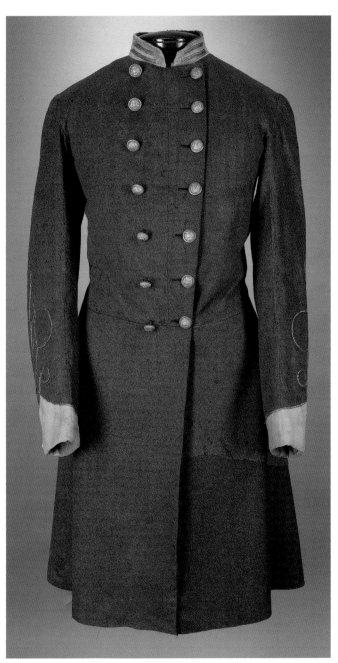

Please visit <u>HA.com</u> to view other collectibles auctions. *A 19.5% Buyer's Premium ($9 min.) Applies To All Lots*

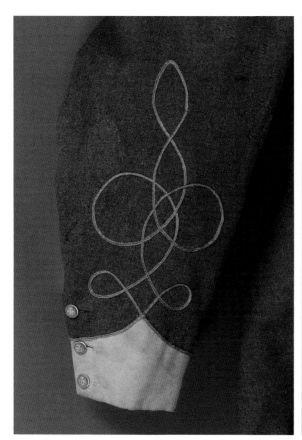

72135   CONFEDERATE FROCK COAT OF LT. WILLIAM ALLEN HANGER, 1ST VIRGINIA CAVALRY – Regulation cadet gray wool broadcloth with yellow cuff and collar trim. The sleeves have a lieutenant's single quatrefoil braid and two collar bars. The coat's double-breasted front has 14 Federal eagle staff buttons, four others are on the tail and three similar cuff buttons are on each sleeve. Repaired moth damage throughout, with the lower portion of the left tail being completely replaced. Note that a bullet hole on the right sleeve has been filled. Interior brown cotton lining has been left substantially as is with all of the loss and separations typically associated with aged fabric. An attractive Confederate junior officer's uniform steeped in history.

Lieutenant Hanger (1831 - 1889) was an Augusta County overseer when he enlisted as 1st Sergeant in the Valley Rangers, Co. "E", 1st Virginia Cavalry. He was appointed 2nd Lieutenant on July 1, 1861 and 1st Lieutenant on April 23, 1862. The previous day, April 22, found Hanger participating in J.E.B. Stuart's raid on Catlett Station, Virginia. During the charge, led personally by J.E.B. Stuart, Hanger was shot in the right arm. The wound never fully healed and the Lieutenant found himself relegated to the Invalid Corps. He was later captured at Cedar Creek on October 19, 1864, Hanger was exchanged and finally paroled on May 19, 1865.

Authentication: With four-page letter of authenticity and thorough technical analysis by Les Jensen.

Provenance: *The Tharpe Collection of American Military History*

Exhibited: *The Liberty Heritage Society Museum*

Estimate: $60,000-$65,000

72136   A VIRGINIA DARK BLUE SLOUCH HAT WITH A GOLD "VA." IN LAUREL WREATH DEVICE – This slouch hat with a distinctive Virginia device surrounded by a laurel wreath is an extremely rare artifact from what is considered to be the first land battle of the Civil War at Big Bethel, Virginia. It was captured from the battlefield by a Union soldier and has been held in a private collection ever since.

A decidedly Confederate victory, the engagement at Big Bethel began when Union Major General Benjamin F. Butler sent troops from Hampton and Newport News to confront Confederate troops at Little and Big Bethel. The Confederates withdrew to concentrate their forces near Big Bethel Church. Commanded by Colonels John B. Magruder and D. H. Hill, the Confederates repulsed the advances of the 5th New York Zouaves killing 79 men including Colonel T. Wynthrop. The Confederates lost only nine men.

This war trophy from that battle, captured by one of Gen. Benjamin Butler's soldiers, is a dark blue heavy felt slouch hat with a 1" silk band of the same color. The gold-colored metal "Va." device is centered in the middle of a metal wreath of a darker gold color. The condition overall is very good with a small hole on the left side of the brim near the bow of the silk band. The interior brown leather band is in excellent condition as well but has separated at the back of the hat. An old museum tag with the words "taken from a rebel on the battlefield of Big Bethel ,Virginia" has been sewn to the top of the hat.

This is a unique and very rare artifact, highly attractive and is from the earliest action of the Civil War.

Provenance: *The Tharpe Collection of American Military History*

Exhibited: *The Liberty Heritage Society Museum*

Estimate: $20,000-$25,000

72137   A CONFEDERATE OFFICER'S SLOUCH HAT WITH GOLD CORD AND ACORNS – This buckskin-colored felt slouch hat, much like the one Confederate General Robert E. Lee often wore, has excellent provenance having been exhibited in a North Carolina collection for many years. The 4" brim is capped by a silk ribbon that encircles the entire hat, coordinating with the 1" ribbed silk hatband. A striking, intricately woven silk hat cord with two officer's acorn ends accentuates the beauty of this instantly recognizable, elegant headgear of the Confederacy.

A hat very similar to this one is illustrated in Time-Life's *Echoes of Glory - Arms and Equipment of the Confederacy* (page 166). It is noted that typically officer's hats had acorns at the end of the hat cords while enlisted men's bore tassels. There are many stories in the literature of the Civil War where General Lee is depicted as wearing a hat just like this one shown here. With a rolled-in crown, this hat remains in very good condition. There is a small hole on the left side of the brim just behind the hatband bow and two small holes at the left rear of the crown. The inner leather hatband has some deterioration at the front but is otherwise intact and in good condition.

Provenance: *The Tharpe Collection of American Military History*

Exhibited: *The Liberty Heritage Society Museum*

Estimate: $20,000-$30,000

72138   CONFEDERATE LOUISIANA "WASHINGTON ARTILLERY" OFFICER'S ARTILLERY KEPI, 6.5" wide x 9" long, high red wool crown, dark blue wool hatband, single line of gold trim, stamped brass crossed cannon insignia, stamped brass "W A" on front of hatband, patent leather visor and remnants of chinstrap secured by two 16mm eagle staff buttons. The interior lacks a true sweatband, however has a strip of blue wool placed along the inside front. The lining is made from coarse brown cotton cloth. An especially good-looking kepi, this one retains vibrant coloring. It has only one tiny pinhole, which is to the right of the insignia. The visor shows a light crazing as should be expected with any antique leather.

The interior stitching is somewhat loose, but still in place. Exterior stitching is tight. An exceptional opportunity to acquire a distinctive kepi, with original insignia intact, from the most famous artillery unit of the Civil War. The Washington Artillery of New Orleans, organized in 1838, was an exclusive militia organization open only to the city's gentry. The brave men of the Washington Artillery fought gallantly in every battle during four years' service with Lee's Army of Northern Virginia.

Provenance: *The Tharpe Collection of American Military History*

Exhibited: *The Liberty Heritage Society Museum*

Estimate: $30,000-$35,000

72139   A VIRGINIA CAVALRY OFFICER'S HAT WITH A FIVE-POINTED STAR, CROSSED SABERS AND OSTRICH PLUME – This Confederate cavalry officer's hat is a striking example of the Southern cavalier's headdress. The 3¼" brim turned up to one side, tacked to the crown with a five-pointed star, this type of hat was worn by the dashing cavalrymen of the South, especially from Virginia, and by many infantry officers as well, including General William Mahone of the Battle of the Crater fame.

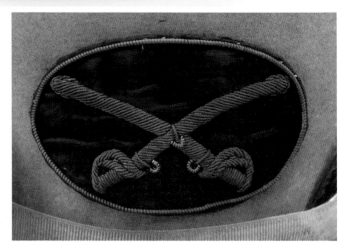

The crossed-sabers gold braid cavalry device is affixed to the front of the hat mounted on a black felt oval field ornament that is surrounded by gold braid beadwork. The ribbed silk 1" hatband has the flamboyant ostrich feather inserted at the left side at the bow. The crown is surrounded at the base by a gold officer's cord that ends with the officer's acorn devices at each end. The inner leather hatband that would have been original to the hat is missing. Otherwise in good condition, this buckskin-colored hat has been repaired at the top of the crown around the oval approximately halfway where it had at one time been separated from the crown itself.

This is a fine example of the most dashing headgear of the Civil War. Only a few are known to exist, especially with the distinctive five-pointed star, ostrich plume and cavalry devices intact.

Provenance: *The Tharpe Collection of American Military History*

Exhibited: *The Liberty Heritage Society Museum*

Estimate: $30,000-$35,000

72140   VIRGINIA LIEUTENANT'S REGULATION CONFEDERATE KEPI, 7" wide x 10" long, grey wool crown and sides with black wool trim, single gold braid indicating rank and forming a quatrefoil on the crown, patent leather visor, leather chinstrap with a small brass buckle secured by two 16mm Virginia gilt buttons (backmark not visible). The interior has a wide brown leather sweatband and is lined with a butternut cotton fabric. Overall this classic Confederate officer's kepi is quite sound and in much better condition than most surviving Civil War headgear. Fewer than half a dozen pinholes dot the grey wool, these being along the edge of the hatband and, as such, nearly invisible. The exterior leather has minimal crazing throughout and one fold line along the visor. The buttons have a rich, never-cleaned gilt patina. The interior is somewhat soiled from use. All stitching is tight. This kepi presents an excellent opportunity to own a museum quality Confederate officer's kepi.

Provenance: *The Tharpe Collection of American Military History*

Exhibited: *The Liberty Heritage Society Museum*

Estimate: $35,000-$45,000

72141 CONFEDERATE OFFICER'S KEPI FROM SOUTH CAROLINA, 6.75" x 8.5", with a high crown consisting of light blue wool trimmed conservatively with gray braid. A 1.75" dark blue wool band circles the base and carries an embroidered device consisting of a laurel wreath enclosing "SC". The visor is of black patent leather with a green underside. A brown leather sweatband and cotton lining are inside the kepi. The crown shows some mothing, otherwise the wool elements are sound. Some crazing to the visor, moderate interior staining and wear. Overall a very presentable example of Confederate junior officer's headgear with good color and an interesting history. A photocopied letter of provenance from the North Missouri Historical Society accompanies the kepi. According to the letter, the kepi was acquired at an Iowa estate auction that had several Civil War items that had been brought home by a Union veteran. The letter's author, Jerry Davis, writes in part: "*...I tried to piece together the story as best I could where his unit would have encountered a South Carolina cavalry unit and the most likely cavalry unit would have been the 6th South Carolina Cavalry called the 'Dixie Rangers' assigned to Butler's brigade. The oral history of the kepie (sp) is that the Union caught the Confederates asleep and captured them without a fight.*"

Estimate: $15,000-$20,000

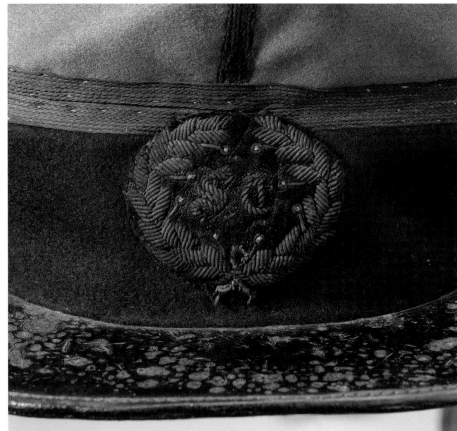

The Finest Obtainable Confederate Sword Belt Rig

72142 CONFEDERATE LIEUTENANT GENERAL'S "BATTLE FLAG" SWORD BELT SET SIMILAR TO GENERAL HOOD'S. The centerpiece of this wartime treasure is, of course, the silver Confederate Battle Flag waving proudly from its staff set in a laurel wreath. This magnificent Southern icon is applied to a fine English-made 51mm x 44mm gilt brass sword belt plate having a stippled face and smooth beveled edges. The resulting contrast between silver and gold is stunning. A maker's stamp reading "Webb & Bonella / 23/ Old Bond Street / London" is on the back of the plate between two brass pins securing the flag device from behind. The plate and its keeper are sewn to a light brown leather belt embellished with four horizontal rows of gold bullion. Supplementary brass hardware on the rig includes three adjustment buckles, two studs, two attachment rings and a sword hanger. The plate's silver elements are lightly toned and show evidence of a previous cleaning since there are small dabs of white residue in some recesses. The belt remains as supple as it must have been during the 1860s. There is, however, some minor surface crazing, wear along the edges, and a foot-long split on the inside where the stitching has loosened along a seam. Such is to expected and does not detract from the overall appeal of this great piece of Confederate history. A similar belt rig held by the Museum of the Confederacy figures prominently in a wartime photograph of General Hood. The belt in the image, however, has three bands of bullion rather than four and the plate is not marked by the maker. Less than six of these extremely rare Confederate buckles are known to exist. This is the finest one in existence and the rarest Confederate belt buckle.

Estimate: $80,000-$90,000

Virginia Confederate General Officer's Custom Belt Rig

72143   RARE AND UNUSUAL CONFEDERATE GENERAL OFFICER'S BELT RIG UTILIZING A VIRGINIA STAFF BUTTON. An enterprising Confederate officer of the Old Dominion fashioned a unique belt plate for himself by wiring the face of a Steele & Johnson Virginia uniform button to the tongue portion of a two-piece militia belt plate. The plate is smaller than most being 75mm x 41mm, and is an ornate gilt brass affair decorated with scrolled floral designs at the belt attachment loops. The wreath consists of laurel and has an opening just large enough to accommodate the Virginia button. Copper wire, some solder and three neat holes were all it took to affix the button's face to the tongue. The color and toning of this addition matches the rest of the plate exactly, giving it an as-made look. Other brass elements on this rig include an adjuster and a D-ring. The belt is made of burlap covered by fine red leather, this being exposed on the interior but hidden by rich gilt embroidered brocade on the exterior. The belt's golden embellishment strongly suggests that it once was worn by a Confederate general. The plate is in excellent condition; however, the belt shows considerable wear, has some splits and suffers a small area of loss. Overall an exceptional belt rig demonstrating that ingenuity that was not a trait exclusive to Yankees.

Provenance: *The Tharpe Collection of American Military History*

Exhibited: *The Liberty Heritage Society Museum*

Estimate: $20,000-$30,000

72144   VIRGINIA SWORD BELT PLATE ON LEATHER. The cast brass plate measures 84mm x 50mm and is nearly identical to Plate 435 in *Confederate Belt Buckles and Plates* by Steve E. Mullinax. Its bold, distinctive and almost modern, design consists of "VIRGINIA" within a laurel wreath set against a stippled field. The plate and keeper have matching "811" benchmarks and are sewn to a U.S. officer's sword belt. The belt proper remains intact, however its two leather sword straps have deteriorated over the years with only remnants being attached to the belt, which has moderate crazing throughout. A rare and attractive belt rig.

Provenance: *The Tharpe Collection of American Military History*

Exhibited: *The Liberty Heritage Society Museum*

Estimate: $10,000-$20,000

72145 **VIRGINIA SWORD BELT PLATE ON LEATHER,** 88mm x 51mm, cast and die-stamped brass, ca. late 1850s - 1861. See Plate 434 in *Confederate Belt Buckles and Plates* by Steve E. Mullinax. Following the general form of the Model 1851 U. S. sword belt plate, the face of this prewar plate displays the Virginia State Seal within an oblong oval cartouche set against a stippled background. The Roman personification of Virtue, Virtus, is shown standing over a defeated Tyranny. This device, used by Virginia since 1776, would have seemed especially appropriate to her volunteer forces of 1861. The plate's back and keeper are both stamped with the benchmark "219", indicating an original pairing since the day they were made. The plate is affixed to a russet leather belt and has a brass ring stitched to its back. An unusual feature of this particular specimen is that the plate's tongue has been repaired with two copper rivets set into pre-drilled holes. All brass elements in this rig enjoy a natural old toning. The leather is somewhat stiff, yet remains solid.

Provenance: *The Tharpe Collection of American Military History from Norm Flayderman.*

Exhibited: *The Liberty Heritage Society Museum.*

Estimate: $10,000-$20,000

72146   A REMARKABLE TWO-PIECE GOLD VIRGINIA CONFEDERATE BELT PLATE BELONGING TO MOSBY RANGER C. F. WOOD OF WARRENTON, VIRGINIA − Rarely does a Confederate plate in this condition reach the market. This near-pristine gold-plated jeweler made buckle set is a museum piece in quality, as visually attractive as it is historically important. The central disk which is inserted into the receiving mechanism of the buckle is the Virginia state seal with 'Virginia' above the figure of Virtus, the Roman goddess of virtue with the Latin motto 'Sic Semper Tyrannis' when translated meaning 'thus always to tyrants', appearing below the figure.

While there is some of the gilt having been rubbed from the clothing of the figure of Virtus, the overall condition of the disk portion of the buckle is magnificent. Virtus stands in a victorious pose with her foot ceremoniously on top of the defeated tyrant whose crown has fallen from his head. A variant of the 1776 approved design is still in use as Virginia's state seal today. There is an inspector's mark '3' on the obverse of the buckle beside the disk next to the rectangular attachment where a leather belt would be attached.

The receiving device of the buckle is a magnificent oak wreath, intricately engraved and broken at the top and bottom by ribbons forming two St. Andrew's crosses. This part of the buckle incorporates the rectangular portion where the leather belt would be attached. Inside the interior of the oak wreath where the disk is inserted is another, separate inspector's mark of a reversed '4'. The plate measures 80mm x 50mm and is similar to Plate 418 in *Confederate Belt Buckles and Plates* by Steve E. Mullinax. A letter of authenticity from Mullinax accompanied this buckle.

This is a highly treasured gold Virginia Confederate two-piece belt buckle in almost unseen, fine condition.

Provenance: *The Tharpe Collection of American Military History*

Exhibited: *The Liberty Heritage Society Museum*

Estimate: $18,000-$24,000

Magnificent and Extremely Rare "CS In The Shield" Confederate Officer's Belt Plate

72147   EXTREMELY RARE TWO-PIECE "CS IN THE SHIELD" CONFEDERATE OFFICER'S BELT PLATE, 51mm x 75mm, interlocking gilt stamped brass tongue with replica cast wreath portion. Similar to Plate 065, which belonged to Confederate General Walter Lane, as illustrated in *Confederate Belt Buckles and Plates* by Steve E. Mullinax. The high relief Confederate droop-wing eagle on this plate is behind a shield defiantly displaying the letters "CS". This attractive device is reminiscent of Confederate officer's buttons made by English firms such as S. Buckley of Birmingham. The eagle's use here and its superb execution suggest the plate is probably a British import run through the blockade into the Confederacy, which explains their rarity, as less than six are known to exist. In excellent, original condition. Another example is unlikely to appear on the market in the foreseeable future.

Provenance: *Ken Ferreo, The Tharpe Collection of Military History*

Exhibited: *The Liberty Heritage Society Museum.*

Estimate: $25,000-$30,000

A Virginia Button From "Stonewall" Jackson's Uniform

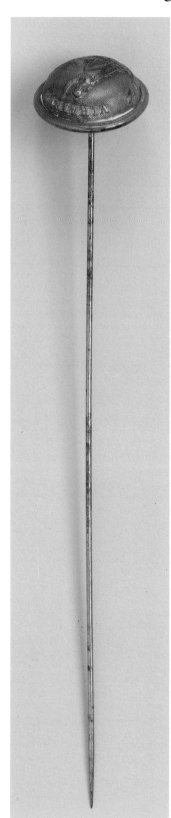

72148   VIRGINIA BUTTON HATPIN WITH PROVENANCE, STONEWALL JACKSON'S – 5.5"
long, made from a three-piece state seal button having the pre-war backmark of the well-known Richmond
firm Mitchell & Tyler. The shank of this button was removed with a long steel pin being soldered in its place.
An accompanying typed card shows light aging and states that the button is "…from the Richard D. Steuart
Collection…supposedly from the uniform coat of 'Stonewall Jackson.'" The button has excellent old toning
and is free of pushes or dents. Its former owner, Richard D. Steuart of Baltimore, was a highly regarded author
and collector of Confederate memorabilia during the mid-20th century.

Provenance: *The William Turner Collection*

Estimate: $6,000-$8,000

72149   LOUISIANA BELT PLATE ON ORIGINAL LEATHER, 55 x 79 mm, die-struck face with a laurel wreath and small stars surrounding a nesting pelican feeding five young. The back has three brass attachment hooks soldered directly to its lead fill. Similar to Plate 286 in Steve Mullinax's *Confederate Belt Buckles & Plates.* The plate has spectacular lightly tones brass with hints of red and green verdigris. Usual crazing to moderately stiff leather.

Estimate: $6,000-$9,000

72150   TWO-PIECE MARYLAND BELT PLATE, 56 x 85 mm, cast brass with die-struck tongue showing Maryland state seal, Roman numerals etched on belt loop. Similar to Plate 299 in *Confederate Belt Buckles and Plates* by Steve E. Mullinax. This example does not seem to have been gilt. An older tag attached to the plate notes that it was worn by a George Lewman, who died in 1905. It appears to have been cleaned many years ago. excellent condition.

Estimate: $1,000-$2,000

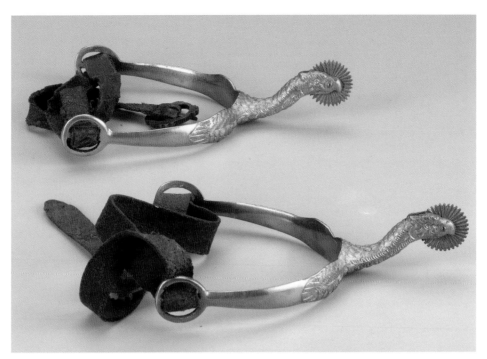

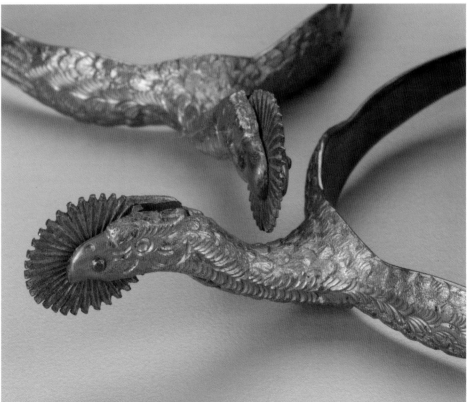

72151   THE SPURS OF COLONEL EDWIN J. HARVIE – STAFF OF GENERAL ROBERT E. LEE – Colonel Edwin J. Harvie served General Robert E. Lee as Assistant Inspector General. A native of Amelia County, Virginia, Harvie served as Inspector General on General Joseph Johnston's staff and then on Lee's staff until the end of the war. A graduate of the Virginia Military Institute and scion of an old James River colonial family, he served in fifty-four battles during the war. After the war he was a businessman at Richmond, Virginia.

These gilt spurs are in excellent condition with the gilding at over 90% intact. The shaft of the spur is formed as an eagle with wings spread back to the sides of the spurs. The rowels of the spurs are in a sunburst design and are carved toward the center of the disk.

The leather and buckles are still in place with some cracking of the leather. These spurs have witnessed much history as they were worn by one of General Lee's staff officers.

Provenance: *The Tharpe Collection of American Military History*

Exhibited: *The Liberty Heritage Society Museum*

Estimate: $2,000-$3,000

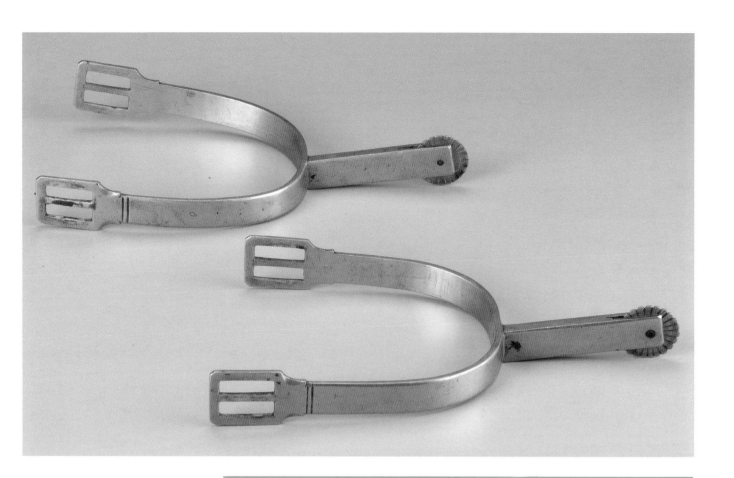

72152 A PAIR OF SILVER CONFEDERATE SPURS – This pair of utilitarian silver spurs have great character. The simple, clean lines belie the fact that they could still be strapped on and used today. The smooth sunburst rowel still functions perfectly. The only designs the maker attempted are two vertical, parallel lines near the hole where the leather would be attached. The sloped edges near the lines are all slightly different, each hand-made by a craftsman more interested in practical usage and not decoration. They are very typical of Confederate spurs of the Civil War.

Provenance: *The Tharpe Collection of American Military History*

Exhibited: *The Liberty Heritage Society Museum*

Estimate: $1,000-$2,000

72153   PAIR OF GOLD EPAULETTES IDENTIFIED TO COLONEL JONATHAN CATLETT GIBSON, 49TH VIRGINIA VOLUNTEERS,
5" x 7" These epaulettes have 2.5" tassels, heavy gold bullion with yellow silk underside, with original Mitchell & Tyler presentation box. The box, of sturdy board, carries two labels, one on the lid and another on its side. Mitchell & Tyler were well known military outfitters and are especially recognized among collectors for uniform buttons carrying their backmark. The upper label of the box gives the company's location as Richmond while the side label notes that these are lieutenant's epaulettes. The epaulettes are in excellent condition with the box having some chipping and a seam separation along the lid. Both items are in pristine condition. Colonel Gibson, a native of Culpeper County, Virginia entered Confederate service in 1861. A participant in First Manassas, he rose to succeed "Extra Billy" Smith as colonel of the 49th Virginia. Gibson led the regiment at Gettysburg and was wounded three times before war's end. After the war, he practiced law and held a seat in Virginia's General Assembly. Gibson was part of the guard that escorted John Brown to the gallows in December, 1859.

Provenance: *The Tharpe Collection of American Military History*

Exhibited: *The Liberty Heritage Society Museum*

Estimate: $8,000-$10,000

72154 INSIGNIA FOR THE M1858 "HARDEE" HAT BELONGING TO COLONEL CATLETT GIBSON. Included are a stamped brass "Jeff Davis" eagle pin, 2" x 2.5", and a stamped brass infantry bugle on a black velvet oval bordered in gold, 3.25" x 2.5". Both items are in pristine condition.

Provenance: *The Tharpe Collection of American Military History*

Exhibited: *The Liberty Heritage Society Museum*

Estimate: $2,000-$3,000

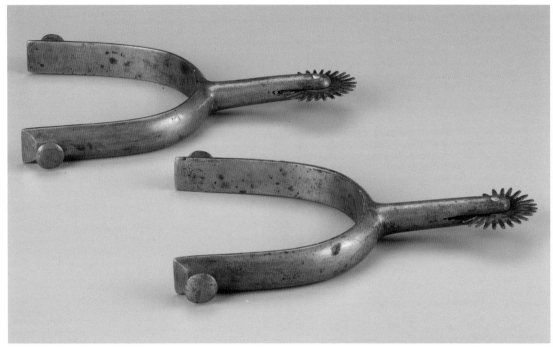

72155 BLACK HORSE TROOP DR. MCGILL, A PAIR OF HEAVY BRASS CONFEDERATE SPURS − This pair of Confederate spurs are a no-frills, heavy duty set designed for battle. They are attributed to Dr. McGill of the famed Confederate Black Horse Troop. With the sideways mounted starburst rowels attached at the end of the 5" spur, these are highly attractive and a great example of the Confederate cavalryman's spurs. The brass has a nice and even patina with some rust at the rowels, these spurs show much field use making them even more desirable.

Provenance: *The Tharpe Collection of American Military History*

Exhibited: *The Liberty Heritage Society Museum*

Estimate: $1,000-$2,000

Simply The Ultimate Civil War Canteen Available

72156   ULTRA RARE EMBOSSED "CS" CONFEDERATE TIN DRUM CANTEEN WITH LINEN SHOULDER STRAP, 6.75" diameter x 1.75" wide, 48" strap, ca.1861. Both faces of this fine canteen sport a raised central disc flanked by a "C" and an "S". As such, it is the only style of Confederate canteen thus marked by the manufacturer, believed to be made in New Orleans in 1861.This well made item is of three-piece soldered tin construction with an applied spout and three brackets for securing the strap. It is fitted with an original heavy linen strap sewn into position. One face has three small dents and there is another along its side. Otherwise, the canteen is as made. The surfaces are generally clean with only the lightest rusting on some of the high points. The strap, though stable, is worn with moderate fraying throughout and splits at its center.

A crushed specimen of this canteen type was found on the Manassas battlefield some years ago. For another example of the "CS" tin drum canteen see page 210 in Time-Life's

Arms and Equipment of the Confederacy. The editors of that excellent reference suggest that these canteens were made in New Orleans for Louisiana troops. This is the absolute finest example known to exist. It is 1 of only 4 known and is one of the great rarities of Civil War collecting.

Provenance: *The Tharpe Collection of American Military History*

Exhibited: *The Liberty Heritage Society Museum*

Estimate: $30,000-$40,000

72157 UNION SOLDIER'S CAPTURED CONFEDERATE CANTEEN, 7.25" diameter, cedar construction with two iron bands securing sides and three iron sling brackets, one face is boldly carved "*I. S. Moore. Co C. 103rd O. V. I.*" by its captor while the other is simply carved "J. H. Winton" by its original owner. Minor scuffing and wear with some shrinkage causing seams to open. Excellent patina, fine condition.

Isaac S. Moore joined the 103rd Ohio Infantry as a corporal in July, 1862 and was demoted to private sometime before mustering out in Raleigh, North Carolina some three years later. Moore's regiment served in Kentucky, Tennessee, Georgia and the Carolinas. There were a number of Confederate Wintons in Tennessee Infantry who would qualify as possible original owners of this canteen since their regiments opposed Sherman in Tennessee and Georgia.

Estimate: $2,000-$3,000

72158 CONFEDERATE WOOD DRUM CANTEEN IDENTIFIED TO A PRIVATE IN THE 20TH TENNESSEE. Cedar with double iron bands and strap retaining bands, about 7.25" in diameter, 2.5" thick, retains about 16" of the original web strap with iron buckle present, general wear from usage, wood darkened with age, spout crudely enlarged, else very good condition. Crudely carved on one side of the canteen are the initials "*J. J. C.*" and on the other in the same style a crude decorative pattern of lines. This canteen belonged to a private in the 20th Tennessee Infantry.

Estimate: $2,500-$3,000

72159   A TIN PORTABLE CONFEDERATE KITCHEN – This novel tin Confederate camp pot is marked 'Orange, Va.' was highly portable, allowing the soldier to carry this device with him onto the battlefield for use back at camp later. The two-piece kitchen is composed of a lower 4" canister that holds oil and a covered wick that provides the heat to warm the contents of the upper 4" diameter by 3" deep tin pot. The upper pot has a tin handle and ring on the accompanying lid. The upper pot is supported by three posts (one missing) that fit snugly into three receptacles in the lower pan to hold the pot above the flame. This is an interesting and rare set of Civil War camp kitchen accouterments.

Provenance: *The William Turner Collection*

Estimate: $2,500-$3,500

**72160   A BEAUTIFUL UNION HARDEE
CAVALRY HAT** – This Hardee hat is in exceptionally
good condition, almost unseen in the texture and color
of the black felt, the condition of the cavalry device and
the striking gold bullion eagle pin.

A design named for cavalry commander William J.
Hardee in 1858, a man who would three years later leave
the Union Army to fight for the Confederacy, this Hardee
hat was adopted that year as the 'Model 1858' It is one
of the most stylish hats found during the Civil War with
it's 8" ostrich plume, medallion device held by a federal
staff officer's pin and decorative acorns that cap the gold
hat cord.

The 3" brim is double-sewn and turned up on the right
side and fastened by the highly-elaborate gold bullion
eagle pin mounted on an oval felt disk. The underside of
the brim is trimmed with ½" gold lace trim which has
somewhat faded. The lace is missing from the top of the
hat brim.

The hat band, in originally yellow gold braid is wrapped
around a 1" silk hatband. Inside the hat, the 2" leather
hat band is in excellent condition. There is no lining in
the hat.

This is a great museum piece from a Union cavalry officer during the Civil War.

Authentication: Les Jensen

Estimate: $12,000-$16,000

72161 UNION 6TH ARTILLERY MAJOR'S KEPI, 7.25" wide x 10" long, dark blue wool throughout with three rows of stitched black braid forming a quatrefoil on the crown. The face displays embroidered crossed cannon behind a red shield emblazoned with a silver "6". The bill and chinstrap are of patent leather with the latter able to be adjusted by a small brass buckle and being secured by two 16mm eagle "A" buttons". The interior is lined with black silk and has a sweatband of tan leather. The kepi is in fantastic condition overall, having only two pinholes and exhibiting the most minimal crazing on the leather.

Provenance: *The Tharpe Collection of American Military History*

Exhibited: *The Liberty Heritage Society Museum*

Estimate: $6,000-$8,000

72162   UNION MODEL 1858 CAVALRY OFFICER'S FORAGE "MCDOWELL" CAP, 8.25" wide x 9" long, leather panel inside crown maker-marked by Shute & Son, Washington St., Boston. Dark blue wool throughout with characteristic high crown and small leather bill. An oval felt panel with embroidered cavalry saber insignia is sewn to the face. The leather chinstrap retains its original brass buckle and is secured by two 16mm Eagle "C" buttons produced by Scovill. The cap's interior has a wide leather sweatband and is lined on the sides with a dark green silk. Expected crazing to the leather elements and wear to the sweatband: otherwise, excellent condition. This is a superb and classic early Civil War "McDowell" cap.

Provenance: *The Tharpe Collection of American Military History*

Exhibited: *The Liberty Heritage Society Museum*

Estimate: $8,000-$10,000

72163   A SPECTACULAR CIVIL WAR ZOUAVE COMPLETE UNIFORM (AND ACCOUTREMENTS) – THE UNIFORM OF W. BERIAH CHANDLER, BATTLE OF GETTYSBURG, LITTLE ROUND TOP – This Zouave complete uniform is an incredible rarity, complete with the jacket with ornate chevrons, ballooned, chasseur-style pants, sash and leggings plus the very rare fez hat - and more. Zouave uniform sets are very rare, only a few are known to exist. This grouping is extremely rare in that it is in prime condition and is attributed to a soldier who fought at Gettysburg. Amazingly, it is accompanied by Private, later 'Principal Musician' W, Beriah Chandler's leggings, leather gaiters - even his sky-blue canteen and Drum Major's baton.

W. Beriah Chandler enlisted at Whitestown, New York on October 6, 1862 for the duration of the war, leaving service after the war as a 2nd Lieutenant. He was a member of the 146th New York Infantry, the Garrard's Tigers under the command of West Point graduate Colonel Kenner Garrard. The regiment would first be assigned to the defenses of Washington, DC but would soon see battle at Fredericksburg and then Chancellorsville. However, important to this uniform, Colonel Garrard had succeeded in obtaining new Zouave uniforms for his soldiers, including Beriah Chandler, just before the most important battle of the Civil War - Gettysburg.

According to historical evidence of the delivery of the unit's uniforms, W. Beriah Chandler was issued this Zouave uniform on June 3, 1863, just one month before he would see battle at Gettysburg. Manufactured at the famed Schuylkill Arsenal, Colonel Garrard made several trips to check on the progress of the uniforms' manufacture before their delivery. Designed according to the Turcos pattern of the French Army, unlike the traditional Zouave designs, these uniforms would have yellow piping, lace and edge work, making them even more distinctive and rare.

This uniform, as were the entire Schuylkill Arsenal uniforms made for the 146th New York, were entirely hand-sewn. The sky-blue jacket and ballooned chasseur-style pants are made from twilled wool. The jacket is a six-piece design with two-piece sleeves and is lined with jean material. A beautiful yellow ½" lace trim accents the jacket's border and on the front on the typical Zouave pattern. The back of the jacket is double-vented. A chevron is applied on each lower sleeve and intersects the sleeve just above the second of the three small eagle functioning cuff buttons that are on each sleeve. There is a Schuylkill Arsenal stencil inside the right sleeve and the jacket fastens at the front top with a looped and braided blue cord with a pin. The jacket is in overall excellent condition.

The most striking features of the jacket are the 'Principal Musician' insignias with three arcs over three inverted chevrons with a central five-pointed star made from gold braid that are sewn to each sleeve. Chandler would have had these applied to his uniform after the Battle of Gettysburg since he was promoted to Principal Musician on July 31, 1864 after his unit participated at the Mine Explosion during the Siege of Petersburg.

The chasseur trousers are unique to this Zouave unit as well. These blue wool trousers are untrimmed and have a wider waistband than other Zouave pants. There are 7" long pockets on each side and the pants have a six-button front with two buttons missing.

At the rear of the trousers there is a buckle used to adjust the fit at the waist. The trousers have a baggy appearance and have small buttons that function at the bottom of the pant leg. There is a watch pocket at the top right waist where the front of the pants are gathered. The overall condition of the pants is good with some holes midway down the front and at the seat. There is also a Schuylkill Arsenal stencil inside the pants at the back center as well.

The accompanying fez and tassel are wool as well and are a departure from the Turcos design in that Colonel Garrard had them made with a yellow tassel instead of the Turcos blue. The fez is made of fine red wool with a fine gold cloth trim while the tassel is of heavy wool yard and a macramé-capped acorn.

The red sash is made of red light wool and is approximately 11" wide allowing for shrinkage. It is approximately 103" long and has a hand-stitched yellow piping along the border on one side and is in excellent condition. An additional, narrower 5" sash approximately 90" long, including the long tassels, is included and was worn over the wider sash. This sash has several tears toward one end and is slightly faded from its original redder tone.

It is even more rare that the leggings and gaiters are present to complete this rare grouping of a Zouave uniform. In the uniform of Private, later Principal Musician Chandler we have the complete set of leather leggings that were worn to protect the leg above the ankle toward the knee. While they have obviously seen much use, the buckles and even the lacings are still present.

The heavy cloth white gaiters that were worn under the leggings are completely intact with the buttons complete on the inside as well as the bottom arch support buttons.

Chandler would have certainly worn this uniform as he led the musicians in their cadence and music that the 146th New York would hear at drill, marching into combat, even as the musicians would play patriotic music to intimidate the enemy, often picking up weapons when the fighting came close at hand. But duty as a musician was no easy task during the Civil War. The hard fighting units such as the Zouaves, the cavalry units under General George Armstrong Custer and General Philip Sheridan all had fighting musicians who played inspirational music on the front lines. Indeed, General Custer demanded a mounted band in his 7th Cavalry after the war.

In that sense, Chandler would see his share of action, especially at Gettysburg on July 2, 1863. The 146th New York Infantry would be under General Weed's brigade that day as they charged up Little Round Top. As Weed was killed, the regiment was part of the first troops to reach and hold 'Round Top Ridge'. Colonel Garrard would be promoted to Brigadier General for his and his unit's bravery that day. From that engagement we not only have Chandler's uniform but his canteen as well.

Owned and carried by Chandler, this Hadden, Porter and Booth Model 1858 canteen was manufactured in Philadelphia. It has its original sky-blue wool cloth covering and heavy white strap. The cork has been replaced and there is a 4" tear of the cloth on one side at the bottom left. There is only slight rusting underneath the cloth, otherwise, this canteen is in excellent condition.

As a the leader of the musicians in his unit, Chandler would play a ceremonial role as well, leading the band in ceremonies, particularly in parades whenever the occasion arose. One such event was the Grand Review "Victory Parade" at Washington, DC just after the war on May 23, 1865. From this service in the Civil War we have Chandler's Drum Major baton. At a full four feet in length, this wooden and brass baton is wrapped in blue and white woolen cording and has a 7½" massive brass cap. This heavy brass globular device measures 13" in diameter and has seen much field wear. Engraved in a foliate design, it has many dents and scratches and tapers to the wooden staff where it is attached with two screws. A 1" brass cap is attached to the bottom of the baton.

This is an amazing archive from a Zouave soldier in the Civil War. Not only is the uniform complete, in excellent condition, but also is attributed to a specific soldier who fought at Little Round Top during the Battle of Gettysburg and later marched proudly in the Grand Review at the close of the war. The fact that we have the accouterments of his canteen and Drum Major's baton make this an especially rare and historic collection.

Provenance: *Direct Descent From the Chandler Family*

Authentication: Les Jensen

Estimate: $120,000-$160,000

72165   A UNION GENERAL'S FROCK COAT WITH DRESS EPAULETS AND HAND-SEWN STARS UNDERNEATH – This striking Union general's double-breasted frock coat conforms to the 1861 uniform regulations for a general's uniform in every way. This coat shows field wear on the coat overall as well as at the collar. Made of a dark blue wool with dark trim, it has two rows of 8 staff officer's buttons down the front with three smaller buttons on each cuff. There are four buttons at the center vent at the back. The coat measures 36" down the front from the neck to the bottom of the unseamed, rough-cut bottom and 40" at the back. The sleeves measure 24" at the outside.

The frock coat comes with brigadier general's dress epaulets with the gold bullion coils, fine gold silk thread small federal eagle button, and single gold bullion star. A single star is sewn onto the coat under the epaulets, a common practice on the battlefield to minimize visibility by enemy sharpshooters. The coat has the typical dark green lining and unusual blue-striped lining.

This is a fine and elaborate example of a Civil War brigadier general's officer uniform, perfect as a display piece and in very good condition.

Provenance: *The Tharpe Collection of American Military History*

Exhibited: *The Liberty Heritage Society Museum*

Estimate: $15,000-$18,000

72166   A UNION NEW YORK ARTILLERY 2ND LIEUTENANT'S UNIFORM
– This single-breasted Union Artillery 2nd Lieutenant's frock coat with New York eagle "Excelsior" buttons, made by Hortsmann Brothers and Allen of New York, is made of very fine dark blue broadcloth, well-constructed with a six-panel pattern. Nine buttons down the front are accentuated by three smaller buttons on each cuff of the 20½" sleeves. Each of the buttons bears the New York state militia seal surmounted by an eagle encircled by 13 stars.

The collar of this frock coat is of the low variety with a small matching button on either side. On each shoulder of the coat are the red, gold-braided Smith's patent shoulder straps indicative of an artillery 2nd Lieutenant. The back of the coat incorporates the conventional design with a center vent with four large matching buttons. The lining is of fine cloth in a green-hued windowpane pattern and two vest pockets. The greenish tone is extended to the sleeve linings which are of that color striped through a more coarse white cloth. The coat is in overall excellent condition with some of the gold braiding pulled loose from the right shoulder strap alone.

Estimate: $8,000-$10,000

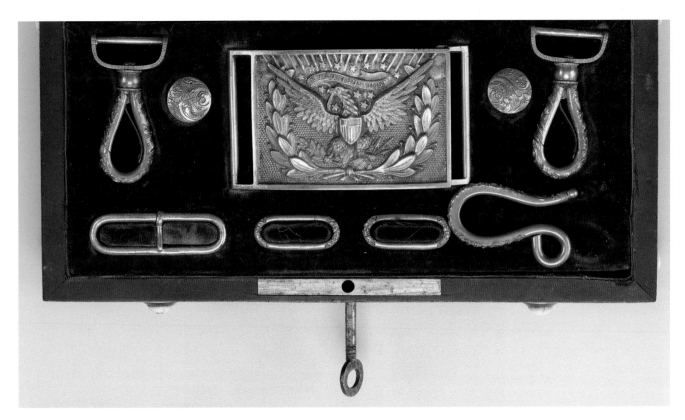

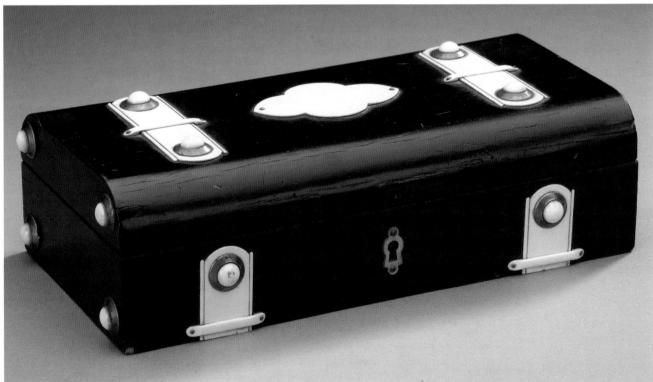

72167   SOLID SILVER FEDERAL SWORD BELT PLATE WITH ATTACHMENTS IN PRESENTATION BOX – A magnificent silver set consisting of an M1851 sword belt plate with keeper, two belt studs, an adjuster, two "O" rings, two snap-on sword hangers and a sword hook. A far cry from standard issue sword belt set furniture, these beautiful items finely crafted with extra embellishments that go far beyond their utility. Even the studs and rings have been engraved with scrolled foliate designs. Marketed by military outfitters Schuyler, Hartley and Graham, New York, the collection is possibly a salesman's sample and is housed in a custom 9" x 2.75" x 4.5" velvet-lined lacquered black box decorated with ivory. Complete with its original latch and key. The silver items are in excellent condition. A remarkable U.S. Army officer's sword belt set.

Provenance: *Ken Ferreo, The Tharpe Collection of American Military History*

Exhibited: *The Liberty Heritage Society Museum.*

Estimate: $10,000-$15,000

72168   CAPTAIN EDGAR HINKLEY, 10TH NEW YORK CAVALRY; GETTYSBURG, APPOMATTOX – HIS SPURS, BELT BUCKLE AND SHOULDER STRAPS – Edgar Hinkley was a captain in the 10th New York Cavalry which saw action at such notable battles as Fredericksburg, Gettysburg, Cold Harbor, Yellow Tavern, Five Forks, and Sayler's Creek. His unit was also present at the surrender of Confederate General Robert E. Lee at Appomattox Court House. Captain Hinkley was captain of Company H at Gettysburg as his men fought at Brinkerhoff's Ridge against the 2nd Virginia Infantry.

This grouping includes ornate and distinctive spurs with the extension being in the form of a chimera with a sunburst rowel. The chimera, a mythological beast with the head of a lion and wings of an eagle retains most of its gilt while the highly engraved rowel is a dark silver. Continuing the contrast of the dark silver to the gilt are the foliate, raised detail work over the lower edge of the wings and around the side of the spurs. While the outside of the spurs retain most of its gilt, the inside shows much boot wear from use. They are cased in a Schuyler, Hartley, and Graham case.

Also included are Captain Hinkley's shoulder boards from his uniform. With the yellow coloring of the cavalry unit having almost completely faded between his two captain's bars of the straps, the gold braid work has faded and has been soiled as well.

Captain Hinkley's brass Union belt buckle has also survived the war and is included with this grouping. The federal eagle is still proudly spreading its wings under the E. Pluribus Unum motto, however the buckle has shown much wear, particularly at the shield at the center of the eagle.

This is a remarkable set of historical items from a Captain who fought throughout the war, seeing action at Gettysburg and witnessing the end of the war at Appomattox.

Provenance: *The Tharpe Collection of American Military History*

Exhibited: *The Liberty Heritage Society Museum*

Estimate: $4,000-$5,000

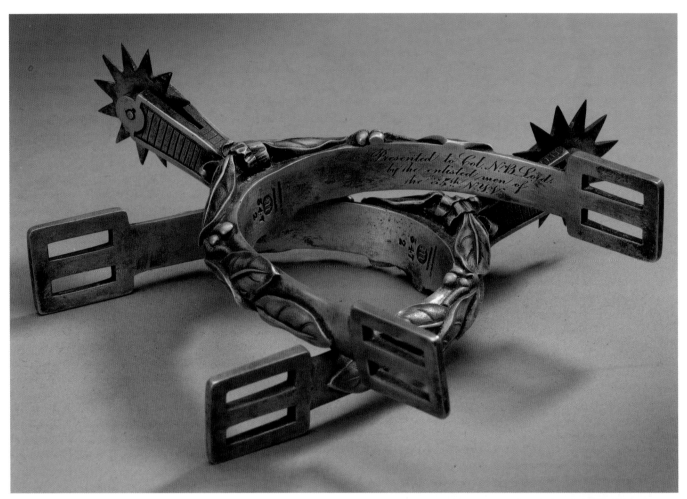

72169   A REMARKABLE PAIR OF STERLING SILVER TIFFANY SPURS OWNED BY COLONEL NEWTON B. LORD OF THE 35TH NEW YORK INFANTRY – Colonel Newton B. Lord rose to the rank of Colonel in the United States Army during the Civil War, apparently with much admiration from his men. This pair of sterling silver Tiffany and Company spurs bear the engraving, "Presented to Col. N. B. Lord by the enlisted men of the 35th N.Y.V."

At the outbreak of the war Newton B. Lord was a foundryman at Jefferson County, New York. Receiving permission to raise a militia company called the Jefferson Grays, he led them as their captain in May 1861. Upon the organization of a regiment designated as the 35th New York Volunteers, he was promoted to colonel on August 2, 1861. Colonel Lord went on to lead his men at Binn's Hill near Falls Church, Virginia, Antietam and at Fredericksburg. It was surely during this time frame that he was presented these Tiffany sterling silver spurs as he was transferred to the 20th New York Volunteer Cavalry shortly thereafter.

These heavy and ornate spurs are each marked "Tiffany & Co." and "sterling" on the inside near the heel of the spur. Incorporating a foliate design on each side of the spurs, the rowels of each spur are very sharp and are 12-pointed for maximum efficiency in the field. The original leather straps have been preserved and are pliable with one strap broken near the buckle. The silver buckles are of a foliate design as well. The entire grouping is enclosed in its blue silk and velvet-lined mahogany presentation box. The lid of the box bears a silver shield device which has not been engraved. The brass hardware is intact and original.

These are a beautiful set of officer's spurs, sterling silver and made by the famous jewelers and silversmiths Tiffany Company, New York, presented to a Union colonel by his men.

Provenance: *The Norman Flayderman Collection; The Tharpe Collection of American Military History.*

Exhibited: *The Liberty Heritage Society Museum.*

Estimate: $10,000-$15,000

72170   A GOLD AND ENAMEL 27TH MASSACHUSETTS VOLUNTEERS MEDAL – This is a beautiful and interesting medal in excellent condition. Made of gold and decorated with white and red enamel, the medal is unique in that it incorporates designations of multiple units within the composition of the medal. Made for a soldier of the 27th Massachusetts Volunteer Infantry, it commemorates the unit that saw service at Petersburg and Cold Harbor and lost 9 officers and 128 enlisted men during the course of the Civil War.

Measuring 1¼" x 2¼", the upper pin-backed shield of the medal is white enamel with a gold cannon and anchor motif, nicely engraved as well. This is the badge of the US Army's 9th Corps. The pendant device attached below the shield is in the form of a cross fleury, the symbol of the 18th Corps with an enameled central red star, the designation of the 1st Division.

The four stations of the cross are engraved clockwise with the words, "27th, Mass., Vols., Regt." This is a beautiful, unique and intricately engraved medal from the 27th Massachusetts Volunteer Infantry in the Civil War.

Provenance: *The John Ford Collection, The Tharpe Collection of American Military History*

Exhibited: *The Liberty Heritage Society Museum*

Estimate: $3,000-$5,000

72171 A BEAUTIFUL GOLD SOLDIER'S MEDAL OF THE 3RD PENNSYLVANIA CAVALRY – GETTYSBURG – This gold soldier's pendant of the 3rd Pennsylvania Cavalry Volunteers is finely crafted of solid gold, the reverse finely engraved with the battles in which the unit fought. Organized at Philadelphia in July and August of 1861, the unit saw duty at the defense of Washington, DC but soon saw action at Yorktown, Williamsburg and Seven Pines. They went on to the Battle of Antietam and Fredericksburg and then to Chancellorsville.

But it may be for their action at Gettysburg that the 3rd Pennsylvania Cavalry is most remembered. Fighting in General John Buford's 1st Division, the unit saw much action fighting with Custer in repulsing the Confederate cavalry led by General J.E.B. Stuart. Captain William E. Miller of the unit was awarded the Congressional Medal of Honor for his actions at Gettysburg.

This soldier's medal from the 3rd Pennsylvania Cavalry measures approximately 1" across, has foliate engraving around its Maltese cross borders and is in superb condition. The loop attachment is still at the top of the medal as well.

Provenance: *The Norman Flayderman Collection; The Tharpe Collection of American Military History*

Exhibited: *The Liberty Heritage Society Museum*

Estimate: $6,000-$8,000

72172　A GOLD PRESENTATION MEDAL FOR CIVIL WAR RECRUITMENT

- As the Civil War seemed imminent, state militias began recruiting young men in case they were needed for service in the United States armed forces. They had no idea of how many men they would ultimately need to fight the nation's bloodiest conflict.

This large gold medal in the shape of a shield is a recruiting award to a Sergeant William M. Baldwin. Measuring 1½" x 2½", it was presented to him by Major William Nary on May 10, 1860 by the 'Franklin Guard' for "his superior exertions in recruiting the company". Engraved on both sides with jeweler's quality script the shield is surmounted by a highly intricate eagle with its wings spread. The loop at the top for a necklace to be attached is in perfect condition as is the entire pendant, obviously treasured by someone for over 160 years.

This is a beautiful large gold medal that is a reminder of the lead-up to the Civil War.

Provenance: *The Tharpe Collection of American Military History*

Exhibited: *The Liberty Heritage Society Museum*

Estimate: $8,000-$12,000

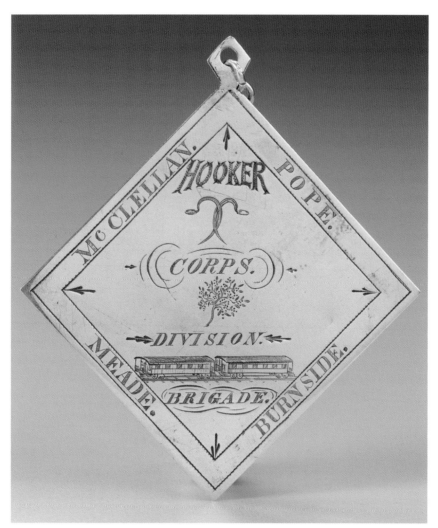

**72173   A SILVER SOLDIER'S MEDAL – SERGEANT
CHARLES F. BROWNE – GETTYSBURG –** Charles F. Browne
was a sergeant with the 1st Regiment of Massachusetts Infantry.
Organized at Boston on May 23, 1861, the regiment fought at
Bull Run, Fredericksburg, and Chancellorsville. As this silver
soldier's pendant clearly shows, they also saw action at the Battle
of Gettysburg. This large 1¾" pendant is highly engraved on one
side with Sergeant Browne's name and his unit designation. The
location of the regiment's formation, 'Boston', is also engraved on
the same side. In the middle of the medal are the major battles,
including Gettysburg, at which the regiment fought.

On the reverse of the pendant Union generals' names are engraved. McClellan, Pope, Burnside and Meade appear at the four
sides with 'Hooker' inside the border of the engraving at the top
near the attachment loop. Under Hooker is ornate engraving interspersed between the words 'Corps', 'Division' and 'Brigade' in
progressively small script denoting the smaller size of the units.
In the center of the pendant on this side is a small, decorative foliate engraving with two railroad cars engraved between the words
'Division' and 'Brigade.

This is a beautiful and unusual engraved Civil War silver medal in
excellent condition.

Provenance: *The Norman Flayderman Collection, The Tharpe
Collection of American Military History*

Exhibited: *The Liberty Heritage Society Museum*

Estimate: $6,000-$8,000

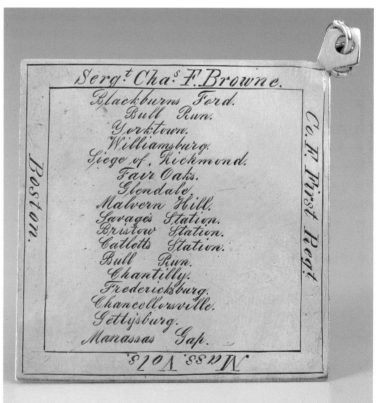

72174   A PAIR OF BRASS TIFFANY MARKED SPURS – This is a pair of rare Tiffany spurs made of a simple design by the renowned New York jeweler during the Civil War. Tiffany made spurs for special clients and marked their products inside the spur at the inside near the front "Tiffany & Co. New York". With a sunburst rowel and a serrated edge below the spur, this attractive but simple design was a trademark of the jeweler's work. These brass spurs have seen much use and have a golden patina but are in sound condition.

Provenance: *The Tharpe Collection of American Military History*

Exhibited: *The Liberty Heritage Society Museum*

Estimate: $2,000-$3,000

**72175   A PAIR OF PARTIAL-GILT EAGLE-HEAD
SPURS – CIVIL WAR –** These Civil War spurs are
ornately made with eagles' head designs holding the
sunburst style rowels. They retain some of the original
gilt, approximately 40%, with one of the spurs having its
original strap complete. The other spur has a remnant of
its strap which includes the buckle. Looking at the rowel
of the spur, it can be seen that the eagle's head is actually
the upturned head of an eagle, the wings of which are the
sides of the spurs.

This is a pair of very attractive Civil War spurs with one of
the complete straps attached.

Provenance: *The Tharpe Collection of American Military
History*

Exhibited: *The Liberty Heritage Society Museum*

Estimate: $1,000-$2,000

72176   THE BRASS AND GILT SPURS OF UNION COLONEL JOHN C. CRANE OF THE 1ST MASSACHUSETTS HEAVY ARTILLERY
– Colonel John C. Crane was assigned to the Quartermaster Corps from Missouri and served throughout the war coordinating supplies, particularly as transported by the railroads. He would encounter many grateful subordinate officers, thankful for the supplies he would deliver to them in order to ensure their survival and win the war.

These gilt brass spurs were presented by one such officer, Lieutenant Colonel Levi P. Wright of the 1st Massachusetts Heavy Artillery. The 1st Massachusetts fought at Spottsylvania, Cold Harbor and the assault on Petersburg and was within two miles of Appomattox Court House when General Robert E. Lee surrendered.

The brass and gilt spurs are made in the form of a spread-winged eagle and measure approximately 5" in length. The eagle holds the starburst rowel in its beak as the wings form the sides of the spur. Both sides of each spur are engraved with the left sides bearing the inscription, 'From Lt. Col. L. I. Wright, 1st Mass. H. Arty.' while the right sides of the spurs have the dedication, 'To Col. J. C. Crane' with a starburst engraving underneath. This is a beautiful pair of spurs dedicated to a commander from an appreciative subordinate.

Provenance: *The Tharpe Collection of American Military History*

Exhibited: *The Liberty Heritage Society Museum*

Estimate: $2,500-$3,500

72177   A VERY RARE CIVIL WAR UNION ARMY STAFF OFFICER'S SILK AND LEATHER BELT AND CARTRIDGE BOX - This is a very rare surviving silk, brass and leather Civil War staff officer's belt and cartridge box. In remarkably good condition, this belt retains the lion's head device and chains that are connected to the heavy federal shield replete with the "E. Pluribus Unum" motto, both made of heavy gilt brass. The heavy patent leather cartridge box is trimmed in thick brass and boasts a federal eagle on the front made of heavy brass with some gilt present. The connecting strap that secures the flap of the box is missing.

This staff officer's dress belt and cartridge box is illustrated in the Schuyler, Hartley and Graham's *Arms and Military Goods Regulations for the Uniform of the Army, Navy, Marine and Revenue Corps* published in 1864 (plate Number 51). This was a standard reference for authorized Union military uniforms, weapons and insignia during the Civil War. The leather of this belt is very pliable with some cracking on the cartridge box with the brass in very good condition. This is a remarkable chance to obtain a rare staff officer's accoutrement from the Civil War.

Estimate: $3,000-$5,000

UNION SWORDS

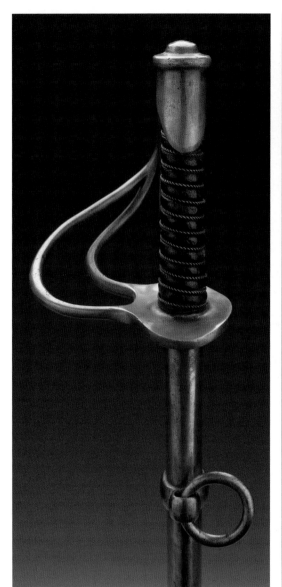

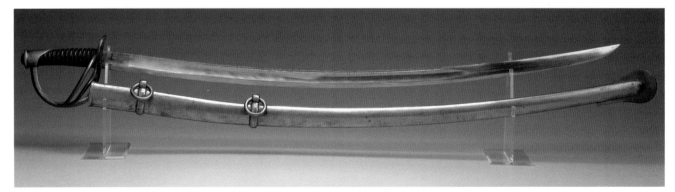

72178   MODEL 1840 CAVALRY SABER WITH SCABBARD 1ST MAINE CAVALRY 1861 – This import wrist-breaker cavalry saber is stamped for the 1st Maine Cavalry. The blade is 36⅛" and has a secondary fuller; the overall length of the sword is 41¼." The right side of the blade, at the ricasso, is die stamped "US/ADK/1861," the left side ricasso is stamped "1/Me./CAV;" the "V" is very faintly stamped. The grip of the sword has its original leather and twisted wire warp, and very little wear shows on the leather. The sword has a beautiful patina and a bright, shiny blade and scabbard. Overall the condition of the saber is excellent. The uniqueness of this sword is that it is an 1840 Model cavalry saber special ordered to outfit the 1st Maine Cavalry and is marked and date stamped 1861. The First Maine suffered more casualties than any other troop, North or South, in the war.

Provenance: *The Tharpe Collection of American Military History*

Exhibited: *The Liberty Heritage Society Museum*

Estimate: $4,000-$6,000

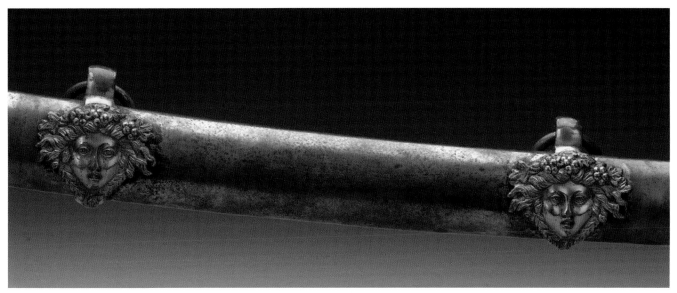

72179   GENERAL ROBERT COWDIN'S CIVIL WAR PRESENTATION CAVALRY SABER – This Schuyler, Hartley and Graham presentation sword was given to Brigadier General Robert Cowdin on January 1, 1863 by his staff. This sword has an elaborate guard and grip with a blade and scabbard that are equally impressive.

Robert Cowdin was born in Jamaica, Vermont on September 8, 1805 and moved to Massachusetts at the age of twenty. Already a member of the state militia at the outbreak of the Civil War, he was named Colonel of the 1st Massachusetts Infantry as the war began. He led his regiment at the Battle of First Bull Run, Williamsburg, and at Chantilly. He was appointed brigadier general just three months before this sword was presented to him by his staff as he served at the defenses of Washington, DC.

This ornate saber has a 36" curved blade with fine scroll etching on each side. On the obverse appears 'US' between the foliate etching while on the reverse, a spread-winged eagle with a ribbon bearing the words 'E. Pluribus Unum' above its head are nicely done. At the ricasso the maker's mark of 'Schuyler Hartley & Graham' is etched while on the mark of 'W. Caluberg Solingen' the maker of the blade is stamped. Schuyler used only the finest blades and advertised many different styles of engraving and blades.

The grip of the sword is very decorative being made of silver bands with a shamrock design etching with narrow brass and gilt etched bands. The guard is of three curved, highly gilded bars curved to the pommel. The inside and the outside of the guard are highly engraved in a floral pattern terminating at the tang with a cherubic device. Atop the grip under the pommel is a large bearded medallion device nicely gilded as well.

The metal scabbard is decorated at the throat with a gilded and intricately engraved band above two large gold medallions at 4" and 12" down the scabbard. The drag is also very ornamental extended 6" from the end of the scabbard. Highly etched, this part of the sword and scabbard shows the most loss of the gilt as it has seen much use. Between the two medallions on the scabbard is the inscription to General Cowdin as follows:

Presented to
Brig. Gen. Robt. Cowdin
By His Staff
Jany 1st 1863

This is an overall very attractive presentation sword and scabbard given to a brigadier general during the Civil War.

Provenance: *The Tharpe Collection of American Military History*

Exhibited: *The Liberty Heritage Society Museum*

Estimate: $10,000-$15,000

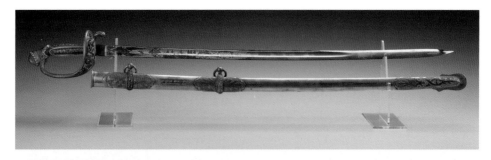

72180   AN ORNATE SILVER AND GOLD PRESENTATION SWORD, LIEUTENANT GEORGE HENRY WING – This highly gilded and silver sword was presented to Lieutenant George Henry Wing of the 14th New York heavy Artillery, Company L, on April 14, 1864. It has a highly gilded blade and scabbard mounts and was specially made by Schuyler, Hartley and Graham of Philadelphia. Schuyler was famous for its fine presentation swords to which they would go to any length of gilding and use of silver.

This is one of the best examples of their craftsmanship, one of their "Rich Presentation" grade swords. The 32" blade is intricately etched and gilded 13" up the double fuller on both sides. The obverse of the blade starts with the standing knight Clauberg Solingen blade maker's mark above which is etched a foliate pattern under an elaborate stand of colors and crossed cannon. Further up the blade is an eagle, spread-winged with the 'E. Pluribus Unum' ribbon in its beak. Following another foliate patter is another stand of arms. All areas up the fuller outside the etching are coated in gold. The etching and gold work extend over the top of the sword to the reverse.

The reverse has a stand of colors starting at the ricasso followed by the foliate device. An elaborate artillery scene with six soldiers and cannon ready for battle is centered around an oval depicting a female warrior with the word 'Eureka' at the top of the oval. Another etched foliate pattern separates the final 'U. S.' etching at the end of the fuller. The remainder of the blade is not etched and retains a mirror finish. The leather washer is still intact.

The foliate openwork of the guard has lost most of its original gilding as has the knucklebow which leads to an ornately carved pommel and pommel cap which has a large oval shell-like device. The 4" grip is made of silver and has been worked into an interesting ribbed design with quarter-moon shapes separated by disks, all silver.

The scabbard is of heavy steel and has heavily carved mounts and mount rings that retain about 30% of their original gilding as does the drag. The gilded throat cap surmounts the first mount of the two 4½" mounts which are engraved on one side and are identical. The heavy foliate pattern is broken by the mount rings which have a holly leaf and berry carving. The elaborate drag extends 6½" from the end of the sword. It bears the same style engraving as the mounts and is engraved on one side as well. The scabbard is inscribed between the two mounts as follows:

> Presented to
> Lieut. George Henry Wing
> by the Members of Co. L
> 14th Reg.
> Artillery N.Y.S.V.
> Willet's Point, New York Harbor, April 14, 1864

Lieutenant George Henry Wing obviously handled this sword regularly as witnessed by the heavy use of the grip. Fortunately the blade has been preserved at approximately 90% of its original gilding.

The 14th New York Heavy Artillery was formed in January 1864 and for a time were stationed at harbor duty in New York as noted in the dedication of the sword, The unit would see much action however through the rest of the war: at the battles of the Wilderness and Spottsylvania; taking part in the Siege of Petersburg, including the Mine Explosion; and participating in the Grand Review 'Victory Parade' at the close of the war.

This is beautiful sword carried by a young lieutenant through some of the most famous battles of the Civil War.

Estimate: $6,000-$8,000

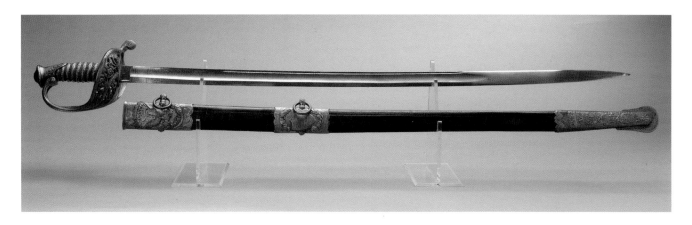

72181   CAPTAIN CHARLES STRICKLAND 20TH MAINE PRESENTATION SWORD – BATTLE OF GETTYSBURG. Captain Charles Strickland of the 20th Maine Infantry was presented this ornate field officer's sword on August 30, 1862 for a wound received while rendering services during the Peninsular Campaign in Virginia. This unit was one of the most famous of the Civil War, fighting at Little Round Top at the Battle of Gettysburg. Led by Colonel Joshua Lawrence Chamberlain, the unit has been memorialized in books and film for their exploits in holding off the Confederate assault and eventually charging into the 15th Alabama to take the day.

This sword presented to Captain Strickland was made in New York by James P. Fitch and measures 32" in length. Starting at the ricasso with an engraved sunrise design, this blade is elaborately etched through the 22" fuller with the 'U.S.' appearing 6" from the ricasso. On the reverse, working up from the maker's mark at the ricasso, the same elaborate floral etching appears with a spread-winged eagle at 6" up the blade just below a ribbon with 'E. Pluribus Unum'. Further up the blade are a stand of arms below an American flag.

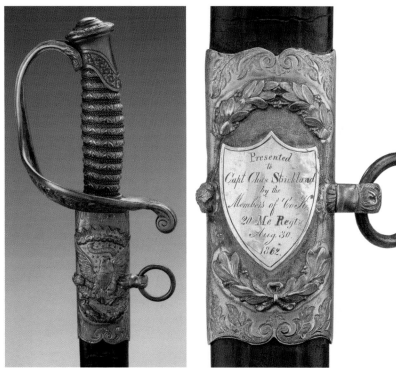

The hilt consists of a carved silver and twisted wire ornate grip capped by a pommel engraved with a floral design. The guard has a tightly carved floral design throughout extending to the quillon that terminates in a scroll pattern. The hilt retains approximately 30% of its original gilt.

The metal and leather scabbard has an ornate throat that extends over 4" down the scabbard. Retaining about 80% of its original gilt, it is in the form of a federal eagle with wings spread, a shield at its center with the 'E. Pluribus Unum' ribbon in its mouth in front of a field of stars surmounted by a sunburst. Below the eagle is a laurel wreath. On the reverse of the throat there is elaborate engraving scrollwork which is bisected by a laurel wreath through the attachment screw fits as well as the upper ring.

Down the leather part of the scabbard about 5" is the second ring attached to a 3½" gilt metal mount which is highly engraved front and back. On the front is the silver presentation shield onto which is engraved the following:

Presented
To
Capt. Chas. Strickland
By the
Members of Co. K
20 Me. Regt.
Aug 30
1862

The gilt drag of the scabbard extends a full 6" from the end of the scabbard and bears equally fine engraving. It retains approximately 30% of its original gilt.

This is a rare field officer's presentations sword given to a young captain at the start of the war who was part of one of the most famous units of the Civil War.

Provenance: *The Tharpe Collection of American Military History*

Exhibited: *The Liberty Heritage Society Museum*

Estimate: $30,000-$40,000

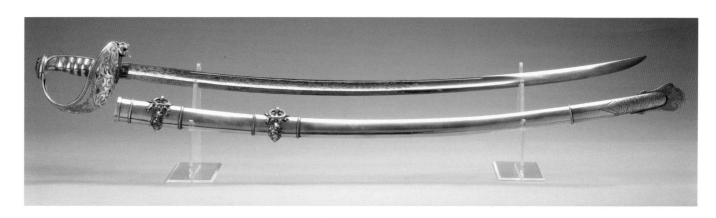

72182   A VERY RARE AND ORNATE SILVER TIFFANY PRESENTATION CIVIL WAR SWORD – CAPTAIN W. A. TREADWELL, 14TH NEW YORK HEAVY ARTILLERY – BATTLES OF THE WILDERNESS, COLD HARBOR, PETERSBURG, THE GRAND REVIEW – This extraordinary, magnificent silver Tiffany sword was presented to Captain William A. Treadwell of the 14th New York Heavy Artillery, a unit that would see service at major battles of the Civil War. A masterpiece crafted by the premier designer Louis Comfort Tiffany, it is also an important historical jewel owned by a captain in a unit that saw some of the heaviest fighting in the war.

Captain William A. Treadwell was appointed captain of the 14th New York Heavy Artillery in September 1863 and saw duty at the Battle of the Wilderness, Cold Harbor, the Siege and Mine Explosion at Petersburg and in the Appomattox Campaign. This sword would have accompanied him at the Grand Review 'Victory Parade' at the close of the war in Washington, DC.

The sword hilt and scabbard are constructed of sterling silver. The obverse of the blade is marked by the blade's maker 'Collins & Co. Hartford Conn.' at the ricasso below elaborate scrollwork inside which appears the engraved 'Tiffany & Co. N.Y.' mark of the New York jeweler that crafted this magnificent silver work. Continuing up the 35" blade and 26" double fuller, is an engraving of a soldier, sword in hand surmounted by additional elaborate scrollwork that continues a full 20" up the blade. A 'U. S.' separated by scrollwork is engraved at the midpoint of the designs.

On the reverse at the ricasso is the date '1861' followed by scroll engraving up the blade 4" to an engraved image of a cavalry officer. Above the cavalier is additional scroll engraving among a stand of arms surmounted by floral and foliate scrollwork. A scalloped red felt washer is at the ricasso.

Perhaps the most striking work on the sword is Tiffany's treatment of the hilt, especially the guard. The guard is an elaborately engraved basket-style guard with tightly carved openwork topped by a federal eagle with arrows in each of its claws, a shield at its breast. Hoop-shaped etching trims the entire guard terminating at the pommel with a massive Medusa-headed cap. Opposite is an open-mouthed panther head at the quillon, its tongue toward the top of the ricasso. The grip is sterling silver with banding and an engraved backstrap with a foliate design.

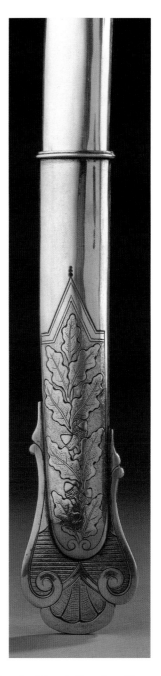

The scabbard of this sword is marked at the throat with Tiffany's cartouche and the '925.1000' number signifying sterling silver. The mounts are elaborate oak leaf devices finished with a large bow at the rings. Between the two mounts appears the following engraving:

Presented in behalf of
Company "G" 14th Regt. NYHA
TO
Capt. W. A. Treadwell

Below the dedication is inscribed "*Vera amicitia est sempiterna*", translated from the Latin meaning 'true friendship is eternal'.

The drag of the scabbard is engraved on the opposite side with an oak leaf pattern topped by an inverted chevron. The tip of the drag is scalloped and engraved as well.

A scabbard very similar to this Tiffany example may be found in John H. Thillman's book *Civil War Cavalry and Artillery Sabers* (page 423).

This is a remarkable, singularly important Civil War officer's sword from the famous New York jewelers and artisans Tiffany and Company. Historically important in that it was carried by an officer that fought through some of the most important engagements of the Civil War, it is in remarkable condition with only some light pitting along the blade. It is truly a masterpiece of Tiffany silver.

Provenance: *The Tharpe Collection of American Military History*

Exhibited: *The Liberty Heritage Society Museum*

Estimate: $80,000-$120,000

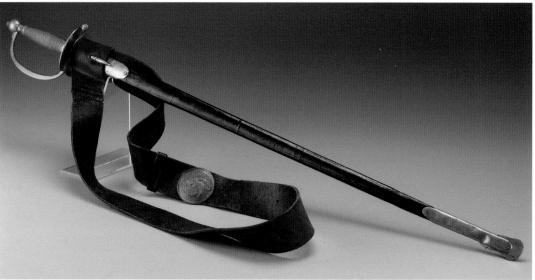

72183   THE SWORD OF SERGEANT FRANCIS BURT, 10TH CONNECTICUT INFANTRY – BATTERY WAGNER – This 32" non-commissioned officer's sword made by Collins and Company of Hartford, Connecticut was owned and carried by Sergeant Francis E. Burt of the 10th Connecticut Infantry. It is engraved 'Sergt. F. E. Burt 10th Reg. Ct. Inf.' in plain text on the solid brass 3" guard. The 5" banded brass grip is complemented by a single brass knuckle-bow, pommel cap and quillon. With the blade marked 'Collins & Co. Hartford, Conn. 1862' at the ricasso, the fuller extends nearly the entire length of the blade.

We know quite a lot about this sword's owner, Sergeant Francis E. Burt. Born on December 29, 1836 in Ridgefield, Connecticut, he mustered into the 10th Connecticut Infantry on September 30, 1861. The 25 year-old would take part in 40 battles during the CIvil War including Roanoke Island and New Bern when he was promoted to corporal and then sergeant, the occasion of the presentation of this field-engraved non-commissioned officer's sword. Burt would brave his greatest gunfire at Battery Wagner on July 18, 1863. It was there that Sergeant Burt's 10th Connecticut fought with the legendary 54th Colored Regiment that was annihilated as they assaulted the fort.

Sergeant Burt would serve throughout the war fighting at Saint Augustine, Florida, New Market and at the Battle of Darbytown where he was wounded. He was promoted to first lieutenant of Company C and later fought at Hatcher's Run and was present at the surrender at Appomattox.

This sword comes with its original leather scabbard which has a brass throat with brass frog and drag. Amazingly, this sword and scabbard comes with its 2" leather shoulder belt complete with brass eagle breastplate. This is truly a remarkable grouping with significant historical importance. It comes with a binder of extensive research concerning Burt and his regiment.

Estimate: $6,000-$8,000

GENERAL GRANT

    A 19.5% Buyer's Premium ($9 min.) Applies To All Lots

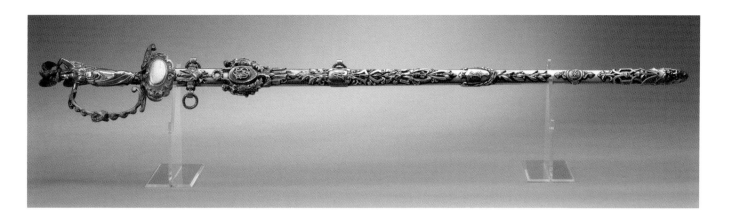

72184   GENERAL ULYSSES S. GRANT'S CIVIL WAR PRESENTATION SWORD AS "GENERAL IN CHIEF OF THE UNITED STATES ARMY 1864". A "Magnificent Sword For General Grant!" read the headline in the *Richmond Examiner* on April 16, 1864. "The Most Beautiful And Costly Sword Yet Manufactured In This Country" proclaimed the *St. Louis Dispatch*. Truly a national treasure, this silver and gold jeweled presentation sword owned by General Ulysses S. Grant is one-of-a-kind, the only such example of precious craftsmanship and historical significance in private hands.

Presented to the future 18th president of the United States, by the citizens of Kentucky who gave this token of their esteem to General Grant upon his promotion to "General in Chief of the Armies of the United States" in 1864, a major turning point in the Civil War. This was a historic event, as Grant was being elevated to the same level of command as only George Washington had ever achieved; prompting Kentucky patriots to raise money to purchase this unique and extremely valuable sword crafted by St. Louis silversmith and jeweler Henry Folsom.

Twenty-six mine cut diamonds compose Grant's monogram "U.S.G." set upon a large amethyst surmounted by a gold sunburst, the sword is crafted of pure silver and gold with the silver grip in the form of the goddess Victory. Over the goddess' head is an American eagle with wings spread. The sword is still in the magnificent original ivory mounted black japanned fitted case that it was presented to him in. The 33-inch blade is intricately etched and engraved with battle scenes, which include a stand of arms, artillery firing, cavalry engagements as well as infantry scenes symbolizing Grant's command of the entire United States armed forces.

Grant was fresh from victories at Lookout Mountain and Missionary Ridge and was brought in from the West by President Lincoln and Congress to win the war that had torn the nation apart for three long years. Within a year of Grant's promotion to General in Chief of the United States Armies the Confederate Army led by Robert E. Lee surrendered and the war was over. America was once again reunited. This was the highest rank ever achieved by any American since the Revolutionary War when George Washington was appointed General in Chief; a title shared by two men both of whom carried the fate of the country in their hands, and would both become great leaders after a war guiding our nation in a time of healing and rebuilding.

Provenance: *1. Ulysses S. Grant - 1864 (sword presented to him by citizens of Kentucky) - 1885 (his death)*
2. Grant Family - 1885-1960s
3. Jay Altmeyer - 1960s-1989 (Altmeyer was a charter member of the American Society of Arms Collectors; the sword sold in 1989 for a then-world record price)
4. Donald Tharpe - 1989-present (Since 1989, the sword has been part of the Tharpe Collection of American Military History)

Exhibited: *Virginia War Memorial Museum, 1999*
American Arms Collectors Semi-Annual Meeting (Best Single Weapon)
Greater Baltimore Antique Arms Collectors Show, 1995 (Best in Show)
The Liberty Heritage Society Musuem

Estimate: $2,000,000-$2,500,000

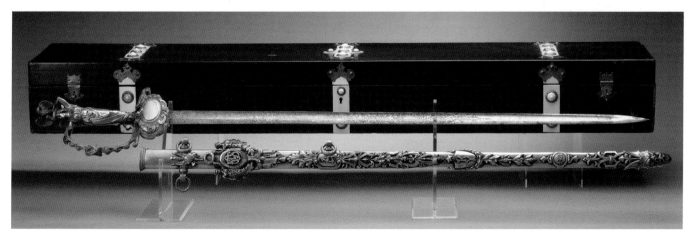

U. S. Grant's Lieutenant General Shoulder Insignia

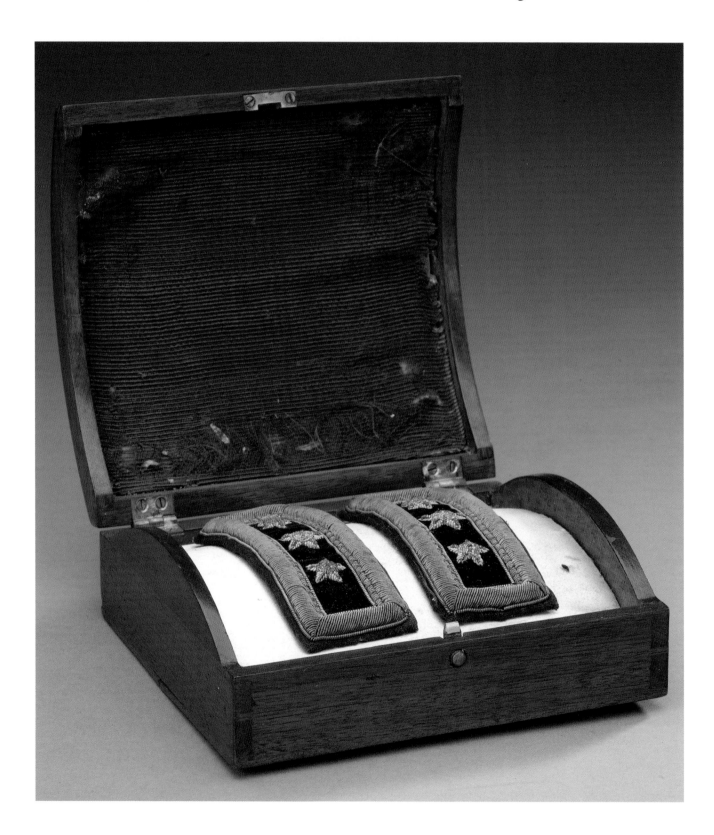

72185   ULYSSES S. GRANT'S BOXED SET OF LIEUTENANT GENERAL'S SHOULDER INSIGNIA CA. 1864 – Each strap measures 4" x 1.5" and rests in a custom dovetailed cherry wood box with an arched lid that has two hinges, 5.5" x 2.25" x 5". The shoulder straps each consist of a metal frame that gives shape to a black felt matrix upon which are sewn three silver bullion stars within a rectangular gold bullion border. The box's interior is lined with white silk while the lid's underside is covered with red fabric. Accompanied by General Grant's daughter's family photographs including her wedding invitation from the White House during Grant's administration.

Overall, the insignia and the box are quite presentable. The straps' bullion elements are lightly soiled and tarnished from usage on his uniform. The stitching remains tight on both straps; however, the black silk undersides show evidence of use. A nice glossy finish with normal light scratches and scuffing. Both interior lining fabrics are worn with some fraying, yet completely cover wooden surfaces as intended.

The historical importance of this insignia cannot be overstated. Grant became the nation's very first "three-star" lieutenant general in March 1864 after Abraham Lincoln appointed him General-in-Chief of the U.S. Army, at which time he received the sword. These are the only known Civil War period insignia for Grant while he was Lieutenant General. It was while holding this rank that U.S.Grant defeated Robert E. Lee's Army of Northern Virginia, thus ensuring the Union's survival. These shoulder straps, then, date to those crucial months in which Grant's abilities and determination brought him everlasting fame as he saved the nation.

Provenance: *Grant daughter family; Wolf Auctions (Cleveland, Ohio); The Tharpe Collection of American Military History*

Exhibited: *The Liberty Heritage Society Museum*

Estimate: $250,000-$350,000

72186   ULYSSES S. GRANT WARTIME CDV SIGNED, *"U.S. Grant Lt. Gen. U.S.A.",* Anthony backmark. Although Grant here appears as a major general early in the war, this signature must date to March, 1864 or later given the rank he uses. The CDV has crisp corners and retains nice tonal contrasts. A very dark and bold signature. Very Fine condition.

Estimate: $4,000-$4,500

72187   AN OIL PAINTING OF GENERAL ULYSSES S. GRANT BY EDWARD DALTON MARCHANT – (1806-1887) – This oil portrait of General Ulysses S. Grant was done from life by the noted portraiture artist Edward Dalton Marchant. Shown as a lieutenant general, this must have been completed in March 1864 around the time that President Lincoln called for Marchant to the White House where Marchant completed a portrait of the president.

The half-length portrait of Grant in full dress uniform measures 14" x 17" and is in very good condition with slight crackling at Grant's forehead and light crackling in the gray background.. Grant stands beside an American flag with a scroll in his hand, his gold bullion dress epaulets in vivid contrast to the dark blue dress frock coat he wears.

Edward Dalton Marchant, a native of Edgartown, Massachusetts had a long and illustrious career due to his longevity and access to high-profile public figures, completing portraits from John Adams to Abraham Lincoln and other prominent Americans such as General Grant. He worked at Philadelphia, Boston, Washington, DC, and New Jersey where he died in 1887.

The portrait is on its original stretcher and is in a period wood gilt frame which has slight chips at the left and top right. There is a nameplate at the bottom with *Gen. Ulysses S. Grant by E. D. Marchant, 1806-1887*. This is an important portrait by a noted artist during the Civil War. At the same time, Grant received his presentation sword featured in this auction.

Provenance: *The Tharpe Collection of American Military History*

Exhitibted: *The Liberty Heritage Society Museum*

Estimate: $70,000-$75,000

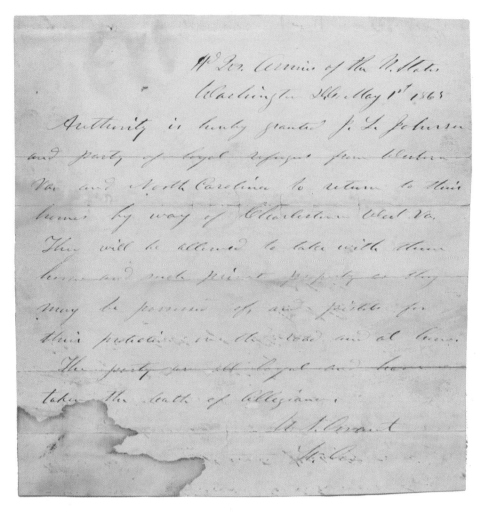

72188   IMPORTANT ULYSSES S. GRANT AUTOGRAPH DOCUMENT SIGNED – "SURRENDER OF THE ARMY OF TENNESSEE" – *"U.S. Grant Lt Gen"*, one page, 7.25" x 7.75", Washington, D.C., May 1, 1865. Writing from the *"H Qrs. Armies of the United States"*, Lieutenant General Grant states here: *"Authority is hereby granted J. L. Johnson and party of loyal refugees from western Va. and North Carolina to return to their homes by way of Charleston West Va. They will be allowed to take with them horses and such private property as they may be possessed of, and pistols for their protection on the road and at home. The party are all loyal and have taken the Oath of Allegiance."* soiling with stain in lower left margins, smoothed folds. Very good condition. This travel pass, being personally penned by Grant, is a very rare document in of itself. Its historical significance rests in that it repeats the basic terms of surrender as dictated to the officers serving under Generals Lee and Johnston. Confederate officers below the rank of general were allowed to keep their horses and sidearms once they had given a parole and signed the "oath".

Estimate: $25,000-$35,000

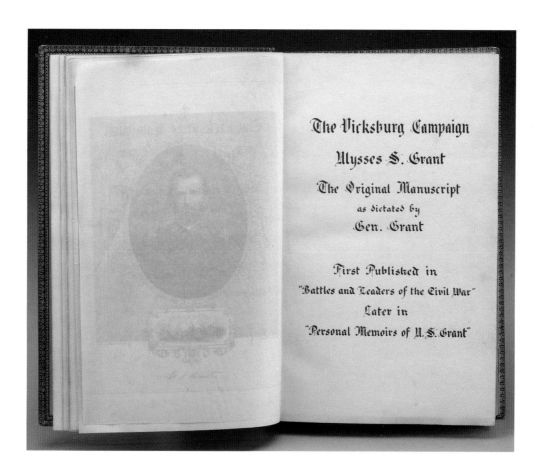

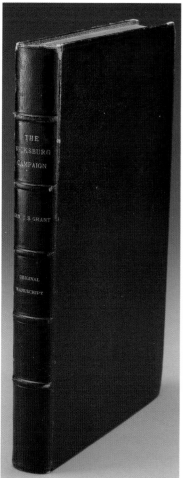

72189   GENERAL ULYSSES S. GRANT'S ORIGINAL MANUSCRIPT "SEIGE OF VICKSBURG" – Ulysses S. Grant dictated his memoirs and wrote them out himself only late in life as he was dying of throat cancer. This is the original manuscript with several holographic corrections and additions made in Grant's own hand. At 246 pages, the memoir is written on the recto only and on lined paper. The memoir was bound in beautiful Morocco leather in the twentieth century and is prefaced by an engraved frontispiece portrait of Grant. This spectacular 12½" x 7⅞" volume was once owned by William Randolph Hearst.

This section of Grant's memoirs concerns the taking of Vicksburg, the city President Abraham Lincoln saw as the key to the downfall of the Confederacy. A key supply point for the Confederate army, Grant devised a brilliant plan to maneuver his army into position to bombard the city and starve the residents into submission. In this manuscript Grant details the siege and makes notes in his own hand. At page 36 he amends as follows:

> I now determined to move independently of Banks, and clear out the rebel force in rear of Vicksburg, and invest or capture the city.

In this historically important and singular example of Grant's personal memoir as he dictated it and wrote corrections and additions in his own hand, Grant's military genius can be read as he dictated it to his clerk. This memoir was intended to be published in Century Magazine but quickly became part of a larger work titled *Battles and Leaders of the Civil War*. The memoir was later used as chapter 33 through 38 in his *Personal Memoirs of U. S. Grant*.

This is the only known example of Grant's memoirs known to be in private hands, the manuscript of his Personal Memoirs being in the possession of the Library of Congress, making this a historically important archive of the chief tactician of the United States Army in the Civil War.

Estimate: $50,000-up

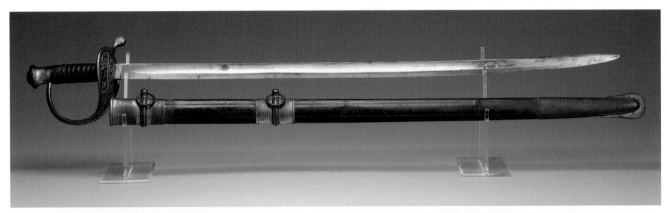

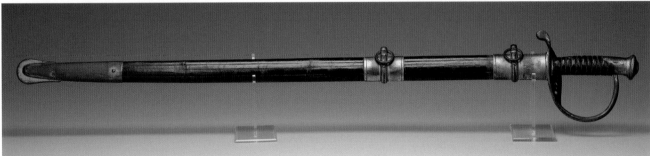

72190   CONFEDERATE OFFICERS FIELD & STAFF SWORD WITH LEATHER SCABBARD BY L. T. CUNNINGHAM, COLLEGE HILL ARSENAL, NASHVILLE, TENNESSEE − This sword is engraved on the throat of the top mount in English script:

> *Lt. E. M. Johnston*
> *Com. A 11th*
> *Miss. Regt.*

Lieutenant Johnston was part of a unit that was formed at Oxford and Corinth, Mississippi and fought at First Manassas, Antietam, and Gettysburg. It was at that monumental battle that they were on the left flank of the famed 'Pickett's Charge'.

L. T. Cunningham at the College Hill Arsenal located in Nashville manufactured swords for the State of Tennessee, the Confederate Government, and private individuals until the fall of Nashville to the Federal Troops April 1, 1861. This example is etched on both sides of the blade to within 5¾" of the tip. The right side of the blade is etched with a scroll pattern, the presentation panel is blank. The left side of the blade is distinctively etched with a 1st National Confederate flag and the letters "CSA." The blade length is 30⅜", the overall length of the sword is 36." The blade is bright and shiny with minor pitting and has its original red leather washer. The hilt of the sword

is the field & staff pattern with the "CS" in the guard; the pommel is unadorned. The leather and twisted brass wire wrap are original to the sword. The scabbard, which appears to be contemporary with the sword and is one of two examples known, is an Ames Manufactured product and is beautifully engraved with Lt. E. M. Johnston's name and company. Both the sword and mounts of the scabbard retain the majority of the original gold gild. This is an excellent example of the College Hill Arsenal field & staff officers' sword that is identified to its user.

Provenance: *The Tharpe Collection of American Military History*

Exhibited: *The Liberty Heritage Society Museum*

Estimate: $60,000-$65,000

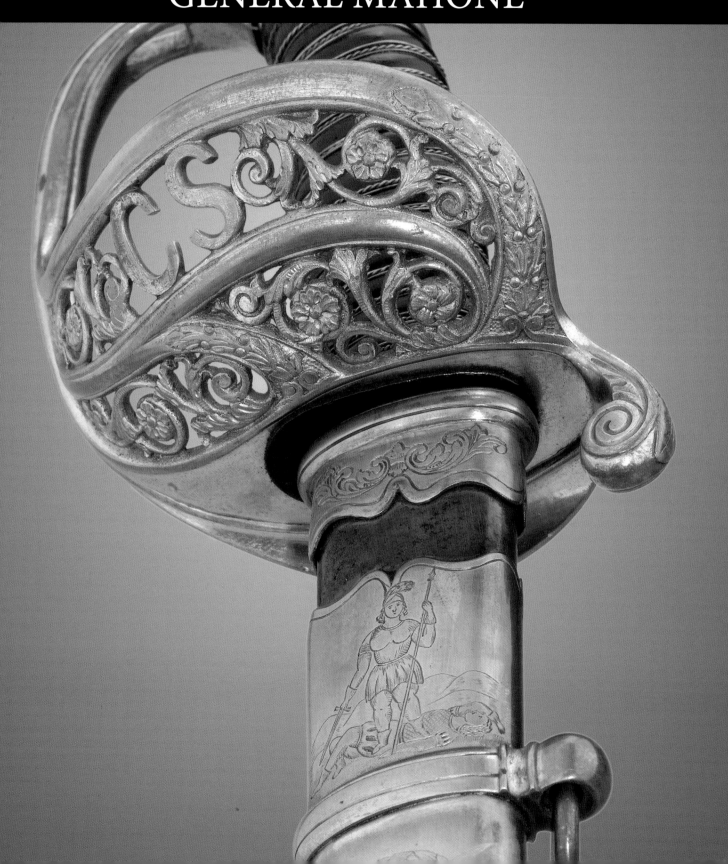

The Last Confederate Sword

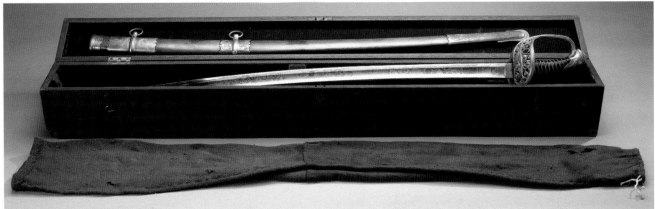

72191   MAJOR GENERAL WILLIAM MAHONE'S PRESENTATION SWORD THE LAST CSA SWORD - A magnificently detailed presentation sword, historically important in every way, Major General William Mahone received this sword from the grateful citizenry of Petersburg, Virginia for saving their city during the six-month siege of their city. This Boyle and Gamble sword was made especially for General Mahone in Richmond, Virginia and is like no other produced by this famous manufacturer. With elaborate etching on the blade as well as the scabbard, the people of Petersburg spared no expense in honoring their great defender. It is noteworthy that this sword was likely the last truly Confederate-made sword, making it the rarest Confederate presentation sword existent.

William Mahone was a true son of the South. Born in Southampton County, Virginia in 1826, he was educated at the Virginia Military Institute and was a quick study in engineering, a career he would follow before and after the war, serving him well during the conflict as he resigned the presidency of the Norfolk and Petersburg Railroad to serve the Confederacy. While physically lacking in stature, Mahone's talents were immediately recognized as he was appointed to Brigadier General on November 16, 1861. He served throughout the war with the Army of Northern Virginia in all the major campaigns except for Antietam as he was recovering from wounds he suffered at Second Manassas.

But it was for the Siege of Petersburg that he was awarded this war trophy that has no comparison in the annals of history. Union General Ambrose Burnside had laid siege to the Virginia town and had grown tired of the ten-month ordeal that was General Mahone's bitter defense of the city. A seemingly nonsensical scheme was hatched by a regiment of Pennsylvania former coal miners that involved digging a tunnel under the Confederate trenches with theidea of exploding a cache of gunpowder right beneath them, breaking the stalemate and winning the battle. The plan proved disastrous.

Early on the morning of July 30, 1864, fully one month after the Union engineers and coal miners had dug their tunnel under the Confederate

trenches, filling their subterranean earthworks with gunpowder,the Union troops lit the fuse. Nine companies of the 19th and 22nd South Carolina were rocketed into the air with the dead and dying falling into a 170 feet long crater created by the blast. Had the Union forces been satisfied with the disaster of the devastation created by their subterfuge, the battle may have been won. After the dust had settled, the Union forces rushed into the crater going after what was left of the Confederates, a grievous tactical error by Union General James Ledlie's division. Instead of waiting at the rim of the crater, the Union troops poured into the crater itself making them easy targets for General Mahone's men. When the shooting was over, "like shooting ducks", as the Confederates would later remark, General Mahone's troops had pushed the Union forces back inflicting 3,798 losses compared to the Confederates' nearly 1,500 men.

The ten-month siege of their hometown had taken its toll on the people of Petersburg. In the twilight of the war they looked to honor the man that had led the defense of their city and, for that one day, had repulsed the Union forces that had a stranglehold on the city, the second largest city in Virginia with a population of around 20,000 people in 1865. Their appreciation came in the form of this ornate Boyle and Gamble presentation sword commissioned by the grateful citizenry. The actual presentation was reported that March day in 1865 by the Richmond Daily Dispatch as follows: "The presentation took place in the presence of a large assemblage of officers, soldiers,citizens, and ladies, who gathered together to witness the pleasing event." By then Mahone had been promoted to Major General. He took the sword in its black walnut presentation case with the red sash and general officer's sword belt with the interlocking Virginia buckle as his memento of his service to his beloved Virginia and the Confederacy, cherishing it for the rest of his life.

The Boyle and Gamble sword is truly one-of-a-kind, but the scabbard within which it is encased is remarkable in itself. Slightly curved and 35" in length, the scabbard's steel body is brazed along the lower reverse side. Complemented by a gilded throat, top mount (with ring), center mount and drag, these features are all gently scalloped. The throat of the scabbard shows a 'C' scroll and floral motif engraving with the top featuring a

rendering of the seal of the Commonwealth of Virginia above a sword and wreath device. Such subtle touches as the richer, more deep copper content of the top mount make this Boyle and Gamble stand out from their standard sword line, ensuring that the viewer would know it was made for a very special soldier.

Perhaps the most distinctive feature of the scabbard is the center mount which is emblazoned with the Confederate battle flag within a wreath above a bugle and bayonet crossed in front of a drum. Leaving no detail on the scabbard to chance, Boyle and Gamble engraved the drag of the scabbard featuring a plumed, helmeted knight amid an array of lances and trophy flags above a quiver of arrows and a mace. This design surmounts an intricately scrolled motif which finishes out the scabbard.

After seeing the scabbard, the viewer is only given a taste of what is to follow, concealed within being the Boyle and Gamble presentation sword itself. The regulation, slightly curved 33¾" blade bears the maker's name 'BOYLE AND GAMBLE/RICHMOND VA', appearing proudly as their signature on the ricasso of the reverse. The eye is drawn to the fact that the fuller of the blade is stopped rather than tapered, unlike other Boyle and Gamble swords. Intricate engraving filling the length of the blade includes ornate floral motifs, a shield, drums, a quiver of arrows, a crossbow, a highly-stylized Confederate flag and a pennant on a staff. Further up the blade is the eagle-ensconced presentation as follows:

> PRESENTED TO
> MAJOR GENERAL WILLIAM MAHONE
> BY THE CITIZENS OF PETERSBURG VA
> IN APPRECIATION OF HIS SKILL ENERGY
> AND GALLANTRY
> IN DEFENSE OF THEIR CITY DURING THE CAMPAIGN OF 1864

The obverse of the sword is equally delightful with the sword maker using all the tools, imagination and skill to the fullest advantage. The hilt-most end of the obverse incorporates a beautifully etched floral design and cross-hatching similar to an effect used on the reverse of the blade. A standing figure of the goddess Liberty carrying a dagger in her right hand while holding an unfurled Confederate flag in her left surmounts the letters 'CS' at the hilt of the blade. Elaborate floral etched designs flow up the blade terminating in a symbol of the rising sun of the Confederacy motif that echoes the drag of the scabbard.

The hilt of the sword measures 6" and is of the staff officer's style bearing one more branch than the foot officer's hilt. Within the upper branches is the openwork large 'CS' with surrounding open branches on either side and below. The quillon terminates with additional scrollwork and the knuckle bow at the rear of the hilt at the pommel cap, which is domed to receive the tang of the blade. Wrapped with black leather, the grip has a fine grade twisted brass wire on either side. Still in its elaborate walnut case lined with blue velvet and brass furniture hinges, Boyle and Gamble would have utilized the wood and hinges from furniture to make this presentation box as supplies were scarce during the last days of the Confederacy. Original 'homespun shammy' dyed light blue is still inside the case.

As history was made at Petersburg, the war would end shortly after the presentation of this wartime work of art, the last of its kind ever to be made in the Confederacy. General William Mahone returned to his railroad and later entered politics rising to a United States Senate seat serving his beloved Virginia. Although honored during and after the war for his service, this incredible presentation sword, a reminder of a grateful city for saving their home and families, was perhaps his and now our greatest treasure - "The Last Sword of the Confederacy".

HISTORICAL PERSPECTIVE OF THE MAHONE SWORD DELIVERED IN A SPEECH BY DONALD THARPE BEFORE THE AMERICAN ARMS COLLECTOR'S SOCIETY

On Wednesday, March 22, 1865, the Richmond [Va.] *Daily Dispatch* reported the presentation of a sword, belt, and sash to Maj. Gen. William Mahone by the citizens of Petersburg. "The presentation," the paper reported, "took place in the presence of a large assemblage of officers, soldiers, citizens and ladies, who gathered together to witness the pleasing event."

Those embattled witnesses at Petersburg, a city under siege for ten months, would likely see little else that was pleasing in the next several weeks. On March 25th, just two days later, the final campaign of the Army of Northern Virginia began when Gen. Lee attempted to break Gen. Grant's tightening deathgrip on Petersburg by taking the Federal-held Fort Stedman, just east of the city. They initially met with success, but the relentless Federals retook the fort. The Confederates ultimately lost the strategic position as well as the lives of 3,500 of their already tragically depleted troops. Petersburg fell just one week later.

It was the twilight of the Confederacy; it was also the twilight of Richmond, Virginia manufacturer Boyle & Gamble, military contractors to the Confederate government and makers of Mahone's presentation sword. Originally makers of circular saws for sawmills, Boyle & Gamble was first mentioned in an 1860 newspaper article in which reporters told of going into their extensive saw factory near the Shockoe Warehouse. Their work as sword makers for the Confederacy clearly began early in the conflict; a May 27, 1861, article in the Daily Missouri Republican ran under the headline "Attack on a Secession Sword Factory." The story relat-

ed that the factory of Boyle & Gamble had been set aflame the day before; perpetrators and extent of damages are unknown.

The firm's relationship with the new Southern government continued. On September 2, 1861, Boyle, Gamble & Macfee+ were granted a patent (No. 18) by the Confederate States Patent Office to make a sword bayonets that attached to shoulder arms. Further, the April 17, 1862 *Daily Enquirer* reported that Boyle, Gamble & Co was making a large supply of swords for the establishment of Mitchell & Tyler, which was under contract with the Confederate States government. The following September, a contract was made between Boyle, Gamble & Co. and Maj. Stansbury, commander of the Richmond Armory and Arsenal for the production of sword-sabre bayonets.

The firm's products during the war years were not limited to edged weaponry. They also made axes, curry combs, shoe hammers, and - in a magnificent leap from the utilitarian to the unique - the handle of the seal used by the Confederate States Treasury Department. Still, they were known then and are known now for their high-grade swords. Of these, the most beautiful are the handsomely etched presentation swords bestowed upon Maj. Gen William Mahone and other such personages as Brig. Gen. Thomas A. Harris, Gen. John McCausland, and Maj. J. Thompson Brown.

On April 9, 1862, the *Daily Dispatch* reported having seen Maj. Brown's ornate sword and closed with: "The best of it is, that it was all made in the Southern Confederacy, and intended as an instrument to punish the enemies of that Confederacy." It is quite likely that Maj. Gen. Mahone's sword is the last Boyle & Gamble blade of which that could be said. Presented as it was just weeks before the fall of Richmond, the flight of Jefferson Davis, and the surrender at Appomattox, it likely represents our last glimpse of the true Confederate-made swords of the war. Further, of the scored of blades of this type this author examined, it is without equal in workmanship. It is not without irony that the Confederacy should reach its apex in sword-making as the government reached its nadir.

William Mahone, recipient of the sword, was a true son of the Old Dominion. Born in Southhampton County, Virginia, on December 1, 1826, and educated at Virginia Military Institute, he studied engineering while a teacher at Rappahannock Military Academy. He went on to engineer several Virginia railroads, and at the outbreak of war was president and superintendent of the Norfolk & Petersburg Railroad. When Virginia seceded, he was quick to cast his lot with the fledgling Confederacy and was almost immediately appointed colonel of the 6th Virginia Infantry, in which capacity he commanded at the capture of Norfolk.

Promoted to brigadier general on November 16, 1861, he served continuously with the Army of Northern Virginia throughout the rest of the war, from Seven Pines to the Crater. The only battle missing in his impressive wartime resume is Antietam, at which time Mahone was recovering from wounds suffered at the Battle of Second Manassas. White physically small of stature, being referred toas "Little Billy Mahone," he seemed to grow with his responsibilities. By war's end, he had risen to the rank of major general and was one of only three division commanders till alive at Appomattox, by which time he had become one of Lee's most trusted lieutenants. In the years after the war, Lee is said to have felt that of the surviving leaders in the army, Mahone made the largest contribution to organization and command.

In fact, Mahone's contribution to the Cause did not precisely end with the surrender: a surviving manuscript he wrote between 1890 and 1894 sheds much light on the waning days of the war. Writing first in pencil, then in pen, on stationery from the Hotel Chamberlin on McPherson Square in Washington, Mahone began. "In compliance with your request I give you an account of what I saw and heard from Gen Lee's lines covering Richmond and Petersburg to the close of his army's career at Appomattox."

This document - in all, 73 pages of painstaking longhand script - has come down to us as a model of recollective powers and careful description. It also reveals the scrappy attitude and dogged determination that made Mahone a valued fighter, a successful commander, and ultimately a survivor in the War Between the States. The document offers us the single best account of the Appomattox as witness by a high-ranking officer of the Third Corps. It is, by tunes, poignant and pugnacious:

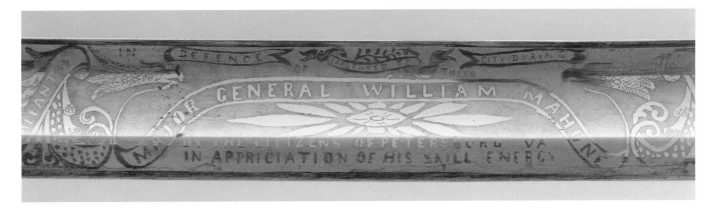

"After the completion of the details of surrender, which were my part, I went over to Gen Lee's Headquarters to bid him good bye [April 10]. I sat with him in the front part of his tent. He was obviously full of grief - offering however no out [ward] signed beyond the watering eye.... Gen. Lee observed that he had advised the Confederate authorities at the start - that the contest on which we had entered could not be over estimated and our chance to win was to be found by throwing the whole military or fighting power of the Confederacy vigorously into the struggle - which while not saying so, he manifestly thought had not been done."

Mahone continued:

"In the winter preceding the evacuation he [Lee] said that he advised Mr. Davis to come to terms - that it would be impossible from him when spring came and the campaign opened, for him to get away. Roads bad and transportation poor, while the army confronting him was full handed and fresh with every means of earnest pursuit at hand: and Mr. Davis he replied no you must fight. I stated to Gen. Lee that just then he had made a mistake. That he was in fact the Confederacy - enjoying the affectionate confidence of all that there was of it - and he should have taken matters in [his] own hands-held a conference with his officers - told them the situation and they would have commissioned him in behalf of the army to see Grant and effect a settlement. He replied, but there was the government at Richmond and I said yes, and I would have taken my division down and dispersed it.

Mahone's reminiscence of Lee in those last days is plain-spoken yet eloquent:

"He was the most [hansom] specimen and proudest man I ever saw. He had no appreciation of a joke. Polite, but stern and matter of fact in all things. His long service in the regular army had [left] him with a reverence for authority and a rigid respect for rules and regulation which were unfortunate and hurt full for one in command of [an] army of revolution. He should have gone to the field unfettered and his mere [wish] should have been the law.

The manuscript contains a host of such gems, not the least of which is a suggestion that Lee may have had a premonition of his own death, a notion that more than one contemporary write has made much of: At Amelia Co Ho early next morning [April 5] … He wore all his best clothes - including his gold spurs and magnificent sword and belt. It impressed me that he anticipated some accident to himself and desired to be found in that dress.

Mahone himself likely had no premonition whatsoever of the events that occurred the previous summer at Petersburg, Virginia - events unlike any other in the war, events that helped endear him to Lee, events that led the grateful people of the beleaguered town of Petersburg to present him with the Boyle & Gamble sword. One June 25, 1864, a Union regiment made up of pre-war coal mines from Schuykill County, Pennsylvania, took shovels in hand and began to dig in the red clay of Virginia. They dug for nearly a month, completing a 586' tunnel that was 5' in height and had two lateral galleries totaling 75' - right under the Confederate trenches at Petersburg. "Clap-trap nonsense," the Union engineers had initially said of the plan to blast the Confederate lines from beneath. Nevertheless, for the next four days the subterranean chambers were filled with 320 kegs of powder. Union Maj. Gen Ambrose Burnside had three division commanders draw straws for who would spearhead the assault after the explosion. Brig. Gen James H. Ledlie, perhaps the worst general ever don a blue uniform, picked the short one.

At 4:45 on the morning of July 30, over a month after the first earth was turned for the tunnel, four tons of powder exploded, tossing nine companies of the 19th and 22nd South Carolina into the air. The crater that resulted from the blast measured 170' long and 30' deep. The shocked Confederates on either side fled in panic.

Into the valley of death rushed Ledlie's division - a grievous tactical error. Had they formed around the crater instead of rushing into it, the outcome might have been different. The Confederates regrouped, and soon Southern artillery was raking the Federals trapped in the hollowed-out bowl of earth. It was rather like shooting ducks in a barrel when, by 8:00 that morning, Mahone's seasoned men had sealed the breach in the Confederate lines and surrounded the crater, which was becoming a gaping grave. By 1:00 PM, the Confederates had successfully pushed the surviving Yankees back to their lines. The Union forms suffered 3,798 losses; the Confederacy, some 1,500.

The Crater was only one - if inarguably the loudest - action in the ten-month siege that was the Petersburg Campaign, the longest sustained operation of the war. As the war drew close, the grateful citizenry of Petersburg responded to Mahone's consistent displays of leadership in the campaign by commissioning the Boyle & Gamble sword, appropriately etched:

MAJOR GENERAL WILLIAM MAHONE
BY THE CITIZENS OF PETERSBURG, VA
IN APPRECIATION OF HIS SKILL ENERGY
AND GALLANTRY
IN DEFENSE OF THEIR CITY DURING THE CAMPAIGN OF
1864

The sword was presented in a black walnut box lined in blue fabric, and it was accompanied by a red sash and generals officer's sword belt replete with an interlocking Virginia buckle. The sword was wrapped in a green wool casing with a drawstring top.

The slightly curved scabbard measure 35" and has a steel body brazed along the lower reverse side. It is complemented by a glided throat, top mount (with ring), center mount (with ring), and drag. All of these are gently scalloped.

The throat shows a "C"- scroll and floral motif engraving, and the top mount of the sword bears a rendition of the state seal of the Commonwealth of Virginia and a sword-and-wreath motif. This coppery hue of the top mount gives ample evidence that it possesses a greater copper content than the other mountings. (Copper was in relatively good supply in the South and was put to uses both practical and decorative.)

The center mount is emblazoned atop with the Confederate battle flag within a wreath; the lower motif is a bugle and bayonet crossed in front of a drum.

The drag features a plumed helmet as the centerpiece in panoply of symbols: an array of lances and trophy flags, a shield bearing the sign of the rising sun of the Confederacy, a quiver of arrows, and a mace. Below this intricate assemblage is yet another highly decorative design that terminates the engraved beauty of the scabbard.

The regulation slightly curved blade measure 33¾", and the maker's name - "BOYLE & GAMBLE / RICHMOND VA" - appears proudly on the ricasso of the reverse. Unlike most other Boyle & Gamble blades, the fuller is stopped rather than tapered. Continuing toward its point, the ornately etched blade bears a floral motif, a border of cross-hatching, and a depiction of various military symbols that include a shield, drums, a quiver of arrows, a crossbow, a highly stylized furled Confederate flag, and a pennant on a staff. Further up is the aforementioned presentation panel. Decorative diagonal etching appears on the back of blade along its length.

On the hiltmost end of the blade's obverse there is a floral design and cross-hatching that echoes that one the reverse. The letters "CS" are topped by a standing figure described as the Goddess of Liberty, who carries a drawn dagger in her right hand and hold an unfurled Confederate flag in her left. Flowing up from that design is more floral work, which terminates in the symbol of the rising sun of the Confederacy, much as it appeared on the aforementioned drag of the scabbard. It is worthy of note here that an 1863 Richmond Enquirer article concerning the presentation of a Boyle & Gamble sword to Col. R.W. Martin, 53rd Virginia Regiment, carries the following description: "The scabbard is of steel, and the tail bands and bars plated with gold and carved with ingenious devices on either side, such as the Goddess of Liberty with drawn dagger, the rising sun of the Confederacy, together with the Confederate flag and battle flag crossed..." The similarities in motif are striking.

The hilt, which measures 6", is of the staff officer's style, which boasts one more branch than that of a foot officer's sword. Within the upper branches is the openwork CS; floral openwork appears between both branches. (These sword hilts echo those of the regulation Union staff officer's swords - with, of course, the substitution of "CS" for the Federal "US.")

The quillion terminates with a scroll of motif, and knuckle bow terminates at the rear of the hilt at the pommel cap, which displays a floral motif along its from edge. The pommel cap is domed to receive the tang of the blade, which was peened over to seat it. The grip is wrapped with black leather and has a fine-grade twisted wire bordered by a single strand of wire on either side.

Having done his part for his home state when it was part of the short-lived Confederacy, Mahone went on to serve Virginia after the war as well. He returned to his railroad, which is today known as the Norfolk & Western system, and became active in politics. Although defeated several times in his bid for office, he characteristically preserved and in 1880 was elected senator on the Readjuster ticket, which was essentially the Virginia version of Republican. He was active in Virginia political affairs until his death in Washington, D.C., on October 8, 1895. Little Billy Mahone was laid to rest at Blandford Cemetery in Petersburg, Virginia.

Boyle & Gamble continued to operate after the war, as they are present in the Tredegar Company's business records of 1866 and in post-war Richmond business directories, but their products after Appomattox cannot, of course, be called Confederate.

Just as William Mahone was a survivor, several of his possessions survive. Among these are his copies of Scott's Infantry Tactics, Vol. I, inscribed "William Mahone, V.M.I."; his New York- manufactured boots; his gold suspender clasps with his name engraved; and a gold watch marked Richmond & Tyler, Virginia. But it is his presentation sword that is the finest of these artifacts. The exceptionally fine workmanship alone puts it without peer, and the sterling reputation of its original owner adds extra luster. Even so, its greatest significance lies in the fact that it is likely the last truly Confederate-made sword, skillfully fashioned of enduring metal even as the Confederacy itself dissolved.

Presentation of a sword to Major Gen. Mahone - The sword, belt and sash, ordered by the citizens of Petersburg for Maj. Gen. W.M. Mahone, was presented to that brave and veteran officer on Saturday afternoon near his headquarters in Chesterfield Co. The presentation took place in the presence of a large assemblage of officer's, soldiers, citizens and ladies, who gathers together to witness the pleasing event.

Following official reports of campaign of 1864 ending October 27, 1864. Captured 6,704 prisoners, 15 pieces of artillery, 42 colors, 4,867 small arms, 235 horses, 49 wagons & ambulances, 537 slaves.

Inflicted a loss of 17,704 men. His own loss was 5,248.

Provenance: *The Tharpe Collection of American Military History*

Published: *The American Society of Arms Collectors Bulletin* - Number 72. *North South Trader's Civil War* - Volume XXIV, Number 6. This sword will be featured in Don Tharpe's upcoming book on *Swords of Valor*.

Exhibited: *The Liberty Heritage Society Museum*

Estimate: $400,000-$500,000

Exceptional Confederate Major General William Mahone Photograph

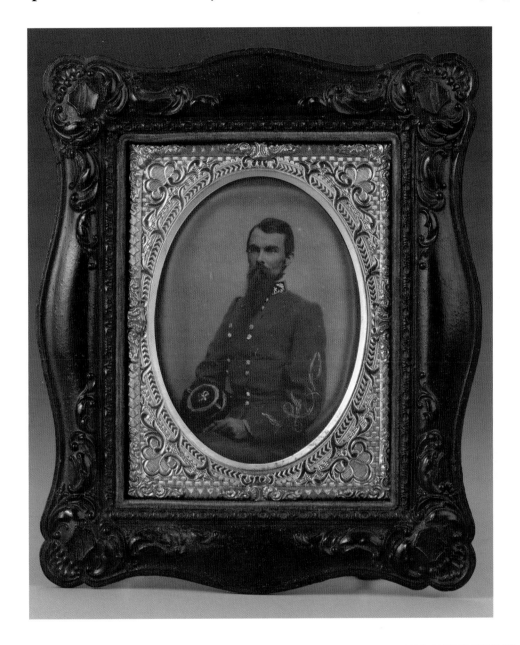

72192   A SUPERB AND UNIQUE WARTIME PHOTOGRAPH OF MAJOR GENERAL WILLIAM MAHONE FROM LIFE IN 1864 – This framed image of General William Mahone gives the viewer an idea of his diminutive stature. Dressed in his Major General's Confederate uniform and holding his kepi in hand, the General's iconic long beard falls onto his frock coat. The beard would be his trademark throughout the rest of his life as it grew gray and longer.

This poignant image of the Confederate warrior was hand-tinted by the photographer showing gold tint at the collar insignia, buttons, on the kepi and the sleeve quarterfoil accentuating this sharp image of the General, the finest in existence.

The photograph is in its original gutta-percha frame with an elaborately engraved shell frame. This is the most famous image of the General and is in pristine condition.

Provenance: *The Don Tharpe Collection of American Military History*

Published: *The American Society of Arms Collectors Bulletin - Number 72.
North South Trader's Civil War - Volume XXIV, Number 6.*

Exhibited: *The Liberty Heritage Society Museum*

Estimate: $30,000-$40,000

72193   MAJOR GENERAL WILLIAM MAHONE'S SASH, BELT SET AND TWO-PIECE VIRGINIA BUCKLE

– This Confederate Major General officer's sword belt, two-piece Virginia buckle and sash were presented to Confederate General William Mahone who was honored by the people of Petersburg, Virginia as their gallant defender due to his tenacity during the ten-month siege of their city. General Mahone was there to thwart the attempts of Union General Ambrose Burnside as Burnside's troops affected one of the most famous maneuvers of the war, the subterranean explosion under the Confederate trenches that became known as the Battle of the Crater. After exploding a cache of gunpowder placed in the trenches, Union General James Ledlie's troops poured into the crater left after the explosion but were decimated by General Mahone's troops.

In March of 1865 the people of Petersburg honored General Mahone with the presentation of this leather general officer's belt set and sash as an accompaniment to his Boyle and Gamble presentation sword given to him on the same occasion. Constructed of fine leather, possibly by Boyle and Gamble, with double rows of silk embroidering and gilt denot-

ing his general's rank, the belt set is accentuated by the fine two-piece Virginia Confederate belt buckle bearing the Virginia state seal and the Latin motto "Sic Semper Tyrannis" at top with "Virginia" at bottom. Between is the standing figure of the Roman goddess Virtus dressed in Amazon garb with a sword in one hand and spear in the other. She is standing on a figure representing tyranny evoking the translation of the motto as "thus always to tyrants". The inner piece of the buckle includes an ornate wreath into which the Virginia seal disk is inserted completing the buckle.

Accompanying the belt and buckle are General Mahone's red general staff officer's silk sash. This too was presented to the General by the citizens of Petersburg, at the same time as this belt as noted by the Richmond Daily Dispatch as follows: "The presentation took place in the presence of a large assemblage of officers, soldiers, citizens, and ladies, who gathered together to witness the pleasing event." These items are in excellent condition and were treasured by General William Mahone from the citizens of his native Petersburg, Virginia for saving their city.

Provenance: *The Tharpe Collection of American Military History*

Published: *The Richmond Daily Dispatch* - 1865
North South Trader's Civil War - Volume XXIV, Number 6.

Exhibited: *The Liberty Heritage Society Museum*

Estimate: $60,000-$70,000

72194   GENERAL WILLIAM MAHONE'S MILITARY FIELD GLASSES BINOCULARS AND CASE – General William Mahone, educated at the Virginia Military Institute was a keen engineer, training he took with him into the Civil War as he commanded the capture of Norfolk. With him were these finely crafted Tumelle Panorama binoculars. Produced by Tumelle of Paris, France, these compact field glasses still function as if new. Engraved on the barrel of each eyepiece 'Tumelle Panorama', the focus wheel shows a slight crack that does not affect the function of the glasses. There is wear to the leather-covered areas of the binoculars and at the eyepiece as should be expected. Since the glasses on each end of the binoculars are in excellent condition, these binoculars were obviously well protected in their velvet-lined leather case which accompanies these field glasses. The case which still closes nicely includes its original leather strap. The case shows much wear as General Mahone viewed all the battles of war from victory to defeat, to the great massacre at the Battle of the Crater, these field glasses offered him a closeup view of war.

Provenance: *The Tharpe Collection of American Military History*

Published: *North South Trader's Civil War* - Volume XXIV, Number 6.

Exhibited: *The Liberty Heritage Society Museum*

Estimate: $10,000-$20,000

72195   OFFICER'S BOOTS OF GENERAL WILLIAM MAHONE – Undoubtedly worn by General William Mahone during the siege of Petersburg, these 'Lorin Brooks' manufactured 15-inch tall boots are in remarkably good condition. Brooks' shop at 438 Broadway in New York handmade these fine leather boots that have withstood Mahone's battles and the test of time. The small size of the boots are not a result of shrinkage but of Mahone's small stature, a fact that belies his fierceness in war. Each boot bears the maker's mark stamped in gold at the front, outside top and includes Mahone's name written in period ink inside each boot. The maker's number of '42984' appears inside each boot as well making the boots a matched pair. Although the boots have seen much usage, they still bear the square nails at the heel that gave General Mahone as much wear as possible. The stitching is still intact and tight while the lower leather remains supple. There is some wear to the outside of the uppers that is indicative of Mahone's horsemanship. General Mahone's wooden boot stretcher or boot jack accompanies the boots as well.

These boots owned and worn by Major General William Mahone are a remarkable example of a Confederate general's uniform ensemble.

Provenance: *The Don Tharpe Collection of American Military History*

Published: *The American Society of Arms Collectors Bulletin-* Volume XXIV, Number 6.

Exhibited: *The Liberty Heritage Society Museum*

Estimate: $20,000-$30,000

72196   CONFEDERATE GENERAL WILLIAM MAHONE'S MITCHELL & TYLER WATCH WITH A ROSE-CUT DIAMOND AT THE MOVEMENT – This gold watch owned and worn by Confederate William Mahone was made in London, England for Mitchell and Tyler of Richmond, Virginia. The elaborately engraved rose gold face has raised Roman numerals and an intricate floral design engraved at the center of the dial. A smaller second dial is located at the bottom and, while the minute hand and second hand of the watch are missing, the watch is highly attractive in its present state.

General Mahone carried this watch extensively as it has seen much wear as evidenced by the missing hands and since the glass is missing from the opening face. The beautiful case opens at three positions. Besides opening at the 2" dial, the mechanism can be opened to reveal the movement of the watch made by John Cragg of London as engraved on the border of the movement. An ornamental rose-cut diamond is beautifully set amidst a highly-engraved setting above the balance staff. The gold cap piece of the movement is engraved 'Made For Mitchell & Tyler. Richmond Va.'.

The back of the case can be opened to reveal the hallmarks associated with this watch. There is an 18 karat gold mark, a mark indicating that the case was made in London and the Mitchell & Tyler name. The entire watch is serial numbered 26742.

Accompanying the watch is a 14" gold watch chain and eagle-head watch fob. This heavy gold chain has the eagle head holding the watch's key which has the stem missing.

This is a beautiful and very rare Mitchell and Tyler gold watch that ran the blockade into the Confederacy of the great Confederate general who may be best known for his valiant defense of Petersburg.

Provenance: *The Tharpe Collection of American Military History*

Published: *North South Trader's Civil War* - Volume XXIV, Number 6.

Exhibited: *The Liberty Heritage Society Museum*

Estimate: $20,000-$30,000

**72197 GENERAL WILLIAM MAHONE'S STERLING SILVER CENTERPIECE
AND LADLE BEARING THE MAHONE BRIGADE EMBLEM** – General Mahone
designed a badge for his Confederate Civil War brigade using a shield with a five-pointed
star in the center. Mahone and his men wore that storied emblem throughout the war. The
general carried the emblem into his private life making the shield and star his personal
'coat of arms' by adding the initial 'M' in the center of the star. He used the emblem on his
personal stationary, his silver, and even on his tomb in Petersburg, Virginia, not far from
the site of the engagement that made him famous, the Battle of the Crater.

His crest is featured on this magnificent sterling silver centerpiece and punch ladle crafted
by the New York silversmiths Ball, Black and Company. The towering centerpiece served as
the focal point of the general's table. It bears the company mark, "New York", and "English
Sterling". The centerpiece measures 13" in height and almost 11" across the top of the bowl.
Decorated with portrait medallions of Greek warriors at the top of each of the three sup-
ports from the base, the centerpiece weighs almost fifty ounces. Ornate engraving adorns
the top of the bowl with intricate floral work around the outside rim. The design incorporates two Mahone Brigade emblems on each side of the rim.

The wonderful ladle has a realistic mermaid at the handle and a gilt clamshell bowl. The ladle is clearly marked "Ball, Black & Co." and "Sterling Silver". The Mahone crest is engraved
on the reverse of the mermaid.

The artisans at Ball, Black, and Company crafted this centerpiece and ladle shortly after
end of the Civil War, using the more desirable "English Sterling" (referring to .925 silver)
rather than coin silver that predominated prior to the war. In 1876 the company became
Black, Starr, and Frost. The company used the. They are magnificent examples of the fine
silver used by the general at family and social occasions.

Provenance: *The Tharpe Collection of American Military History*

Published: *North South Trader's Civil War* - Volume XXIV, Number 6

Exhibited: *The Liberty Heritage Society Museum*

Estimate: $10,000-$20,000

72198 GENERAL WILLIAM MAHONE'S *ENGINEERS' AND MECHANICS' POCKET-BOOK* USED ON THE NORFOLK AND PETERSBURG RAILROAD

– General William Mahone was an accomplished engineer before the Civil War and had risen to the position of Superintendent of the Norfolk and Petersburg Railroad. This engineering manual was the personal property of William Mahone and bears penciled calculations along with the inscription 'W. Mahone of Virginia' at the front of the book. Charles H. Haswell, Chief Engineer of the United States Navy, authored the *Engineers' and Mechanics' Pocket-Book*. This edition was published by Harper and Brothers of 82 Cliff Street, New York and is dated 1848, just after Mahone graduated from the Virginia Military Institute. Mahone engineered at several railroads before becoming the Superintendent at the Norfolk and Petersburg Railroad, later casting his lot with the Confederacy.

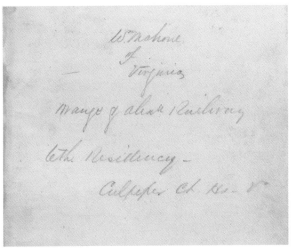

The red leather book has the clasp intact and has only a 1½" split at the bottom of the spine. The upper spine is stamped 'Haswell' in gold. This is an excellent Mahone item that dates to his early, pre-war career as an engineer building and running railroads in Petersburg, a manual he undoubtedly cherished and kept with him and used extensively through the Civil War and throughout the remainder of his life. Indeed, Mahone returned to the railroad industry becoming president of the Norfolk and Western before being elected to the United States Senate from Virginia.

Provenance: The Don Tharpe Collection of American Military History

Estimate: $2,000-$5,000

72199 GENERAL WILLIAM MAHONE'S SIGNED VIRGINIA MILITARY INSTITUTE MANUALS: SCOTT'S *INFANTRY TACTICS*, SIGNED BY MAHONE – Confederate Major General William Mahone, celebrated for his heroic defense of Petersburg during the Civil War, enrolled at Virginia Military Institute on July 20, 1844 at the young age of 17. During the course of his military instruction he was tutored in infantry tactics which he would undoubtedly use in the war that would soon follow. These two volumes completed by the most famous US Army commander in history, Major General Winfield Scott's *Infantry Tactics* were the standard text for military students at the time. Still used at the time of the Civil War some twenty years after they were written, they were used as the basis for William Hardee's updated tactical manuals in 1855.

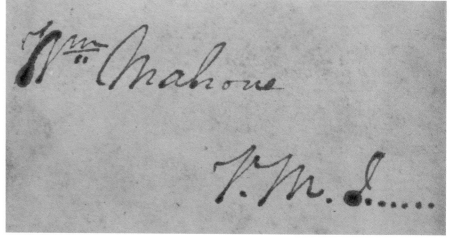

Signed *"Wm. Mahone, VMI"* on the frontispiece of each of the two volumes, these are the "New Edition" printings done in 1843, just a year before Mahone's enrollment at VMI. Both volumes contain pull-out tactical drawings and are in overall good condition with some foxing while the gold eagles and lettering on the binding are still vibrant. Measuring 3½" x 5½" these two manuals would follow General Mahone throughout the war and become a keepsake of his time at VMI and his command during the Civil War.

Born on a farm in Southampton, Virginia on December 1, 1826, Mahone was the son of a tavern owner whose father had come to America from Ireland. The archives at VMI indicate that Mahone was able to attend the elite academy through gambling winnings at his father's tavern. After his father had lost his money to a wealthy traveler Mahone stayed in the game, unbeknownst to this father, and not only won his father's money back but enough to "keep my winnings and educate myself", as he later told fellow Cadet William Pryor. These manuals are rare historical mementos of an important Confederate general, one of only three Confederate Corps commanders still alive at the time of the surrender at Appomattox.

Provenance: *The Don Tharpe Collection of American Military History*

Exhibited: *The Liberty Heritage Society Museum*

Estimate: $3,000-$8,000

Mahone's Copy of Lee's General Order Number 9

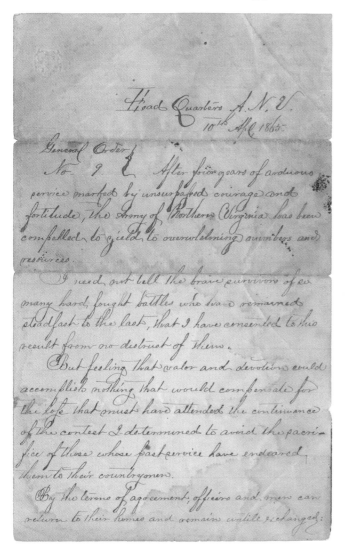

72200   **A TRANSCRIBED, HANDWRITTEN COPY OF GENERAL ROBERT E. LEE'S GENERAL ORDER NUMBER 9 – THE PERSONAL COPY OF GENERAL WILLIAM MAHONE** – General William Mahone, the famed Confederate cavalryman, owned this handwritten copy of General Robert E. Lee's General Order Number 9 issued to all his commanders. General Mahone took part in the Appomattox Campaign just before Lee surrendered and saved this copy, keeping it with him until his death when, years later, this document was sold from his archives.

Measuring 5" x 8" and beautifully written on white, lined paper it is dated '10th April 1865'. In this famous address General Lee states that the Army of Northern Virginia "has been compelled to yield to overwhelming numbers". There is shading present across the top half of the page and three horizontal folds present and some staining from handling. This is an important document owned by this prominent Confederate general.

Estimate: $4,000-$6,000

72201   GENERAL WILLIAM MAHONE'S COIN SILVER 15" WATER PITCHER − General Mahone maintained a luxurious silver service for entertaining. He was a noted engineer and a railroad president before and after the Civil War, as well as being a famed cavalryman and Confederate general. The makers marks are illegible, but the pitcher most likely dates from the 1830s or 1840s.

This 15" coin silver water pitcher has a 5" floral engraved base from which the pitcher extends up to the full 7" diameter of the pitcher. A highly ornate 'COF' is engraved on the front of the pitcher while on the back is engraved a heraldic falcon. Ornate floral engraving appears at the handle and spout and especially at the neck where a floral design dominates. There are very few slight dents and the piece retains its coin silver finish very well.

At approximately 48 troy ounces, this pitcher is highly ornate and decorative and, moreover, was owned and cherished by the great General Mahone, the hero of Petersburg and United States Senator from Virginia.

Provenance: *The Tharpe Collection of American Military History*

Exhibited: *The Liberty Heritage Society Museum*

Estimate: $4,000-$5,000

72202   GENERAL WILLIAM MAHONE'S GOLD SUSPENDER CLASPS – Confederate General William Mahone, perhaps most famous for his action at the Battle of the Crater during the Siege of Petersburg, was educated at the Virginia Military Institute and was president of the Norfolk and Petersburg Railroad before the war. Small in stature but big in bravado, he was loved by the people of Virginia, particularly those of Petersburg who honored him for his bravery in repulsing the attacks of the forces led by Union General Ambrose Burnside. Any personal, wartime uniform effect associated with the General is highly collectible. These two gold suspender buckles belonging to Mahone bear the engraved script "William Mahone' on the reverse. They appear to be of solid gold and incorporate two prongs in a swiveling fastening device and would have completed his dashing general uniform.

Provenance: *The Don Tharpe Collection of Military History*

Published: *North South Trader's Civil War* - Volume XXIV, Number 6.

Exhibited: *The Liberty Heritage Society Museum*

Estimate: $10,000-$20,000

72203   GENERAL WILLIAM MAHONE'S PERSONAL UNITED CONFEDERATE VETERANS LAPEL PINS – Confederate General William Mahone, hero of the Battle of the Crater, became active in the United Confederate Veterans Association after its formation in 1889, the same year he made an unsuccessful run for governor of Virginia. Founded as a benevolent, historical, social and literary society, the UCV held reunions and sponsored charitable benefits to raise money for disabled veterans of the Civil War and for widows and orphans from the war, all the while their members wearing uniquely identifying pins such as these shown here, this being the personal UCV lapel pins worn by General Mahone.

The UCV held many reunions after its inception with the old soldiers gathering together to reminisce and renew acquaintances. The bond between the men forged during the war was unbreakable as witnessed by the many reunion photographs and tokens from those gatherings that exist today. General Mahone's Brigade were particularly close due to the notoriety of the Battle of the Crater at Petersburg. So singularly important was that battle that the men wore lapel pins that memorialized the event, pins such as the sterling silver enameled battle flag pin of General Mahone's. The pin includes the location "Petersburg, Va." as well as the date of the battle, "July 30, 1864". "The Charge of the Crater" and "Mahone's Brigade" are included on the front of the pin as well. With the back stamped 'sterling', the pin and clasp still in perfect condition, General Mahone wore this pin during the reunions.

The second lapel pin owned by General Mahone bears the Mahone Brigade emblem, a blue shield with a centered gold star, a personal design of Mahone's that he took with him after the war. It is even included on his tomb with the initial 'M' in the center of the star as well as on his family silver. This pin bears the words 'Mahone's Brigade' above and below the shield, is made of coated paper and tin and is surrounded by a copper wreath. It is in fine condition and was manufactured by the Whitehead and Hoag Company of Newark, New Jersey as indicated on the reverse. It is of the stickpin variety attachment with all the original attachments to the pin and wreath intact.

Provenance: *The Don Tharpe Collection of American Military History*

Estimate: $1,000-$3,000

72204　CONFEDERATE GENERAL WILLIAM MAHONE PORTRAIT, FAMILY PHOTOS, AND SMALL CUP – William Mahone married Otelia Butler on February 8, 1855. Together they had 13 children, only three of whom would survive until adulthood. This grouping of five photographs of that family, supplemented by a small enameled drinking cup belonging to the family give a rare insight into the family of the man who was one of the most celebrated generals of the Civil War.

The first photograph is an albumen print of William Mahone himself. Measuring approximately 4" x 6" this photograph is taken years after the Civil War as Mahone's trademark beard has obviously grayed considerably. He strikes a stoic pose in a nice vested suit with a gold watch chain dangling from his vest.

The remainder of the photographs concerns Mahone's family. The first is a *carte de visite* of Mahone's wife Otelia and one of their daughters. The name 'Otelia Mahone' is written on the reverse in pencil. Two of the other photographs are of Mahone's sons in cadet military uniform and are partially hand-tinted. Both measure 4" x 6" with all the photographs being in very good condition.

The last photograph is a daguerreotype of one of the Mahone daughters in death, also hand-tinted. The poignant daguerreotype shows the child lying with a small bouquet of flowers in her hand. The photograph is nicely cased in its gutta percha case and copper frame inside with the image in pristine condition. Images such as these were common during the period as families were desirous of having the photographs as a keepsake, a reminder of the departed.

The remaining item is a small multi-colored, enameled drinking cup. Approximately 2" tall and 2" in diameter at the top, this tiny cup is dated 1884 as hallmarked in the base with a maker's mark as well. The cup is Imperial Russian silver in the Pan-Slavic style. The enamel remains in excellent condition.

These photographs along with the small cup are heartfelt reminders of the personal life of a great soldier and a prominent Southern family.

Provenance: *The Tharpe Collection of American Military History*

Estimate: $8,000-$12,000

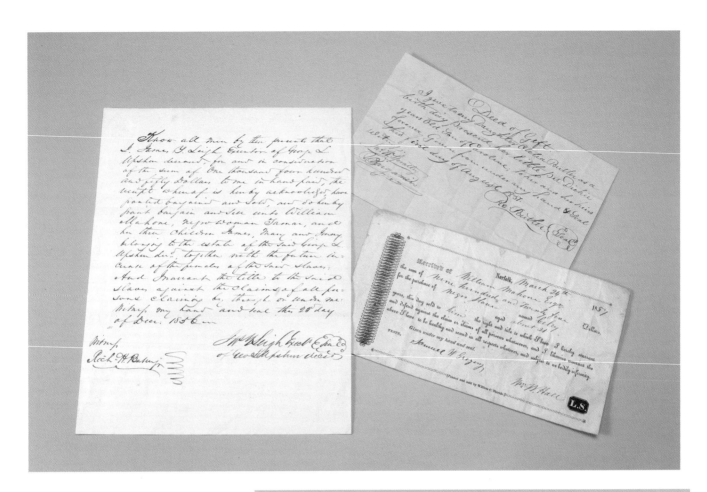

72205 GENERAL WILLIAM MAHONE: A COLLECTION OF MAHONE THREE SLAVE DOCUMENTS – "A LITTLE PET" – Confederate General William Mahone is known to have owned slaves before and during the war. Although he was renowned for his fair treatment and advocacy of emancipation after the war, evidence of Confederate General actual ownership of slaves is very rare. Two of these documents here are receipts for slaves Mahone purchased. The first document is a receipt of $1,450 for a "negro woman Tamar and her three children James, Mary and Jinny…" from the executor of the estate of George Upshur. Dated December 23, 1850, the document measures approximately 8" x 10" and is in very good condition with fold marks on the reverse.

The second receipt is for $925 received from William Mahone for the purchase of a "negro slave" named "Celey". Handwritten into the printed receipt are Mahone's name and the signatures of Samuel Gregory and William Hall. Dated March 24, 1857 at Norfolk, Virginia the 8" x 4¼" document is in very good condition with fold marks and light foxing on the reverse. The printer's name of "William C. Shields" appears at the bottom of the obverse.

The last document is the most moving and controversial, handwritten on blue paper and measures 7⅝" x 4⅞" and is a deed of gift of a slave named Dickie, "son of Caroline" from Robert Butler to his daughter Otelia Butler, the future wife of General William Mahone. Butler refers to Dickie as Mrs. Mahone's "little pet". Dated August 1, 1837, the paper is in excellent condition with strong, dark ink. There are paper folds to the reverse with slight foxing at the folds.

These documents are unique artifacts of slave ownership by one of the Civil War's most prominent generals.

Provenance: *The Tharpe Collection of Military History*

Exhibited: *The Liberty Heritage Society Museum*

Estimate: $2,000-$5,000

72206   CONFEDERATE GENERAL WILLIAM MAHONE'S CANE – PRESENTED TO HIM BY 'THE COLORED CITIZENS OF VIRGINIA'
– Confederate General William Mahone was revered during the Civil War for being the hero of Petersburg, the citizens honoring him with a magnificent presentation sword for his defense of the city. But Mahone was beloved by the people of his home state in Virginia after the war as well, ultimately electing him to the United States Senate where he served until 1887.

Along the way, the former slave owner championed the cause of education for former slaves and their descendants. He was instrumental in securing funds to found the Virginia Normal and Collegiate Institute at Petersburg, the forerunner of the present-day Virginia State University. While serving as a United States Senator, this engraved gold-handled cane was presented to him as a token of the black population's appreciation for his work in education for former slaves and their children.

This 37" cane black cane with an engraved gold knob handle was presented to General Mahone during his service in Washington, DC. The 2½" long knob rises to 1½" in diameter at the end and is elaborately and deeply carved and engraved in a foliate motif. On the end of the gold handle is engraved the following:

> Senator Wm. Mahone
> From the
> Colored Citizens
> of Virginia
> January 30
> 1882

The cane has a brass tip at the end and the overall condition is excellent with the gold knob in pristine and sparkling condition. It was a prized possession of the former Confederate general who went on to serve his state, including the black population by whom he was admired and honored with the presentation of the gold and wood cane.

Provenance: *The Don Tharpe Collection of American Military History*

Published: *North South Trader's Civil War* - Volume XXIV, Number 6.

Exhibited: *The Liberty Heritage Society Museum*

Estimate: $6,000-$8,000

72207   GENERAL WILLIAM MAHONE'S CAMPAIGN CHAIR –
Confederate General William Mahone, a Virginia Military Academy graduate and president of the Norfolk and Petersburg Railroad at the outbreak of
the Civil War, fought with the Army of Northern Virginia throughout the
Civil War. While in the field general officers carried with them as many personal effects as they could, including writing desks and other furniture that
was portable, able to be moved from battle to battle. This 'campaign chair'
belonging to General Mahone was one such item. It does no take much
imagination to envision General Mahone sitting in his headquarters tent or
at fireside during a break in his campaigns. Whether at the Battle of Seven
Pines or at the famous Battle of the Crater at Petersburg, General Mahone
would bring this chair with him at his headquarters to use while planning
or studying the aftermath of battle.

Constructed of black walnut with elegantly carved, three-slat backs separated by a crosspiece, the chair has a scalloped top a cross pieces between
the legs which are supported by sturdy metal rods. Its collapsible, folding
design ensures its portability as it could be laid flat and easily transported
throughout the war. Although it shows the appropriate wear, it is in very
good condition and has a gold cushion that is not original to the chair. This
is a wonderful antique personal effect of General William Mahone used by
him in the field throughout the war.

Provenance: *The Tharpe Collection of Military History*

Published: *North South Trader's Civil War* - Volume XXIV, Number 6.

Exhibited: *The Liberty Heritage Society Museum*

Estimate: $8,000-$12,000

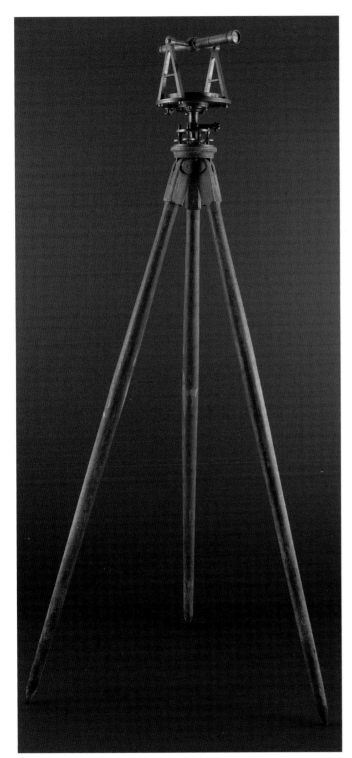

72208 MAJOR GENERAL'S WILLIAM MAHONE'S SURVEYOR'S TRANSIT – FOR THE NORFOLK AND PETERSBURG RAILROAD

– Confederate Major General William Mahone graduated from Virginia Military Institute in 1847 and served as a civil engineer, chief engineer and ultimately president of the Norfolk and Petersburg Railroad. As a Virginian and slaveholder, Mahone sided with the Confederacy but not before lending the resources of his railroad to assist in ramping up the Confederacy for war.

This surveyor's transit and tripod were owned by Mahone and were very likely used by the 1st Virginia Engineers led by Colonel W. W. Blackford who was the chief engineer when the vast system of earthworks were built during the defense of Petersburg. General Mahone was the hero of the Petersburg defense, lauded and decorated by the citizenry for his heroic defense of their city by his magnificent sword featured in this auction. This sort of surveyor's transit would have been a common site during that campaign as well as during the Pennsylvania campaign when such instruments were used to map railroad routes. This one, however, is quite rare and the only one known to exist marked "VA Engineer Battalion".

Manufactured by E. Draper of Philadelphia, this instrument was specially made for the Norfolk and Petersburg Railroad painted on the face of the compass' 5½" glass. The heavy brass transit is affixed to the wooden tripod by heavy metal brass screws. One leg of the tripod is stamped "Va. Engineer Bn. No.1", the unit commanded by Colonel Blackford who was under General Mahone's overall command at Petersburg.

After the war William Mahone returned to engineering and became president of the Norfolk and Western Railroad, the successor company he once ran before the war. He was later elected to the United States Senate from Virginia. This is an excellent example of railroad engineering equipment used to build the Norfolk and Petersburg Railroad and fortification of Petersburg. It is unique, being the only Confederate marked engineers transit known. A remarkable museum showpiece.

Provenance: *The Tharpe Collection of American Military History*

Exhibited: *The Liberty Heritage Society Museum*

Estimate: $8,000-$10,000

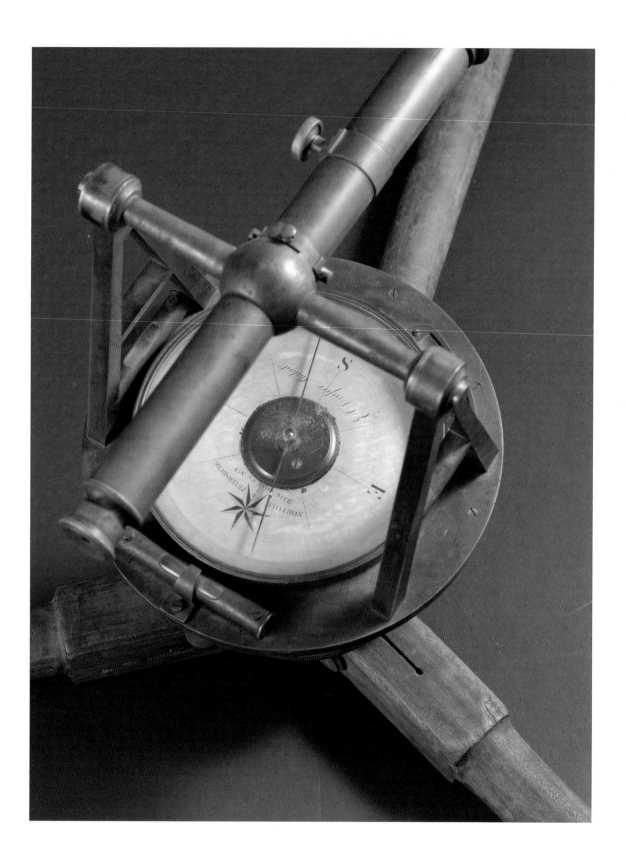

CONFEDERATE SWORDS

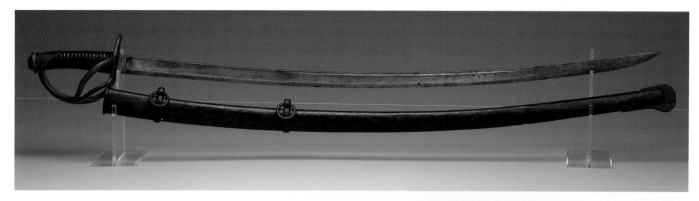

72209   CONFEDERATE MAJOR GENERAL WILLIAMS WICKHAM'S EUROPEAN IMPORT 1840 MODEL WRIST BREAKER – Confederate General Williams Wickham was a lawyer in Virginia at the outbreak of the Civil War when he volunteered as the captain of the Hanover Dragoons. He went on to fight at Bull Run and Gettysburg and took part in General J.E.B. Stuart's raid into Maryland. Like his friend General William Mahone, he served as a railroad president after the war.

This European import 1840 model wrist breaker was used by Major General Williams Wickham, CSA. The sword is in pristine condition. The hilt retains its original leather with twisted brass wire. The blade has an even patina with only minor pitting. The scabbard has its original black paint, which was typical for Virginia cavalry service.

General Williams Wickham also served as a Confederate congressman, transferring his command to General Thomas Rosser when he traveled to Richmond. After the war he served as president of the Chesapeake and Ohio Railroad. A statue of him stands at Monroe Park in Richmond, Virginia.

Provenance: *The Wickham Estate; The Tharpe Collection of American Military History*

Exhibited: *The Liberty Heritage Society Museum*

Estimate: $60,000-$65,000

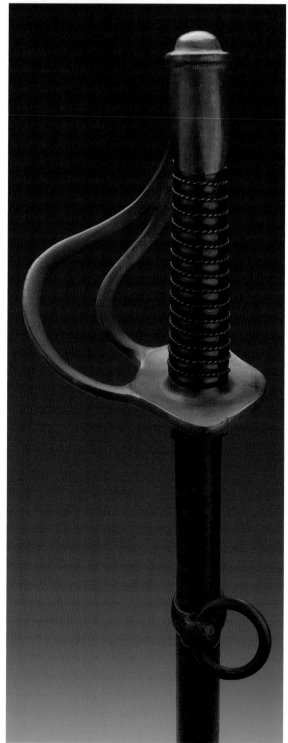

72210 CONFEDERATE GENERAL WILLIAMS WICKHAM TRUNK, SILVER TEA SERVICE, IVORY MATCH SAFE AND POCKET WATCH – Confederate General Williams Wickham was a lawyer in Virginia at the outbreak of the Civil War when he volunteered as the captain of the Hanover Dragoons. He went on to fight at Bull Run and Gettysburg and took part in General JEB Stuart's raid into Maryland. Like his friend General William Mahone, he served as a railroad president after the war.

This five-piece silver service, match safe and pocket watch were owned by Wickham, the silver service being made of coin silver as is the watch. The elaborate floral and garden pattern of the silver continues through the 10" teapot with the hinged top, the 6" sugar and creamer vessels, the sugar tong and spoon. Made by the noted Baltimore silversmiths Kirk and Son, each piece is hallmarked in the base. Each piece is in excellent condition and is engraved "C M".

Included with this service is a silver drinking cup made by the Richmond, Virginia silversmith Mitchell and Tyler. At 3" in diameter at the top, the cup has some small dents and the name of Wickham's daughter, "*Eliza*", engraved in period script on the front.

An unusual piece of silver, a marrow scoop for removing marrow from bones, made in London in 1743, is included. The coin silver watch is double-hinged with a Roman numeral dial and is in running condition with its key and short watch chain included. With a beaded rim, the watch is numbered 23522 and was manufactured by H. and O. Perret of Geneva, Switzerland.

A remarkable and attractive ivory match safe from General Wickham's days as the commander of the 4th Virginia Cavalry is included with this grouping as well. Presented to him by the captain of Company G, Captain W. B. Newton on September 11,1861, the front of the 3" match safe is engraved in high relief with "4th Va. Cav." and an engraved presentation form the Captain to the then-Lieutenant Colonel Wickham on the reverse. The brass hinge is in perfect working order and the bottom of the match safe is carved in a checkered pattern for striking.

General Williams Wickham also served as a Confederate congressman, transferring his command to General Thomas Rosser when he traveled to Richmond. After the war he served as president of the Chesapeake and Ohio Railroad. A statue of him stands at Monroe Park in Richmond, Virginia.

This collection comes with a magnificent 44" x 21½" x 15" Virginia-made field trunk with brass studs, handles, and locks. The interior has a floral pattern lining and two wooden stands on which this heavy trunk may be placed.

This is a valuable and artistic silver service, watch, match safe, and wonderful trunk owned by a Confederate general, Congressman, and prominent businessman from Virginia.

Provenance: *Wickham Estate; The Tharpe Collection of American Military History*

Exhibited: *The Liberty Heritage Society Museum*

Estimate: $8,000-$10,000

72211   CONFEDERATE "DOG RIVER" CAVALRY SABER WITH SCABBARD. The unmarked Confederate cavalry sword retains its original leather and single brass wire wrap on the hilt. The unstopped fuller blade exhibits some pitting and is 31¼". The overall length of the sword is 41". The scabbard is lap seamed on the bottom with an iron drag, two brass ring mounts (the top ring is broken at the seam); the throat is missing. The brass mounts and guard are un-cleaned with even patina. The overall condition of the blade is dark with light pitting.

Estimate: $3,500-$4,500

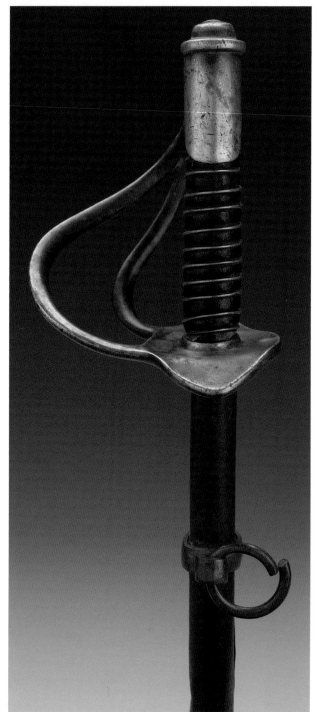

72212   **CONFEDERATE BRASS FIGHTING KNIFE WITH LANGET; SERIAL NO. XXII:** An unmarked (CS Armory) Confederate fighting knife with langet that is serial numbered XXII. The blade of this knife is 14½" the overall length is 20." The handle is solid brass with a langard loop. The meaning of the Roman numeral serial no. XXII is unknown; however, the number is done very similar to the style used by the Confederate States Armory, which operated out of Kenansville, NC. It is known that the firm did produce knives in addition to swords, sabers and cutlasses. This rare knife could well be a product of the firm.

Provenance: *The Tharpe Collection of American Military History*

Exhibited: *The Liberty Heritage Society Museum*

Estimate: $8,000-$12,000

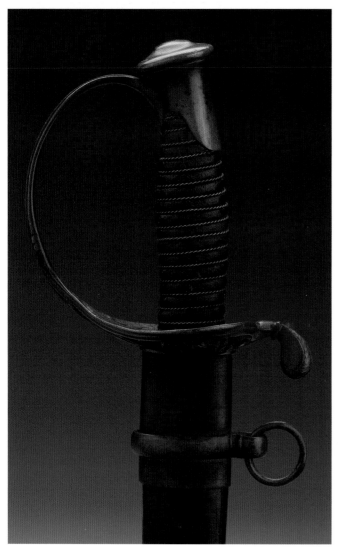

72213 CONFEDERATE OFFICER'S FIELD AND STAFF SWORD WITH ORIGINAL LEATHER SCABBARD BY LOUIS FROELICH, CONFEDERATE STATES ARMORY, KENANSVILLE, NORTH CAROLINA – Louis Froelich produced a wide variety of swords between 1861 and 1865, some of the most treasured Confederate swords of the Civil War. This unique example of the field and staff officers model has stamped on the bow of the guard "L F 1861" making it one of the rarest of Froelich's products. The pattern on the guard, with a five pointed star above the "CS", is similar to a pattern produced by both Boyle & Gamble and B. Douglas. The bright shiny blade is 29⅜" with virtually no pitting, and the overall length of the sword is 35⅝". The leather washer is missing; however, the hilt is tight to the blade. The hilt retains all of its original brown leather and finely twisted brass wire. Some of the original gold gilding may been seen in the recesses of the guard. The original leather scabbard retains 90% of the original black finish and is top-stitched like the Boyle and Gamble products in Richmond. The mounts are original to the sword. The overall condition of this sword is excellent.

Provenance: *The Tharpe Collection of American Military History*

Exhibited: *The Liberty Heritage Society Museum*

Estimate: $35,000-$40,000

72214 CONFEDERATE SIDE KNIFE FASHIONED FROM NAVAL CUTLASS, 10.5" blade, 15.75" overall length. A substantial piece of Southern martial cutlery, this knife was cut down from a Confederate naval cutlass. The brass fish-scale grip has an integral pommel carrying a fouled anchor on one side and CSN on the other. Good metal throughout with deep old toning on the grip.

Provenance: *The Tharpe Collection of American Military History*

Exhibited: *The Liberty Heritage Society Museum*

Estimate: $8,000-$10,000

72215 CONFEDERATE SIDE KNIFE FASHIONED FROM AN ARTILLERY SWORD USED BY RICHMOND HOME GUARDS – 12.5" blade, 18" overall length. This knife, attributed to the Richmond Home Guard, uses the cast brass grip taken from a Confederate artillery short sword. The grip's integral pommel carries depressed stars on both sides and its cross-bar has a crude raised "CS" on either side. The blade is stamped with a pentagram on its ricasso. Excellent surfaces and toning.

Provenance: *The Tharpe Collection of American Military History*

Exhibited: *The Liberty Heritage Society Museum*

Estimate: $10,000-$15,000

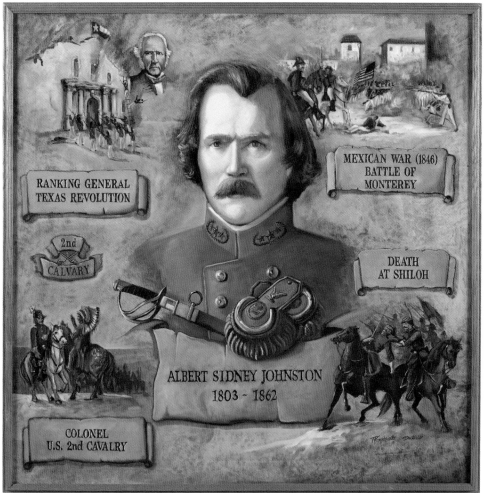

Please visit _HA.com_ to view other collectibles auctions. _A 19.5% Buyer's Premium ($9 min.) Applies To All Lots_

**72216   THE SWORD OF CONFEDERATE GENERAL
ALBERT SIDNEY JOHNSTON – ACCOMPANIED BY AN OIL
PAINTING OF JOHNSTON** – This 1840 Model Ames Cavalry
Saber was carried by Confederate General Albert Sidney Johnston at
the beginning of the Civil War. With a very nice gilt guard, this is a
superb high-grade officer's sword made by the Ames Manufacturing
Company of Chicopee, Massachusetts. Albert Sidney Johnston, an
1826 graduate of the United States Military academy at West Point,
was already an accomplished and famous soldier by the time of the
Civil War. A veteran of the Black Hawk War, a general in the Army
of the Republic of Texas and a Colonel in the Mexican War, he was
a Brigadier General at the outbreak of the Civil War. Offered a position in the United States Army as second in command to General
Winfield Scott, he instead accepted a commission as a General in
the Confederate Army. He was killed at the Battle of Shiloh with the
entire Confederacy mourning his loss. Indeed Confederate President
Jefferson Davis said he was, "the greatest soldier, the ablest man, civil
or military, Confederate or Federal, then living."

This 36" saber is in magnificent condition, the 1¼" wide blade with
the 26" fuller, it is stamped 'US/H.D.K.' at the ricasso with 'Ames Mfg/
Chicopee Mass/1853 on the reverse ricasso above the intact leather
washer. The hilt is highly gilded with a 4" leather grip having 18 turns
of gilt twisted 20 gauge brass wire with 13 twists per inch. The pommel cap has the inspectors' marks of 'A.D.K.' and 'J.W.R.'. The three-
branch knuckle-bow adds weight to the sword which helped it earn
the nickname "Old Wristbreaker".

The scabbard is made of sheet steel and has two mounts at 3" and 11"
down the scabbard with 1" rings. The 4" drag is stamped with the
inspector's mark of 'J.W.R.' with the overall patina of the scabbard being a rich medium gray.

The sword and scabbard are accompanied by a beautiful oil on canvas
painting by T. R. Goldsworthy and David Heslep that commemorates
Johnston's military career. Measuring 42" x 42", the central figure
of Albert Sidney Johnston in his Confederate General's uniform
is surrounded by vignettes of his actions during the Texas War for
Independence, The Mexican War, as a Colonel in the United States
Cavalry in the West and finally a scene depicting his death at the
Battle of Shiloh during the Civil War. This sword is featured in the
painting just below the image of Johnston and above the title of the
picture 'Albert Sidney Johnston, 1803-1862'. The painting is nicely
framed in a 2" oak frame.

This is an historical sword and scabbard owned and used by an illustrious American military hero who was killed at the Battle of Shiloh,
truly one of a kind in every way.

Estimate: $60,000-$65,000

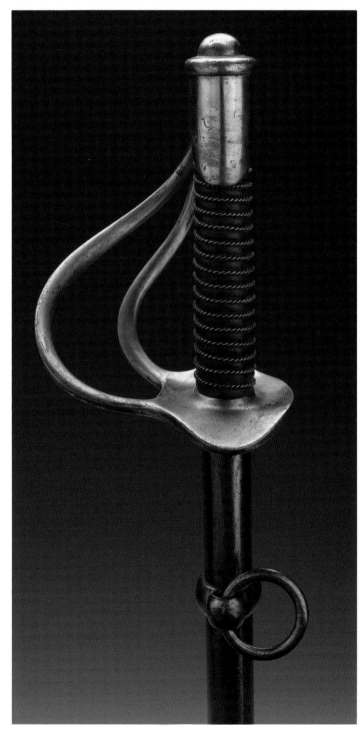

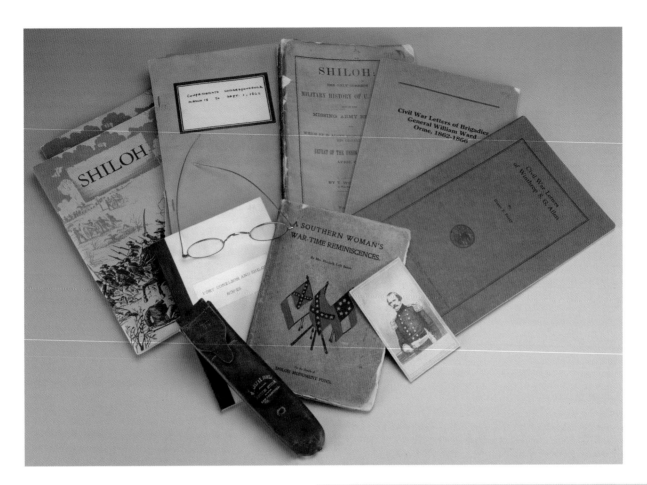

72217   THE EYEGLASSES OF CONFEDERATE GENERAL ALBERT SIDNEY JOHNSTON, A *CARTE DE VISITE* **OF JOHNSTON AND NINE BOOKS** – Albert Sidney Johnston, considered the greatest soldier the Confederacy had to offer at the time, met his death in battle on April 6, 1862 at Shiloh early in the Civil War. An 1826 graduate of the United States Military Academy at West Point, Johnston had already fought in the Black Hawk War, the Texas War of Independence after which he served as the new Republic's Secretary of War and the Mexican War. He had achieved the rank of Brevet Brigadier General in the US Army when the war broke out in 1861.

These gold eyeglasses were the personal property of Johnston measuring 4½" across the front at the oval lenses, still intact and having 5" arms, the glasses are in excellent condition. The eyeglasses have their original leather case bearing the optician's name W. Colfax Jones of San Francisco. Johnston was commanding the Department of the Pacific at the start of the war and most likely purchased the glasses while on duty on the west coast. The glasses and case are accompanied by a *carte de visite* of Johnston in his dress uniform with a backmark of 'E. & H. T. Anthony' of New York. Signed in pencil on the back is 'A. S. Johnston C.S.A.' in another hand.

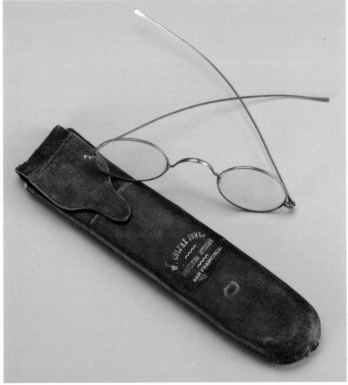

With these items kept by his family are a series of nine books related to the Civil War exploits of General Albert Sidney Johnston. The earliest, a copy of the 1872 *Shiloh* is a 6"x 9" 182 page volume bound in blue paper with the back cover loose. It concerns the 'Defeat of the Union Army at Shiloh'. The second is a 5"x7" paper-bound 1905 book by Elizabeth Lyle Saxon titled *A Southern Woman's War-Time Reminiscences* and was published for the Shiloh Battlefield Memorial Fund. Two of the remaining volumes are war period accounts of Union and Confederate correspondence of the period around the Battle of Shiloh. The remaining five volumes are reprints of letters from General William Ward, Winthrop S. G. Allen who fought at Shiloh, another account of the action Johnston saw at Fort Donelson and Shiloh and two souvenir pamphlets from the Shiloh Military Park.

Estimate: $8,000-$10,000

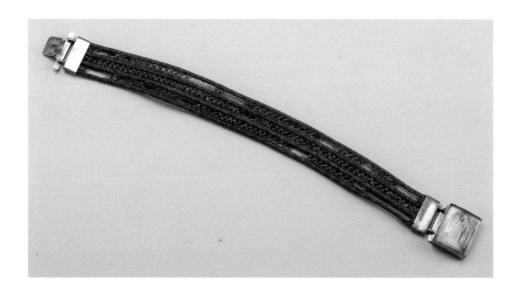

72218   GENERAL ALBERT SIDNEY JOHNSTON'S GOLD AND HAIR BRACELET – This gold clasped and hair mourning bracelet was owned by the great Confederate General Albert Sidney Johnston. The bracelet, 6.5" long, has a gold clasp with a hand-painted image under a crystal, showing a monument with the initials "CS". This bracelet has seen considerable wear but, the braided hair is strong, the crystal and image are very fine, and the clasp functions perfectly.

Estimate: $2,000-$3,000

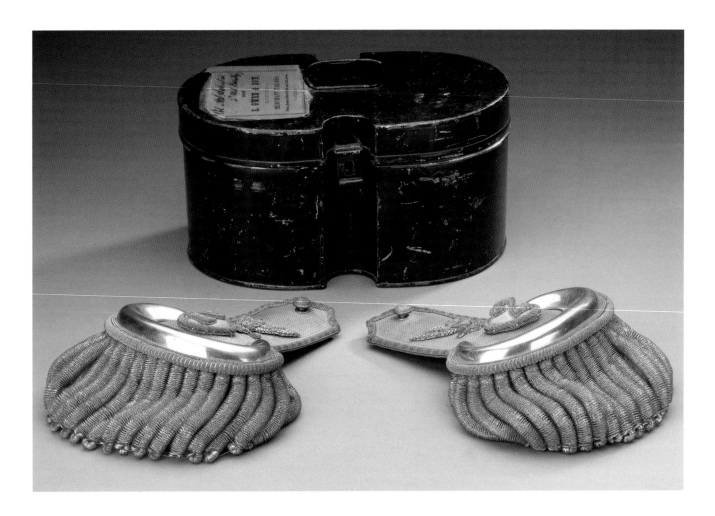

72219   THE GOLD 2ND US CAVALRY EPAULETS OF ALBERT SIDNEY JOHNSTON AS A COLONEL – Two beautiful gold dress epaulets of then-Colonel Albert Sidney Johnston, US Army circa 1855. Albert Sidney Johnston, hero of the Confederacy, killed at the Battle of Shiloh, had a long and respected career as a Union Army officer before the war. A Kentuckian by birth, he spent much of his life in Texas. After graduating from West Point in 1826 he was commissioned a 2nd Lieutenant in the 2nd US Infantry and served in the Blackhawk War. He resigned his commission in 1834 and returned to Kentucky, but he was destined to his serve his country as a soldier.

Later in 1834 Johnston became a farmer in Texas and joined the Texas Army to fight for independence from Mexico, rising to the rank of Senior Brigadier General of the Texas Army and later Secretary of War to the new republic. He resigned in 1840 and returned to Kentucky but his urge to serve as a military officer could not be suppressed. He returned to Texas during the Mexican War and served as a colonel of the Texas Army under General Zachary Taylor. After his election as President of the United States, Taylor appointed Johnston a major in the US Army where Johnston served as a pay-master. By now a career army officer, President Franklin Pierce appointed Johnston as colonel of the newly formed 2nd Cavalry. It is from this era of the great career soldier's life that these two ornate gold epaulets originate.

Still in their original metal case, these two gold dress epaulets were manufactured by the W. H. Hortsman and Sons Company of Philadelphia. They were sold by the E. Owen and Son military merchant tailors of Washington DC. The metal case still bears the tailor's label with the name "A. S. Johnston, 2nd US Cavalry" written in pen on the lid. The brass and gilt epaulets with gold thread and coils that extend down from the shoulder boards display the colonel's spread eagle device on the gold, silk-threaded boards. Significantly, the number '2' denoting the 2nd Cavalry is directly beneath the eagle. A gold Horstman federal eagle button is attached at the collar end of each epaulet.

Albert Sidney Johnston would have only worn these epaulets for a short two years since he was given the brevet promotion of Brigadier General in 1857. This perhaps accounts for the pristine condition in which these epaulets are found today. As the Civil War became eminent, Johnston was serving as com-mander of the Department of the Pacific in California where he resigned his commission to fight for the Confederacy.

As a skilled and experienced soldier having fought in four wars, including the Utah Expedition to put down the Mormon uprising, Johnston could have had high command in the Union Army as well. In May of 1861 he was appointed to the second highest command in the newly formed Confederate Army by President Jefferson Davis. He was much loved by his Confederate troops making his death at the Battle of Shiloh only a year later that much more tragic.

These gold dress epaulets are a rare and historical uniform insignia of a Confederate general's military career.

Estimate: $8,000-$10,000

BOUDE & MILEY.   LEXINGTON, VA.

72220   WILLIAM PRESTON JOHNSTON SIGNED *CARTE DE VISITE,* "*Wm Preston Johnston*", Stonewall Art Gallery, Lexington, Virginia back-mark. This image was taken while Johnston was Chairman of History and English Literature at Washington College in Lexington. One marginal stain, even toning. Very good condition. Son of Confederate General Albert Sidney Johnston, William Preston Johnston initially served his home state of Kentucky. In 1862 he was appointed Aide de Camp to President Davis and labored in that capacity until Davis's capture at war's end.

Estimate: $700-$1,000

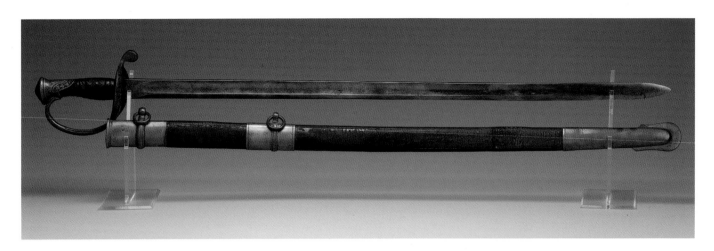

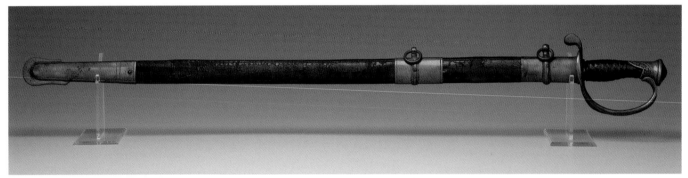

72221   CONFEDERATE FOOT OFFICERS SWORD WITH LEATHER SCABBARD: BY BURGER & BROTHERS OF RICHMOND, VA – P. Burger operated a saw manufactory in Richmond prior to the Civil War along with two of his brothers and Edwin Boyle. Boyle withdrew from the firm in 1861 and became a part of Boyle & Gamble. Burger and his brothers continued with operations producing among other items swords, which may have been assembled from Boyle & Gamble parts. Very few of their swords exist. The known examples of their foot officers' swords that have surfaced have been etched with the name "Burger" at the ricasso.

This 30½" blade is etched on the right side with the firm name, a stand of two Confederate flags. Additionally, "C.S.A.1862" is etched about midway of the blade; the overall length of the sword is 35¼". The left side of the blade is etched with crossed cannon and a presentation ribbon, which is blank; at the ricasso there is a shield, which may have at one time been etched "Richmond." The sword has its original leather washer. The guard and grip appear to be very similar to the products of Boyle & Gamble. The grip retains its original leather and single copper wire wrap. A sword with beautiful patina from a rarely seen Confederate sword maker.

Provenance: *The Tharpe Collection of American Military History*

Exhibited: *The Liberty Heritage Society Museum*

Estimate: $50,000-$60,000

72222   BATTLE-FIELD PICK-UP CONFEDERATE D-GUARD BOWIE KNIFE, 19" blade, 23.75" overall length, wooden grip mounted to iron guard. This classic Southern fighting knife from the battle of Atlanta near Stone Mountain, Georgia enjoys a rich, uncleaned natural patina on all elements. Two splits to wooden grip, else fully intact.

Provenance: *The Tharpe Collection of American Military History*

Exhibited: *The Liberty Heritage Society Museum*

Estimate: $8,000-$10,000

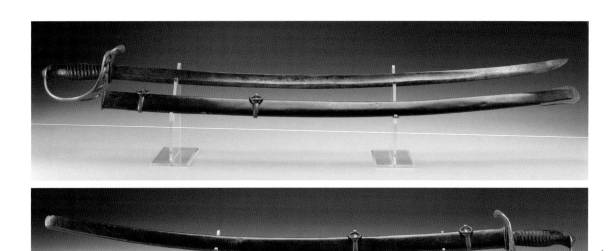

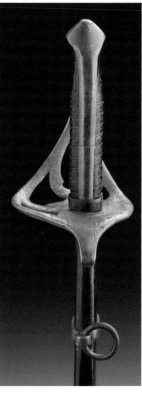

72223   NASHVILLE PLOW WORKS CONFEDERATE CAVALRY SABER WITH ORIGINAL SCABBARD – A unique opportunity to own an authentic Confederate officers cavalry saber, a sword that has been long treasured by collectors with the biblical injunction of turning "plowshares into swords." The facility, operated by principals Messrs. Sharp and Hamilton, was located on 8th Avenue in Nashville near the railroad overpass and operated until Nashville fell to Federal troops on April 1, 1862.

After the fall of Nashville, both Messer's. Sharp and Hamilton were taken into custody by the Federals and charged with treason; they were later released. It is unknown how many swords were produced by the firm nor if other products were made other than the swords. The blade with unstopped fuller is 35½" with an overall length of the sword of 41." The blade has an appealing dark, even patina with very limited pitting. The guard is sand cast without the stippling that is seen on some of their other products.

On the underside of the guard is the distinctive "CSA" and also the firm name "NASHVILLE PLOW WORKS". The back strap/pommel is cast in one piece, and there is a joint in the back strap approximately ⅓ of the way up from the guard, which is not loose from the grip. The sword retains its original leather and finely twisted brass wire wrap. The scabbard's lap seam on the bottom is braized. The mounts, throat and drag are brass, and the drag is loose but stable. The scabbard retains 95 plus percent of its original black paint. Overall condition of the sword is excellent.

Provenance: *The Mullinax Collection*

Estimate: $8,000-$12,000

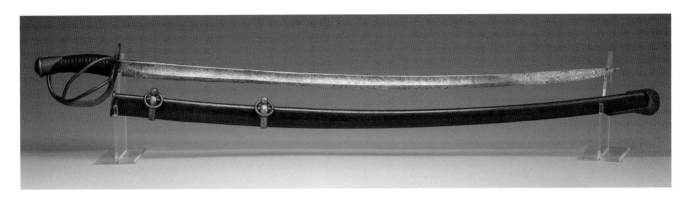

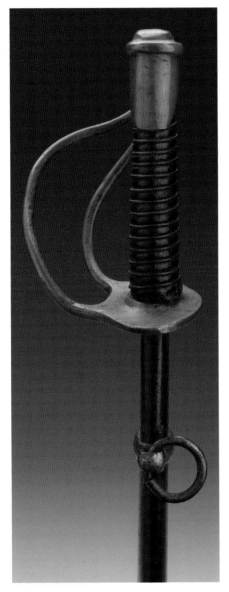
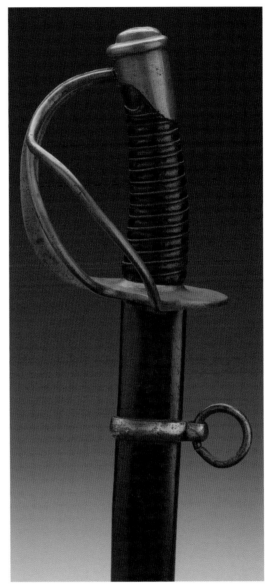

72224   CONFEDERATE HAIMAN CAVALRY SABER WITH SCABBARD, BY L. HAIMAN & BROTHER, COLUMBUS, GEORGIA – Louis Haiman and his brother Elijah operated in Columbus, Georgia throughout the entire Civil War. They produced varied items that they supplied to the Confederacy, including buttons, belts, camp equipment, revolvers, and all types of edged weapons. Their expertise in supplying a variety of edged weapons is quite extensive. Uniquely, the blade on this sword is stamped at the ricasso on the right side, "CSA." The sword retains its original leather and single iron wire wrap on the hilt. The mounts on the scabbard retain most of the original gilt as does the scabbard retain its original brown lacquered finish. The scabbard is lap-seamed on the bottom. The overall condition of this sword is excellent.

Provenance: *The Tharpe Collection of American Military History*

Exhibited: *The Liberty Heritage Society Museum*

Estimate: $30,000-$35,000

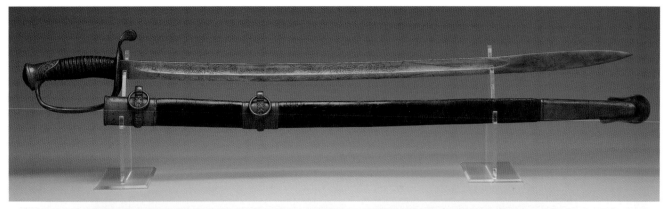

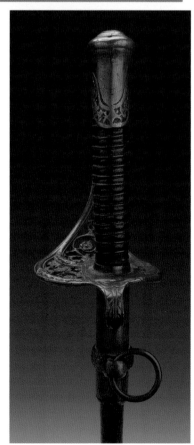

72225 CONFEDERATE LT. MALCOLM L. HUDGINS PRESENTATION STAFF OFFICERS SWORD WITH ORIGINAL LEATHER SCABBARD: BY BOYLE & GAMBLE, RICHMOND, VIRGINIA – The blade is deeply and distinctively etched with the presentation on the right side:

Lieut. Malcolm L. Hudgins
Co. "F" 21st Va. Inftry.

Lieutenant Malcolm L. Hudgins enlisted in the Confederate army on May 16, 1861 at the age of 17. He received his promotion to lieutenant in April 1864. Just six months later, on October 19, 1864, he was wounded and captured at Cedar Creek, undoubtedly the occasion of him losing this sword. He was imprisoned at Old Capitol Prison in Washington, DC on October 29, 1864 and transferred to Fort Delaware in November 1864, where he was exchanged.

An outstanding example of swords produced by Boyle & Gamble. The unstopped blade is 29¼" deeply etched on the right side with a shield containing the letters "CSA", below a Confederate Second National flag; at the ricasso is engraved the firm name, "Boyle/Gamble". The left side of the blade is etched with "CSA" in the middle, a Confederate Second National flag above crossed cannon; at the ricasso is engraved "1863/Richmond". The overall length of the sword is 34½." The scabbard is in beautiful condition with some cracking, top-stitched with minor openings near the drag. The original mounts are adorned with laurel leaves. The pommel is distinctly decorated with laurel leaves.

Boyle & Gamble operated in Richmond, Virginia, throughout the Civil War. They were located on South Sixth Street, a block from the old Virginia Armory, where they produced swords of all types as well as bayonets and knives. The principals of the firm were Edwin Boyle, T. Gamble, and E. MacFee.

Provenance: *The Tharpe Collection of American Military History*

Exhibited: *The Liberty Heritage Society Museum*

Estimate: $70,000-$75,000

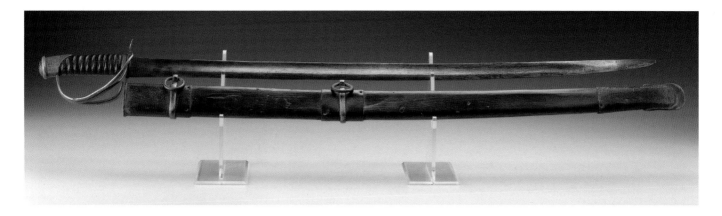

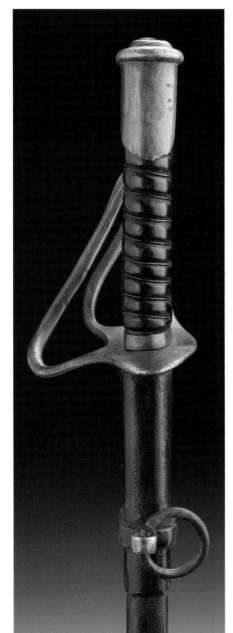

72226   **A CONFEDERATE MARSHALL SABER** – This Hammond Marshall sword was made at the Atlanta factory of this maker who operated from 1861 - 1864. Marshall made a variety of belt plates and other objects for the Confederacy including cavalry and artillery sabers. This 31½" model has a 27" fuller, the leather washer present at the ricasso and the number "37" stamped on the underside of the guard at the ricasso. The leather, single wire-wrapped grip is in good condition with the brass guard and pommel unmarked and is identical to a sword shown on page 153 of Clegg Donald Furr's book *American Swords and Makers' Marks*. The wood and metal scabbard has a 4" throat with ring and a 2½" mount at 12" down the scabbard. The 5¼" drag is held in place by four pins.

This is a rare Confederate sword produced in Atlanta, Georgia during the Civil War.

Estimate: $4,000-$6,000

72227   CONFEDERATE BOYLE & GAMBLE CAVALRY SABER WITH METAL SCABBARD BY BOYLE & GAMBLE, RICHMOND, VIRGINIA – One of the finest known Boyle & Gamble enlisted man's cavalry sabers in existence. Boyle and Gamble operated throughout the Civil War, producing edged weapons of all kinds, knives, and bayonets, as well as other military necessities.

The metal scabbard is lap-seamed on the bottom and retains the majority of its original brown lacquer. The blade length is 34½", and the overall length of the sword is 40¼". The overall condition of the blade is bright and shiny; retaining its original leather washer. The three-branch guard is in excellent condition. The grip retains its original brown leather with twisted copper wire wrap. Truly one of the finest/pristine Confederate cavalry sabers by Boyle & Gamble in existence.

Provenance: *The Tharpe Collection of American Military History*

Exhibited: *The Liberty Heritage Society Museum*

Estimate: $10,000-$20,000

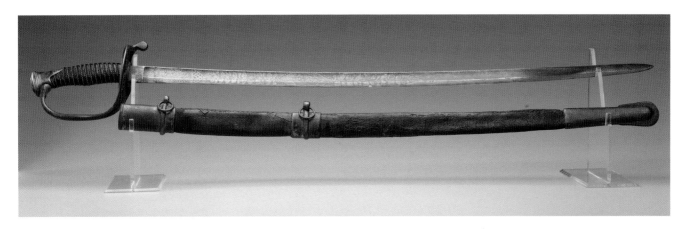

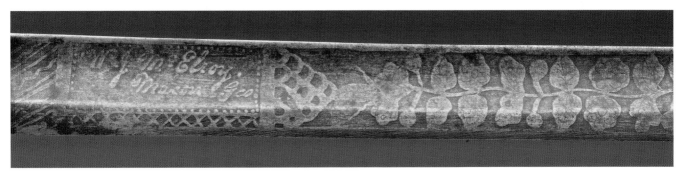

72228   CONFEDERATE PRESENTATION FOOT OFFICER'S SWORD WITH ORIGINAL LEATHER SCABBARD BY W. J. MCELROY OF MACON, GEORGIA – This is a W. J. McElroy presentation staff officer's sword; blade presentation in English script:

L. L. Strozer

Captain L. L. Strozer served in the 25th Georgia Provost Guards, a 1,000-man unit organized to round up deserters.

This sword has its original black leather scabbard with topstitching. The stitching has been re-glued. The mounts retain some of its original gold gild, and the ring on the top mount is original. The middle ring mount appears to be a period replacement. The overall condition of the scabbard is good, dry but stable with cracking and checking. This sword was carried by L. L. Strozer, whose name is etched in the panel on the left side of the blade. Also on this side of the blade is etched a stand of two flags; the etching extends from the ricasso to within 12" of point. The opposite side of the blade is etched with a floral pattern, "CS" in the middle of the blade and a panel near the ricasso with the firm name, "W. J. McElroy, Macon, Geo." The blade is 28¾" from ricasso to tip. Overall, the blade along with hilt is 34½."

The guard has beautiful "attic find" patina with little of the original gold gilt. The top and bottom of the guard are beautifully engraved with an unique oak leaf pattern. The sword's original black leather grip with twisted copper wire is in excellent condition.

Provenance: *The Headley Collection*

Estimate: $25,000-$35,000

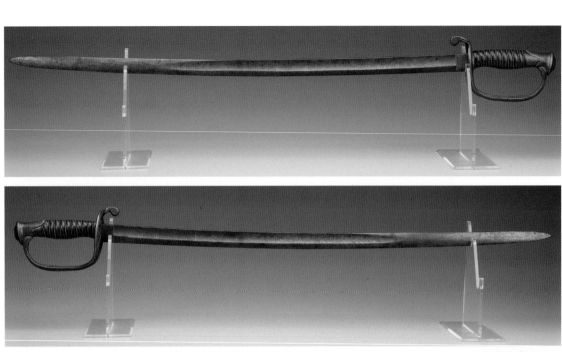

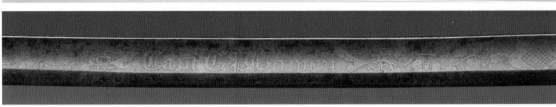

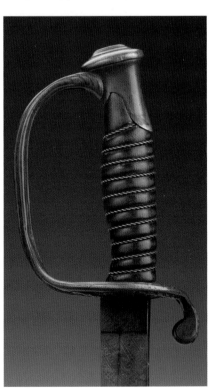

72229   CONFEDERATE PRESENTATION FOOT OFFICERS SWORD BY W. J. MCELROY OF MACON, GA – C. P. Bowen was captain of Company C of the 30th Georgia Infantry. They saw action at Atlanta and Chickamauga and later served at Mobile before surrendering in May 1865. Captain Bowen was born in Jackson County, Georgia, his father being a hero in the War of 1812. This sword was captured from him at the Battle of Nashville.

William J. McElroy went into swordmaking as the winds of war began to blow and operated throughout the Civil War. In addition to the production of all types of swords and sabers, he produced wide and varied products ranging from bayonets and bowie knives of all types, belts, buckles, spurs, and canteens as well as pikes for the State of Georgia. The company was a prolific and noted producer of military supplies to the Confederate Government, the State of Georgia and private individuals.

This beautiful presentation sword was carried by Capt. C. P. Bowen whose name is etched in the presentation panel on the left side of the blade. The etching on both sides of this sword is clear and distinctive. The right side of the blade is etched beginning at the ricasso with a flower over hatching, a panel with the firm name and address in script, "W. J. McElroy/ Macon, Geo.;" and a stand of two flags. On the right is the Confederate First National flag; on the left is the Confederate Battle flag; above that is a diamond pattern with "CS" in old English script. The remainder of this side of the blade to within 11¼" of the tip is etched with laurel vines with leaves.

The left side of the blade is etched to within 11½" of the tip; beginning at the ricasso with the flower over hatching; the presentation panel in a diamond shape etched in old English script, "Capt. C. P, Bowen." The blade is 29⅝" from ricasso to tip, overall the blade along with hilt is 35¼", and the sword is tight to the hilt with no washer. The guard has beautiful patina with none of its original gold gilt remaining. The pommel is plain. The polished wood grip with heavy twisted brass wire wrap is in excellent condition. Truly one of the most beautiful well preserved Confederate presentation swords in private hands.

Estimate: $25,000-$35,000

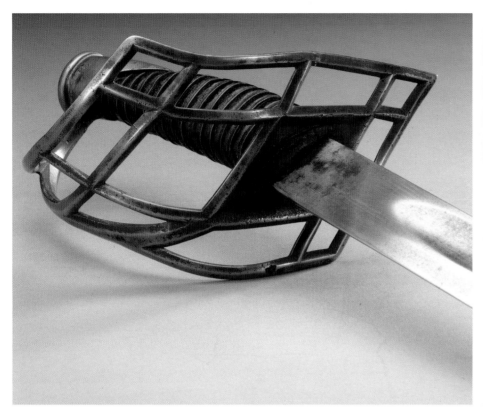

72230   CONFEDERATE OFFICER'S CAVALRY SABER "DIAMOND-SHAPED" SWORD WITH ORIGINAL LEATHER SCABBARD BY BOYLE & GAMBLE, RICHMOND, VIRGINIA. Brass four (4) branch guard with "DIAMOND HATCHED BASKET" design; original leather wrap with single brass wire. Blade is 29⅞", and the overall length of sword is 35½" with original leather washer; unstopped single, fuller beginning 2¼" from ricasso; bands are 1½" heavy brass, attached to mounts that are in a "Coffin" pattern. Scabbard is leather, backstitched. Mounts are solid brass; top mount is 5-15/32" pinned, unique "squared" design throat; middle mount is 3⅜"; drag is 15-17/32" pinned. Carried by Henry A. Hatcher, 2nd Virginia Cavalry.

Boyle & Gamble operated in Richmond, VA, throughout the Civil War, located on South Sixth Street, a block from the old Virginia Armory where they produced swords of all types as well as bayonets and knives. The principals of the firm were Edwin Boyle, T. Gamble, and E. MacFee. This example is the only known example of this style of "Diamond Headed" guard. It is a unique sword that would have been special ordered by Capt. Hatcher of the 2nd Virginia Cavalry.

Provenance: *The Tharpe Collection of American Military History*

Exhibited: *The Liberty Heritage Society Museum*

Estimate: $70,000-$80,000

72231   No lot.

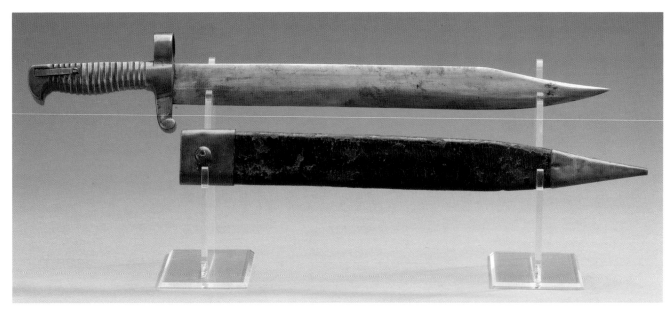

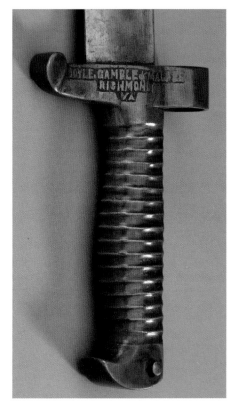

72232   A CONFEDERATE BAYONET 'BOWIE' AND SCABBARD CAPTURED AT THE BATTLE OF FAIR OAKS – ENGRAVED – This is a one-of-a-kind Boyle, Gamble and MacFee bayonet used by a Confederate soldier as a Bowie fighting knife during the Civil War, engraved by its captor and comes from the collection of noted author and collector Norm Flayderman.

Confederates preferred to use their bayonets, when they had them, as fighting knives and here we have a very rare example of just such a weapon *and* its scabbard. This blade has an even, rich patina and an intricately engraved inscription completed sometime after this blade was captured at the Battle of Fair Oaks. Everything on this bayonet Bowie is intact and authentic, even the locking mechanism for the bayonet in the grip. Boyle, Gamble and MacFee of Richmond, Virginia were the premier makers of swords and bayonets for the Confederacy. Their name is proudly stamped across the 3½" guard of this bayonet Bowie. At the top of the grip is stamped the number "52". We know that this weapon was used by a Confederate on the battlefield as it was captured at the Battle of Fair Oaks, Virginia on June 1, 1862, a battle where Confederate General Joseph E. Johnston was severely wounded. At 3" from the ricasso of the bayonet Bowie there begins an elaborate 5½" engraved inscription commemorating the battle and its capture by a fortunate Union private. In an oval shape surrounded by an intricate floral design, the following engraving appears:

Taken by R. Barret of the 15th Regt. Mass. V.M. at the Battle of Fair Oaks, Va. June 1, 1862

The 15th Massachusetts had seen much action before that June day in 1862. They fought at Ball's Bluff and at Yorktown before engaging General Johnston at Fair Oaks and Seven Pines beginning May 31st. Indeed Private Richard Barret as part of Company G of the 15th Massachusetts Infantry was there. The weapons expert collector and author Norm Flayderman had this bayonet Bowie in his collection and once wrote that he had known of "no other inscribed, similar piece. Its rarity quite speaks for itself!"

Amazingly, the leather and brass scabbard is complete and intact and accompanies this bayonet Bowie. With a 2" brass throat and frog and a 3½" drag, it is in good condition making this set not only an extreme rarity of Civil War combat, but a historically important weapon as well.

Provenance: *The Norman Flayderman Collection; The Tharpe Collection of American Military History*

Exhibited: *The Liberty Heritage Society Museum*

Estimate: $55,000-$65,000

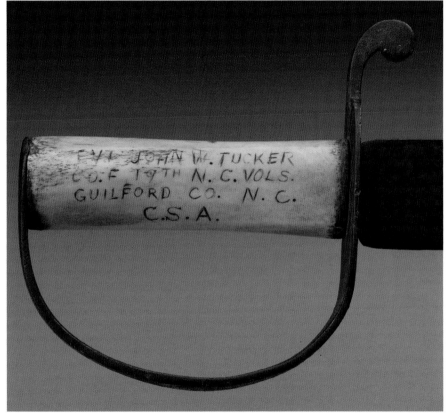

72233   MASSIVE CONFEDERATE "D" GUARD BOWIE KNIFE INSCRIBED TO PRIVATE JOHN W. TUCKER, 19TH NORTH CAROLINA.
This is a beautiful example of a massive Confederate "D" guard Bowie knife as seen in numerous images of Confederates. This wide lipped-pointed example has a blade length of 17⅝" and the overall length of the knife is 23." The guard with quillon is iron; the grip is bone that is engraved by the user in four lines, "PVT. JOHN W. TUCKER/Co. F 19th N.C. VOLS./GUILFORD CO. N.C./C.S.A." The knife is fitted in its leather sheath, stitched on the bottom, and the backside has a loop.

The 19th North Carolina fought at Fredericksburg, Brandy Station and Gettysburg.

Provenance: *The Tharpe Collection of American Military History*

Exhibited: *The Liberty Heritage Society Museum*

Estimate: $25,000-$35,000

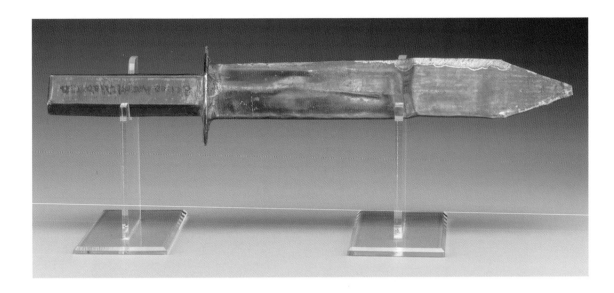

72234 **UNUSUAL TIN CONFEDERATE SIDE KNIFE 'PROTOTYPE',** 9.75" blade, 14" overall length. Sheet tin has been cut, folded and soldered to create a really eccentric hollow production. "*Selma Arsenal Alabama*" is etched onto one side of the grip, while "*Confederate States*" and a small First National flag are on the other side. The lower part of the blade is flattened as is missing its tip. The grip has a small split along one seam. Wear and extremely light rusting typical of old tin. This is believed to be the original model of the rare side knife made by the Confederacy's most productive arsenals.

Provenance: *The William Turner Collection*

Estimate: $2,000-$5,000

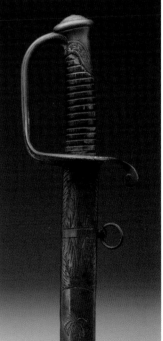

72235   AN EXTREMELY RARE PALMETTO CONFEDERATE SWORD AND SCABBARD – This 29" foot officer's sword has an unmarked blade with a 22" fuller. The blade shows much wear as this is a truly Southern utilitarian sword. It is most rare in that it was possibly made for a state militia member before the Civil War since there are no markings and due to the engravings present on the scabbard.

The grip is made of scored wood and has also seen much use as has the single knucklebow. The scrollwork guard shows a flat finish as does the single bar that extends to the pommel, all worn. The grip is slightly loose but is intact.

Perhaps the most unique aspect of this sword is its scabbard, specially engraved with the South Carolina symbol, the Palmetto tree. Starting at the throat and extending 4½" down the all-metal scabbard is an engraving of a Palmetto tree trunk with foliage. Below is a 5" central engraving of a Palmetto tree. Further down the scabbard is a 4" engraving of more foliage and a Palmetto tree trunk work between two arcs. The remainder of the scabbard is left untouched except for the last 3½" at the drag where again the same Palmetto foliage is etched. The reverse of the scabbard has been left with no artistic engraving.

At the throat on the reverse of the scabbard the initials "H. C." and "1864" have been crudely etched. The brass scabbard displays a dull and worn finish as well. A scabbard similar to this one is published in John H. Thillman's *Civil War Cavalry & Artillery Sabers* (page 63). That particular sword was made for an identified South Carolina militia officer by the Ames Manufacturing Company before the Civil War and bears similar etchings of the Palmetto foliage on the scabbard.

This is a unique and very rare example of a South Carolina soldier's scabbard from the Civil War and is highly collectable.

Estimate: $8,000-$8,500

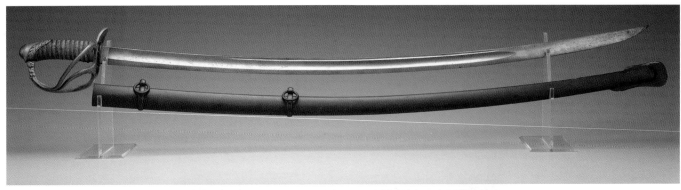

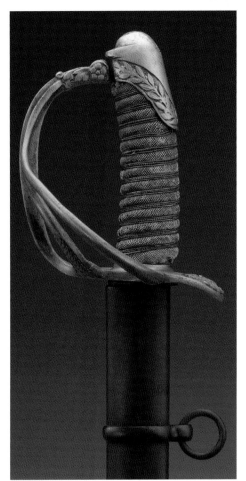

72236   THE CAPTURED SWORD OF LIEUTENANT COLONEL QUINCY MCNEIL OF THE 2ND ILLINOIS CAVALRY – Lieutenant Quincy McNeil was leading his men of the 2nd Illinois Cavalry as they occupied Holly Springs, Mississippi on December 20, 1862 when Confederate General Earl Van Dorn attacked the city, a town General Ulysses S. Grant was using as his supply headquarters.

There are many reports of the famous raid when the Confederates routed the Union troops, many who were caught in bed, comfortable in their position of occupation of the town. Mrs. Ulysses S. Grant was even staying at the home of a Confederate officer who was away at war. Learning of the attack, she left on a rail car before she could be found.

This 36" unmarked cavalry saber is stamped with a period stamp "Quincy McNeil" on the knucklebow. It is noted in accounts of the battle that Lieutenant Colonel Quincy McNeil responded quickly to the attack, unlike his superior officer Colonel Robert C. Murphy of the 8th Wisconsin who was relieved of his command after the invasion. Lieutenant Colonel McNeil formed a defensive perimeter with his six companies at the fairgrounds at Holly Springs and a fierce battle with Van Dorn's troops ensued. In what has been noted as one of the very few actual hand-to-hand sword battles of the Civil War, McNeil's' men were overwhelmed and were captured. It was then that this sword was taken by a Confederate soldier of Van Dorn's army.

The Confederates paroled their captives and proceeded to take whatever they wanted or needed from the Union store and then blew up the Union munitions with much fanfare. They equipped themselves with new Union boots, greatcoats - even cigars. While the officers broke kegs of whiskey to prevent the troops from becoming drunk, bales of cotton were burned. Trains filled with the Union supplies the Van Dorn cavalrymen couldn't take with them were burned.

This 36" blade of the sword is etched with a foliate pattern with the "U. S." device in the middle at 8" down the blade. On the reverse there is an elaborate spread-wing eagle with the "E. Pluribus Unum" ribbon in its claws. The leather washer at the ricasso appears to have been replaced.

The guard closely resembles an Ames product with foliate designs at the knucklebow where McNeil's name is stamped. The attractive grip is made of ray skin and has 12 braided wires securing it to the wood underneath which is showing slightly at the guard end. The knucklebow shows a rosette on each side where it is loose at the pommel cap.

This is a very interesting captured Union officer's saber from one of the most noted Union defeats of the Civil War.

Estimate: $4,000-$5,000

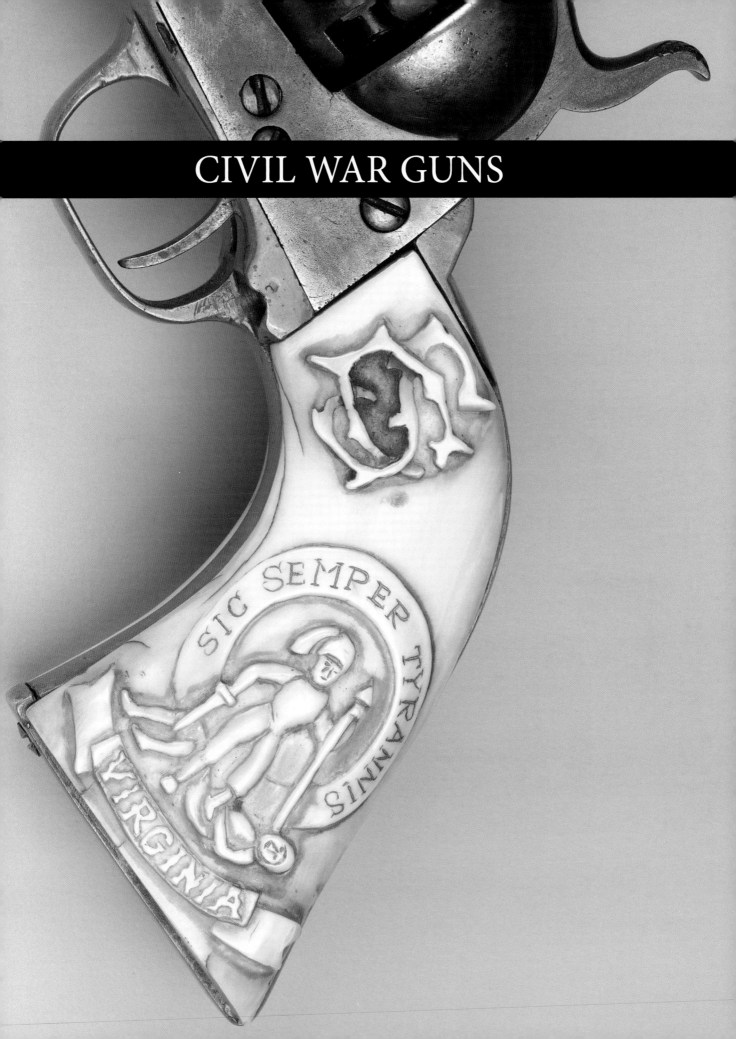

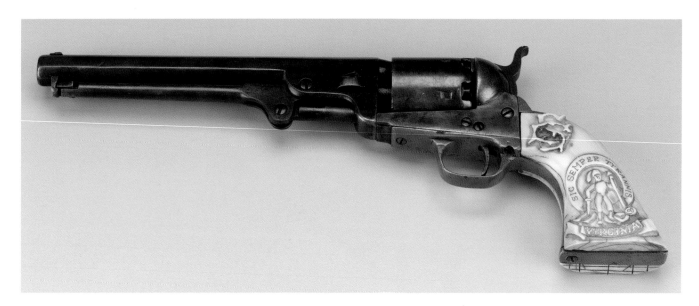

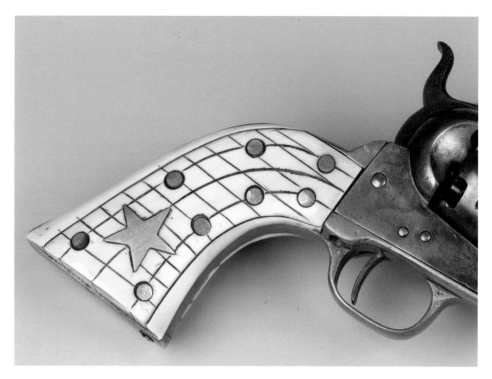

72237   A 'CONFEDERATE COLT' REVOLVER – HAND-CARVED IVORY GRIPS OF VIRGINIA STATE SEAL MARKED MITCHELL & TYLER FROM THE ALBAUGH COLLECTION – This unmarked six-shot 7" barreled .36 caliber revolver is Confederate made based on the .36 caliber Navy model of 1851. The striking detail work on the pistol grips is quite amazing, especially the hand-carved grips made into the form of the Virginia state seal done in deep bas-relief including the Virginia Latin motto "Sic Semper Tyrannis" translated to "thus always to tyrants" above the name "Virginia". An interlocking "CS" has been carved above the state seal. The grips are marked "Mitchell and Tyler" inside indicating they were crafted by the premier military outfitter of the Confederacy in Richmond, Virginia. The reverse of the grips are striking in appearance as well. An arrangement of 8 brass rivets capped by a five-pointed brass star, the ivory is beautifully carved to maximize the utility of the grip.

The revolver has a brass back strap and trigger guard with all other metal parts being iron except for the pinched front sight inset into the top barrel flat, the metal for which may be gold. The back strap and trigger guard exhibit a deep, reddish-yellow patina. This revolver was part of the world-renowned William Albaugh Collection and has been illustrated extensively. This was William Albaugh's favorite Confederate pistol.

There are two accompanying photographs of the gun in the Albaugh collection that are published in his book.

Provenance: *The Tharpe Collection of American Military History; The William Albaugh Collection*

Exhibited: *The Liberty Heritage Society Museum*

Estimate: $40,000-$60,000

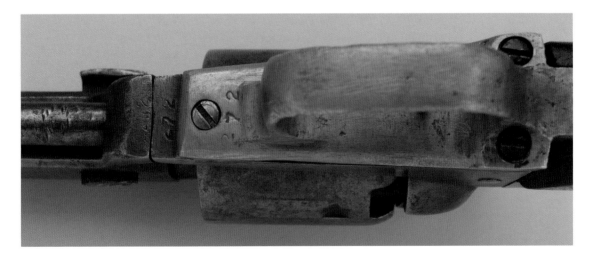

Please visit *HA.com* to view other collectibles auctions. *A 19.5% Buyer's Premium ($9 min.) Applies To All Lots*

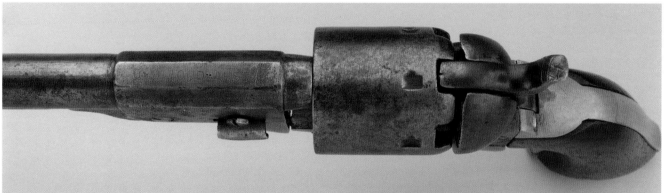

72238   THE RAREST CONFEDERATE REVOLVER EVER MADE, A TEXAS-MADE GEORGE TODD (AUSTIN, TEXAS) .36 CALIBER REVOLVER – This George Todd .36 revolver, serial numbered 272 has been referenced throughout the literature of famous Confederate weapons for over 50 years. From William Albaugh's classic text *Confederate Handguns* to Norm Flayderman's *Guide to Antique American Firearms*, this gun has a storied and spectacular reputation as an extremely rare Texas Confederate weapon.

George Todd came to Texas from Alabama in 1851 and set up his small operation on Second Street in Austin, patterning his revolvers on the .36 caliber Colt Navy model with octagon and round barrels. He stayed in Texas only a short time after the outbreak of the Civil War moving back to Alabama making only a small number of these revolvers in Texas. This six-shot revolver with six stops on an iron frame features a 7½" octagon barrel where "George Todd . Austin" is stamped on a barrel flat. The trigger guard, back strap and front strap are made of brass and at one point have been cleaned and bear some scratches. The serial number "272" appears at the loading lever flat, barrel lug, on the frame in front of the trigger guard, butt strap and trigger guard flat.

The overall condition of the revolver is good with the iron parts having an even patina with only minor pitting throughout. The grips have shrunk somewhat and an approximately 1" piece is missing on the right side near the frame.

This serial number 272 may be the highest number known (Albaugh III) placing this gun at the time of the Civil War in Texas, historically significant, making this the most rare Confederate revolver known. The gun comes with an extensive research file and provenance as well.

Estimate: $40,000-$60,000

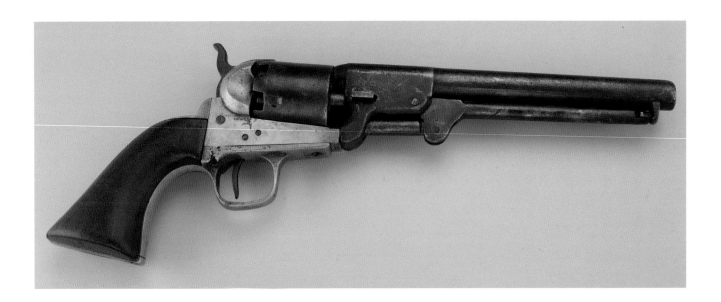

 A 19.5% Buyer's Premium ($9 min.) Applies To All Lots

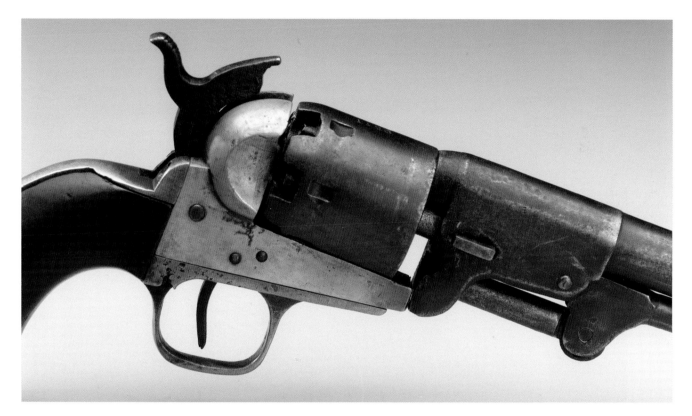

**72239   A GRISWOLD AND GUNNISON CONFEDERATE REVOLVER, PRIVATE JOHN E. MORRIS, 7TH MISSISSIPPI CAVALRY –
FORREST'S CAVALRY –** Private John A. Morris of the 7th Mississippi Cavalry carried this .36 caliber Griswold and Gunnison six-shot revolver during the Civil War until his surrender at Holly Springs, Mississippi on May 4, 1865. Originally from Tuscaloosa, Alabama, Morris joined the 7th Mississippi which was initially called the '1st Partisan Rangers' on September 1, 1862. He was farming near New Albany, Mississippi and joined for the duration of the conflict. The unit would see action in northern Mississippi and eastern Louisiana taking part in the raiding of the Mobile and Ohio Railroad, suffered losses at Tupelo and fought with General Nathan Bedford Forrest at Selma, Alabama.

This is a truly Confederate weapon in every sense. This Griswold and Gunnison, serial number 1123 was manufactured in Griswoldville, Georgia by the firm founded by Samuel Griswold and A. W. Gunnison. The uniqueness about the manufacture of this weapon is due to the fact that they were all produced by mostly slave labor since twenty-two of the twenty-four workers at the factory were slaves. Private Morris must have acquired this revolver shortly after his enlistment since this particular model was manufactured in the spring of 1863. With a 7½" rounded barrel, the revolver is accented by the attractive brass frame and trigger guard. While the major parts of the revolver have the matching serial number 1123, there is a secondary number of "13" on the underside of the loading lever. The walnut grips have somewhat shrunk but overall the revolver is in good condition.

This particular revolver, widely noted in the literature of Confederate weaponry and carried by a soldier of the South throughout the war, is rare in itself. The fact that there were only about 3,700 of these made and due to the use of slave labor in their manufacture, these Griswold and Gunnison revolvers are that much more special to collectors of Civil War weaponry.

Provenance: *The Foote Collection; The Kusrow Collection; The Tharpe Collection of American Military History*

Published: *Confederate Presentation & Inscribed Swords & Revolvers* (pp. 308-309); *Civil War Relics from Georgia; The American Society of Arms Collectors - Bulletin 71*

Estimate: $30,000-$40,000

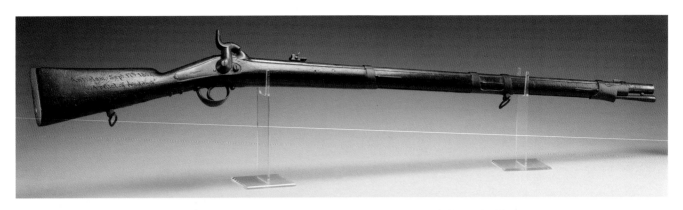

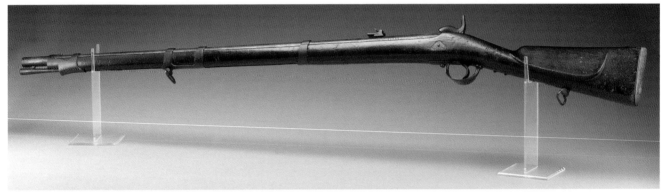

72240   CONFEDERATE MUSKET CAPTURED AT ANTIETAM. A single shot percussion muzzleloader, .58 caliber, 37" barrel, 53" overall length, four bands, adjustable rear sight, checkered hammer, "PJ MALHERBE & CIE / ALIEGE" and "JR" under crown on lockplate, serial numbered "794" in five places, "M" inspector mark on both sides of breech and another crown over "JR" on left side of the breech. Attic condition with deep, natural patina on both wooden and metal elements. This imported Belgian musket was certainly carried by a Confederate in that its walnut stock is carved with the following: "Antietam Sept. 17th 1862 A reclict (sp) of the rebellion Secured by Lieut B C Wilson 107th Reg NYV." Lieutenant Wilson of Elmira, New York enlisted in Co. "I" on August 9, 1862, only to muster out on December 21 of the same year.

Estimate: $6,500-$8,500

72241   CONFEDERATE-USED MODEL 1855 HARPERS FERRY RIFLE, .58 caliber single-shot muzzleloader, 33" barrel, 49" overall, two bands, brass nose cap, lockplate stamped with "U.S. / HARPERS FERRY" and "1860" behind hammer, left side of walnut stock carved "P H HALL 'A' 15th Va.". Light pitting on barrel, somewhat heavier near breech. Good surfaces on lockplate and overall nice patina to the wood. Harpers Ferry muskets are highly collectible given their inherent historic nature. This one, identified to a known Confederate soldier, is especially desirable. The rifle's owner was from Henrico County and enlisted on April 23, 1861. Hall would rise to become a 2nd lieutenant and did survive the war.

Estimate: $4,000-$6,000

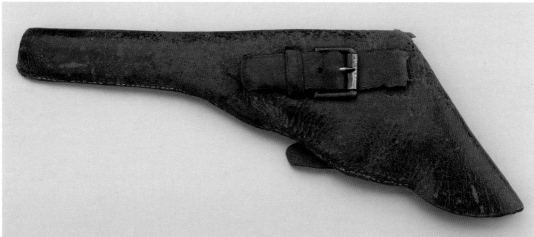

72242   A RARE CONFEDERATE HOLSTER WITH A LEAD FINIAL – This leather Confederate holster is a rarity, handmade with its lead closure finial intact. Measuring 13" from the top of the holster to the open tip, it is in well-worn condition, light brown with crackling of the leather. It has its distinctively Confederate buckle belt attachment in working condition at the back as well.

Estimate: $800-$1,000

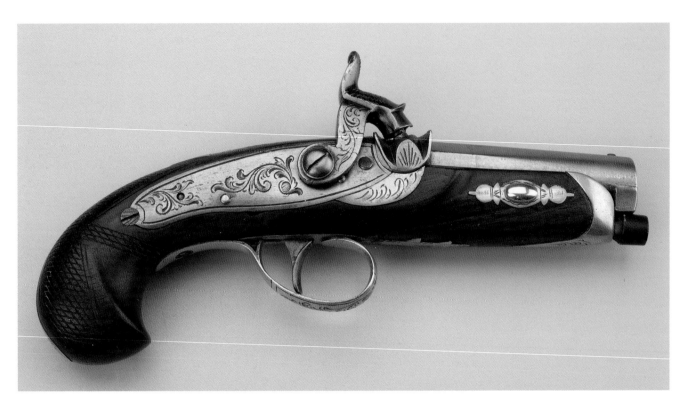

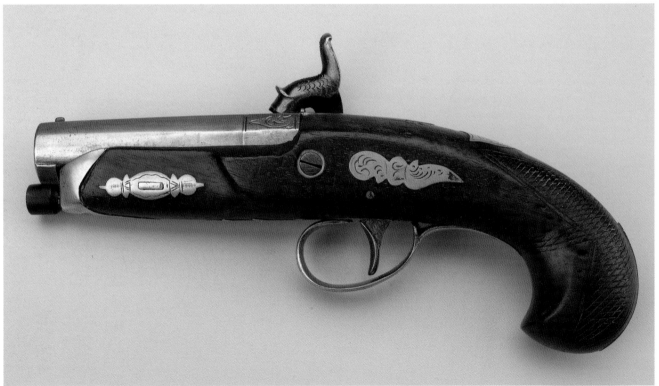

Please visit *HA.com* to view other collectibles auctions. *A 19.5% Buyer's Premium ($9 min.) Applies To All Lots*

**72243   A DERINGER OWNED BY CONFEDERATE MAJOR GENERAL JOHN B.
MAGRUDER** – This .41 caliber Deringer was owned by John Bankhead Magruder when
he was appointed a colonel in the Confederate army in 1861. Magruder had been a career
army officer, having graduated from West Point in 1830. He fought in the Seminole War
and in Mexico and was later stationed at Newport where he earned the nickname "Prince
John" for his courtly manner and lifestyle.

Magruder, a native Virginian, resigned his commission as an army captain in April 1861
and signed on with the Confederacy and was appointed a colonel. He was to be at that
rank only briefly because he became a quick hero to the Confederacy through his victory
at Big Bethel, the first major action of the war.

This Deringer muzzle-loading pistol was owned by him during that brief interval between
his commissioning as a Confederate colonel and his promotion to brigadier general for
his victory at Big Bethel. An ornately engraved .41 caliber pistol, it has a 3" barrel and has
copper-nickel or 'German silver' hardware. The hammer and trigger function perfectly
and the walnut stock is in very good condition. There is an inlaid presentation medallion on the top of the stock behind the barrel bearing the engraved inscription "Col. J. B.
Magruder". The barrel has a nice light gray, even patina and the ramrod is original to the
gun.

Attaining the rank of major general, at the end of the Civil War Magruder refused a parole
and instead traveled to Mexico where he served as a major general under Maximillian
serving in the Franco-Mexican Army. He later returned to the United States and became a
public speaker lecturing about his escapades in the wars in which he fought.

This is a very attractive and historic piece that has descended through a family whose ancestor was given the gun by an attorney at Galveston where
Magruder had his headquarters at the close of the war.

Estimate: $10,000-$12,000

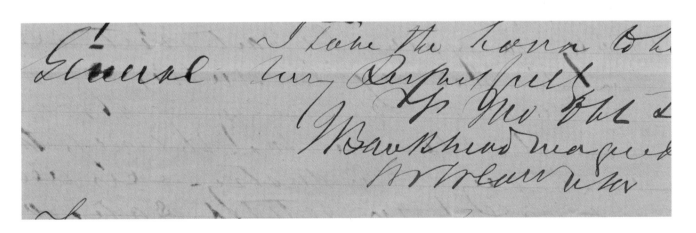

72244   **FUTURE CONFEDERATE GENERAL JOHN B. MAGRUDER AUTOGRAPH LETTER SIGNED,** "*J Bankhead Magruder*", two pages, 7.75" x 9.75", Baton Rouge, Louisiana, January 24, 1857, to Major General Thomas S. Jesup, Washington, D.C. This antebellum letter is penned on the light blue notepaper so fashionable in the 1850s. Magruder, then a Lt. Colonel, here recommends a Lt. A. R. Eddy for an appointment as Assistant Quartermaster. With a second sheet used as a cover postmarked at New Orleans and docketed upon receipt. Very fine condition. A native Virginian and career Army officer, John Bankhead Magruder commanded Confederate forces in the Southwest after a transfer initiated by General Robert E. Lee. He successfully defended Galveston against a Federal assault in 1863.

Estimate: $600-$700

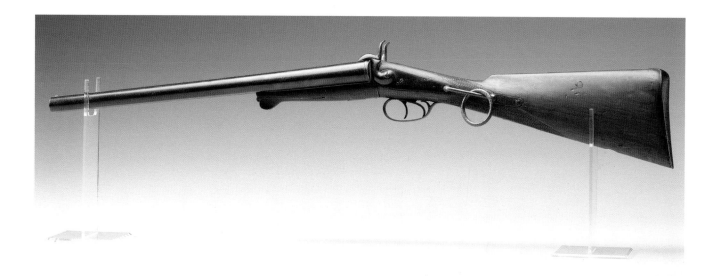

72245   A SAWED-OFF DOUBLE-BARRELED SHOTGUN WITH CAVALRY SLIDE AND RING – This double-barreled .12 gauge shotgun with the cavalry slide and ring device is the type used extensively by Confederate cavalrymen. The 18" barrel would have ensured that this weapon provided the utmost in close-range firepower for the horse soldier. Cursed by the Union troops, these shotguns were a cavalier's best friend when the fighting came at close quarters. Loaded with a variety of projectiles from rocks to nails to a simple slug, these sawed-off weapons with their double hammers and triggers are prized collectors items today and are very scarce.

Most intriguing about this shotgun is the fact that it has a small flag bearing the St. Andrews cross on the right side of the stock. With an iron butt plate, cavalry slide and ring, the shotgun shows moderate wear but is in mechanically sound condition with the lower release lever, hammers and triggers all functioning properly but showing rust pitting and wear. The barrel bears the markings "real twist" on the top indicating that the metal was made using the Damascus twist steel process, possibly in England which could indicate that the weapon ran the Union blockades to reach the Confederacy. There is resulting rust pitting at the breech and running along the gun sight channel toward the front sight which is still intact. This is a significant and attractive Civil War weapon used by gallant cavalrymen for close range fighting.

Provenance: *The Tharpe Collection of American Military History*

Exhibited: *The Liberty Heritage Society Museum*

Estimate: $2,000-$3,000

Please visit *HA.com* to view other collectibles auctions. *A 19.5% Buyer's Premium ($9 min.) Applies To All Lots*

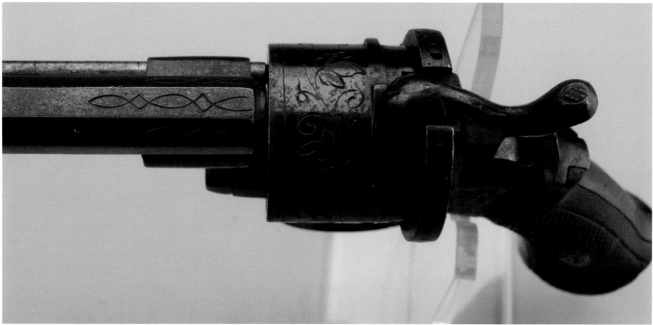

72246   A LE FLEUR CONFEDERATE REVOLVER – This French-made Le Fleur six-shot revolver is highly engraved and in excellent functional condition with the gun cocking and the ejection rod working as well. Very similar to the Lefaucheux revolver, this model is stamped "CSA" on the right side of the 5" octagonal barrel. This is a pinfire model, a mechanism that employs a pin that is at a right angle into the cartridge where the resulting hammer strike causes an internal primer to detonate. The revolver has floral engraving at the cylinder and on the side plate extending to the intact grips which have a lanyard ring.

Estimate: $2,500-$3,500

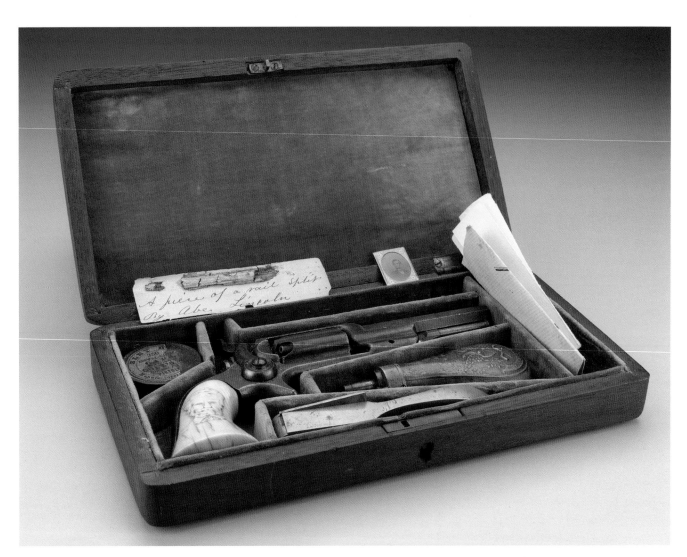

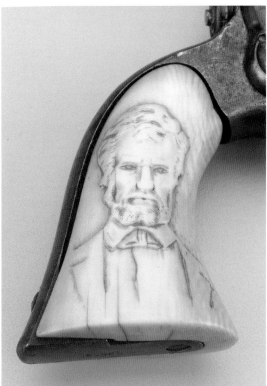

72247 A CASED 1855 COLT SIDEHAMMER REVOLVER WITH IVORY LINCOLN GRIPS – This 1855 model .28 caliber Colt sidehammer model revolver is one of the more uncommon guns found in the Civil War. It is called the 'Root' revolver from the designer Elijah Root. This gun has a 3½" barrel and bears the inscription "Colt's Pt. Address Col. Colt Hartford, Ct, USA 1855" on the top of the barrel. This five-shot model has fluted cylinders and an octagonal barrel.

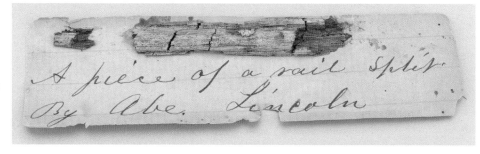

The most interesting aspect of this revolver are the carved ivory grips made into the form of a bust of Abraham Lincoln on one side and a pistol on the reverse. With the serial number 25835, the revolver is housed in a walnut case with 'Colt's Patent' bullet mold, a brass "E. Pluribus Unum" powder flask, a wooden ramrod and empty tin of Ely Brothers percussion caps.

Accompanying the gun are several objects that have been in the family of the owner of this rare gun that are quite interesting. One is a 'gem' tintype of Abraham Lincoln, a good example of the small ¾" x 1" photographs used in the 1860 Lincoln presidential campaign and thereafter as pins and mementoes.

Additional items inside the gun's case include a piece of mid 1800's lined paper with a small scrap of wood attached with the notation 'a piece of rail split by Abe Lincoln' in black ink.

This is an interesting grouping that includes a rare revolver that has been passed down through the generations with a reverent connection to President Abraham Lincoln, whose portrait is carved on the ivory grips.

Estimate: $3,000-$5,000

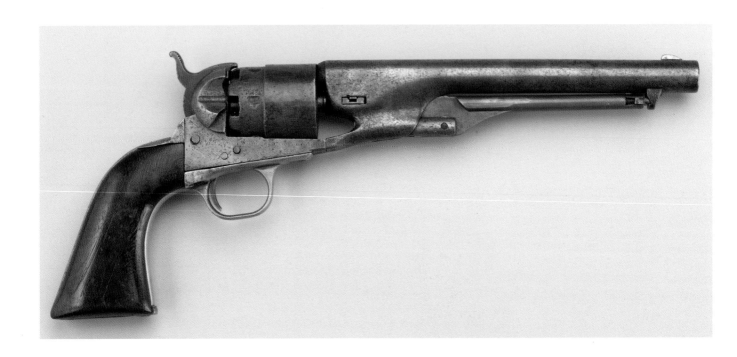

Please visit _HA.com_ to view other collectibles auctions.   _A 19.5% Buyer's Premium ($9 min.) Applies To All Lots_

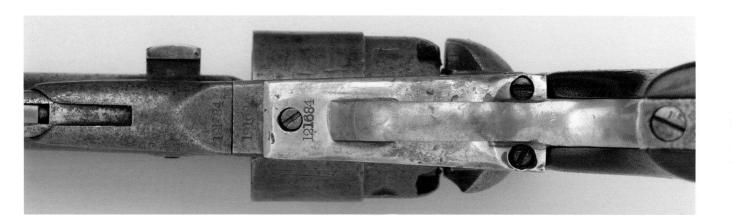

72248 A COLT MODEL 1860 REVOLVER OWNED BY CONGRESSIONAL MEDAL OF HONOR RECIPIENT LIEUTENANT ORSON W. BENNETT – This Colt Model 1860 .44 caliber revolver was owned by Lieutenant Orson W. Bennett of the 102nd US Colored Troops who was awarded the Congressional Medal of Honor for his bravery at Honey Hill, South Carolina on November 30, 1864. Lieutenant Bennett was ordered to capture three Confederate artillery pieces that had been abandoned but were being protected by enemy fire. He chose thirty men and accomplished his mission with only one man wounded.

Bennett was born in Union City, Michigan on November 17, 1841 and enlisted as a private in the 1st Iowa Volunteers at the start of the war and fought until he was wounded at the Battle of Wilson's Creek. After returning home to recuperate, he re-enlisted in the 12th Wisconsin Infantry and later joined the 102nd US Colored troops as a lieutenant. He fought in 17 engagements during the war and was mustered out as a Brevet Major of US Volunteers.

This Colt revolver owned by Bennett has an 8" barrel and brass trigger guard. The walnut grips are in good condition as is the revolver's dark gray patina. The gun bears the serial number "121684". Engraved on the backstrap is the following:

Lt. O. W. Bennett, 102 Regt. U.S.C.T.

This is an important piece of Civil War history carried by a Union soldier who was awarded the Congressional Medal of Honor for his bravery. The revolver comes with a binder of information about Bennett including his muster rolls, a biography and copies of his invalid pension application.

Estimate: $5,000-$6,000

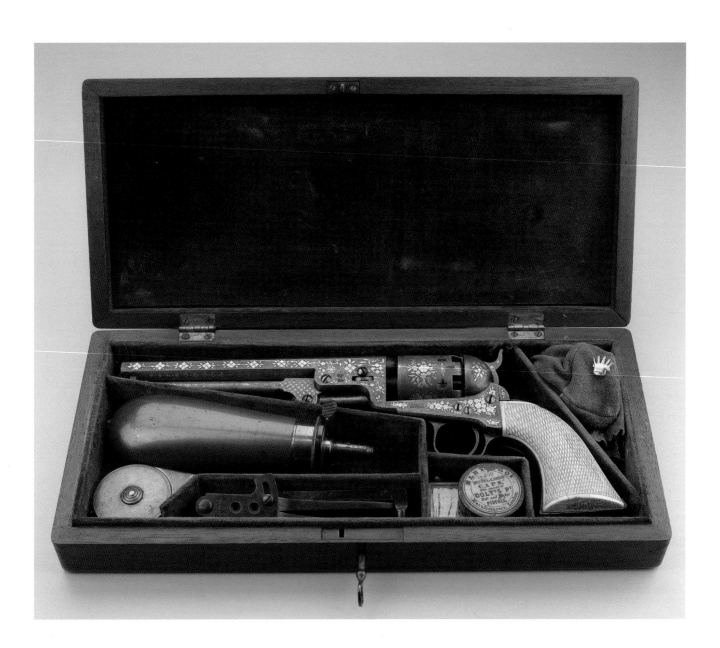

72249   A 24 KARAT GOLD DECORATED COLT MODEL 1851 LONDON NAVY REVOLVER – This exceptionally rare 24 karat gold decorated Colt London Navy revolver bears matching serial numbers of "37061" indicating it was manufactured at Samuel Colt's London, England factory around 1857. Obviously a very special order due to its elaborate use of 24 gold leaf in a decorative floral motif, this .36 caliber six-shot percussion revolver with an octagonal barrel includes intricately carved ivory grips that accentuate the gun's beauty.

Attesting to the overseas fame of his revolvers, the address on the top of the 7½" barrel is simply 'Address. Col. Colt London'. Colonel Colt aggressively marketed his revolvers in England and Colt maintained an agency there until 1904. With complete and matching serial numbers, this weapon bears the appropriate English hallmarks as well. Many such weapons made their way through the Union blockades during the Civil War. This particular revolver with magnificent gold accents would have been made for a very special customer.

The original mahogany case with its original key still contains the accessories for the pistol. Included are a James Dixon and Sons powder horn manufactured at Sheffield, England, a bullet mold, cap puller and percussion cap tool. Additionally, there is a tin of Eley Brothers percussion caps and a box of 'combustible envelope cartridges' for Colt pistols included in the green velvet-lined case which still locks with the original key. A handmade, checkered brown and white heavy wool cloth outer case equipped with a fastening button has kept the case in very good condition for many years. The revolver is in overall very good condition with scattered very light pitting to the metal behind the trigger guard. The craftsman that applied the gold leaf made good use of every surface on the revolver, even the backstrap. The gold has almost completely survived the years and this is an excellent presentation London Colt in its original case, perhaps one of a kind.

Estimate: $20,000-$30,000

Please visit <u>HA.com</u> to view other collectibles auctions. *A 19.5% Buyer's Premium ($9 min.) Applies To All Lots*

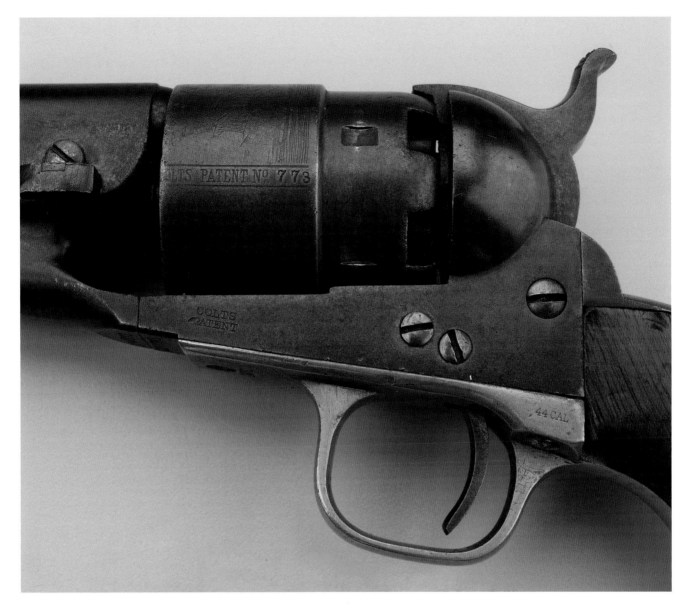

72250　COLT ARMY MODEL 1860 REVOLVER (CASED) – This army model 1860 revolver is cased with an iron bullet mold, brass powder flask, empty tin for percussion caps, assorted conical projectiles, gun tool, key and the wood case. The .44-caliber revolver, serial number "184773", features an 8" round barrel, 6-shot cylinder, loading lever and plunger, and back strap, all made of iron. The trigger guard, front strap and blade front sight are brass. Cylinder is marked "Colt's Patent No. 773" on circumference. The cylinder scene is present and in moderate strength. The serial number appears on the barrel lug, frame in front of trigger guard, trigger guard flat and butt strap. Wedge is unmarked. "Colt's Patent" on left side of frame in 2 lines. ".44 cal" on left side trigger guard near frame. Top of barrel is marked "Address Col. Sam'l Colt, New York, U. S. America."

Wood grip is strong with only minor dings and retains 90% of original varnish.

The 6¼" brass powder flask has a few minor dents but is otherwise undamaged. Neck is marked with a "d", "drame" and "1, 1⅛, 1¼". Top of flask marked "Sykes Patent".

The 2 cavity, iron bullet mold is made for casting both round balls and conical projectiles. Spur cutter is present and marked "Colt's Patent." An L- shaped gun tool (iron) and brass key are present. "Eley Bros." percussion cap tin is present but empty. Label intact. There are indecipherable letters scratched on bottom of tin.

Blue felt lined, wood case measures 15¼" x 7" x 1⅞" and is not cracked but does have minor scratches as would be expected. There is a circular, decorative disc on the lid and the undamaged Colt's 'loading and cleaning' label on the inside of the lid.

Condition: Revolver: very good. Iron parts exhibit an even, dark patina with the only dings near the wedge channel, right side. Original finish remains in evidence on the loading lever. Mechanically sound and strong. Brass parts have sharp edges and an even, mellow patina.
Brass powder flask: Very good. Dark patina on body and lighter on neck and top.
Bullet mold: very good. Mechanically sound. Minor pitting.
Key: Very good. Some wear.
Gun tool: Very good. Evidence of original finish.
Tin: good

Estimate: $10,000-$15,000

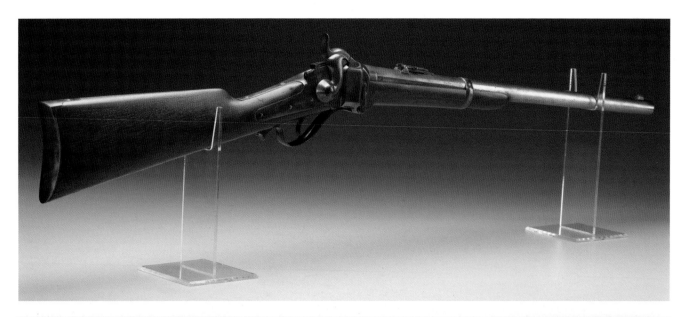

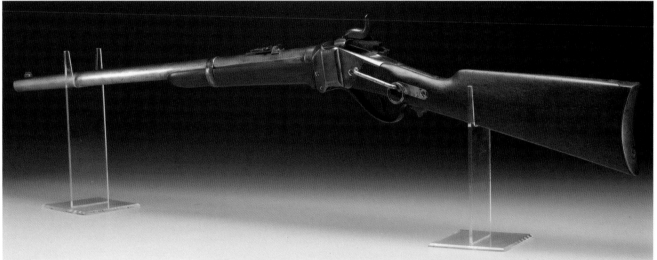

72251   A SHARPS 1863 NEW MODEL .54 CALIBER RIFLE – The most popular carbine of the Civil War was the Sharps, this single shot .54 caliber percussion breech-loader being manufactured in Hartford, Connecticut. It was this type of weapon that fired the first shot at the Battle of Gettysburg.

This Sharps New Model, serial number "C,10509", with a 22" barrel bears numerous Sharps patent marks; "New Model 1863" on the top of the barrel, "R. S. Lawrence Patented February 15, 1859" on the rear sight, as well as the earlier Sharps patent marks appropriate to the rifle. The bore is very clean with the rifling intact and the wood of the stock and the forearm in very good condition with only slight dings. The

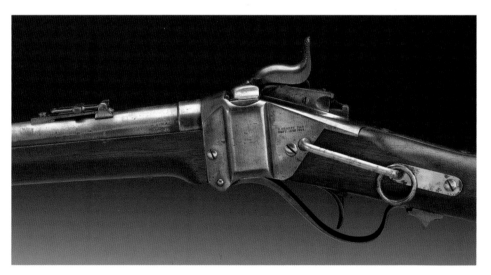

action is in excellent working condition making this an excellent example of a Civil War Sharps. The rifle bears the inspector's marks of "E. A. W." on the barrel which shows good wear down to a light gray patina with some vise marks at the rear. The sling ring bar and ring show considerable wear as well.

This is an excellent example of a Civil War issue Sharps that was prevalent during the war.

Estimate: $4,000-$5,000

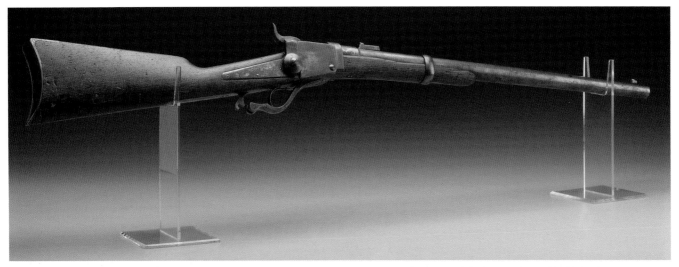

72252   A RARE STARR ARMS CARBINE FROM THE CIVIL WAR AND THE WEST; CAPTAIN JAMES HENRY TEMPEST – The Starr carbines were made in a limited supply for the Union Army by Eben T. Starr of Yonkers, New York. In .54 caliber, these cavalry carbines were re-issued for use in the Indian Wars following the Civil War. Captain James Henry Tempest, an Army captain who fought in the Indian War campaigns throughout Utah, Wyoming and Idaho took this rifle home with him where it has descended through his family to us today. The story of his service is made more remarkable due to his family relationship to a noted figure in Civil War history.

Captain Tempest's daughter married Lewis Norman Ellsworth, the nephew of Colonel Elmer Ellsworth, the first Union officer killed in the Civil War. Colonel Ellsworth was shot by an innkeeper as he hauled down a Confederate flag still flying over a hotel in Alexandria, Virginia at the very start of the war. This rifle was passed down through Lewis Norman Ellsworth's family to his grandson Colonel Steve Ellsworth who has made it available for this sale.

While rare in itself, the story of the association with Colonel Ellsworth of Civil War fame makes this percussion breech-loading .54 caliber carbine even more attractive. At 37" in length it was the perfect saddle gun equipped with a saddle ring, metal butt plate and locking lever at the trigger guard. Considering its record of usage, this gun is in very good condition with the lever action working perfectly. The wood stock and forearm, again while showing wear, have no chips missing and have scratches and wear appropriate for the use in the Civil War and Indian Wars. Serial numbered "33362", the maker's name appears at the breech as follows: "Starr's Patent, Sept. 14th 1858".

This carbine has a great history and is a rare find. It functions perfectly and was fired by the current owner's grandfather for many years as he told the story of his famous relative during the Civil War and his direct descendant from the Indian Wars. It will make a great addition to a Civil War/Indian War collection.

Provenance: *The Ellsworth Family Collection*

Estimate: $3,000-$4,000

72253   BEAUTIFUL MINTY SMITH CARBINE, .50 caliber, single shot percussion breechloader, 20.25" barrel, 39" overall length, walnut stock, iron mountings, sling ring mounted to left of breech, serial "#536" twice on underside at either side of hinge, inspector's initials "LFR" stamped on left side of barrel in front of breech, inspectors' cartouches reading "LFR" and "IIC" stamped into stock on left side behind breech, "ADDRESS POULTNEY & TRIMBLE BALTIMORE U.S.A, MANUFACTURED BY / AM'N. MACH'N. WKS. / SPRINGFIELD MASS. and SMITH'S PATENT / JUNE 23, 1857" all stamped on left side of breech. Never fired, with original blued finish. Magnificent!

Estimate: $12,000-$15,000

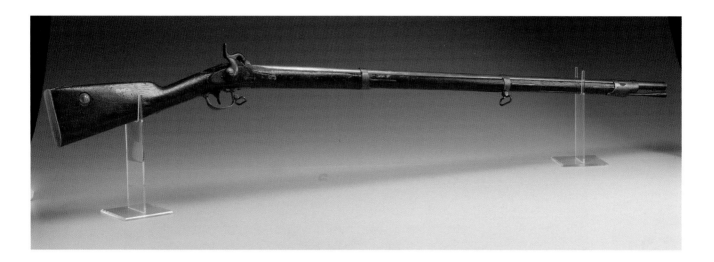

72254   RARE MODEL 1841 SPRINGFIELD ARMORY CADET MUSKET, .57 caliber percussion muzzleloader, 40" barrel, 54" overall length, walnut stock with three barrel bands, iron mountings, bayonet lug on barrel's underside at muzzle, "VP" marking on barrel at breech, "1844" on tang, "SPRING/FIELD 1844" behind hammer on lockplate. With trumpet-shaped ramrod. Cast brass Confederate "Block I" button applied to right side of stock. Small areas of old chipping around lockplate, glossy natural sheen to wood, iron elements have light pitting, some finish remaining to trigger guard and barrel. Very good condition. According to Flayderman, only 450 of these diminutive rifles were produced between 1844 and 1845. This example surely saw Confederate usage in that the US and eagle stampings have been removed from the lockplate. The button might or might not have been a war-time addition.

Estimate: $2,000-$3,000

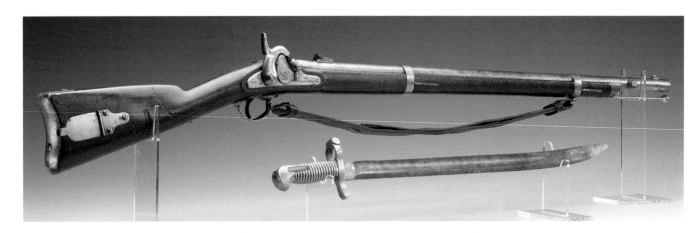

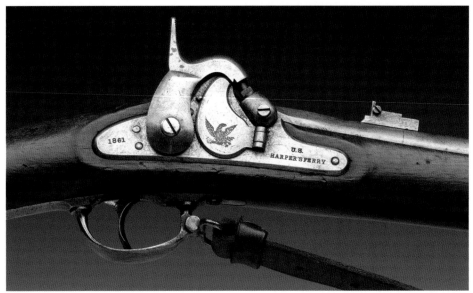

72255   MODEL 1855 HARPERS FERRY MUSKET WITH BAYONET, .58 caliber, single shot percussion muzzleloader, 33" barrel, 49" overall length, two barrel bands, side lug for bayonet, walnut stock, hinged patchbox, "VP" inspector's mark on left side of breech, "U.S / HARPERS FERRY" and American eagle on lockplate, dated "1861" behind hammer and on top of barrel at breech. Complete with supple leather sling and original brass-gripped saber bayonet having an overall length of 26.5". A superb example of this historic firearm with original surfaces free of the pitting so often associated with Civil War longarms. This musket was made on the eve of the Civil War and likely saw Confederate usage.

Provenance: *The Tharpe Collection of American Military History*

Exhibited: *The Liberty Heritage Society Museum*

Estimate: $8,000-$10,000

72256 **COLT ARMY MODEL 1860 REVOLVER** – This 44-caliber revolver, serial number "74492", features an 8" round barrel, 6-shot cylinder loading lever and plunger, and back strap, all made of iron. The trigger guard, front strap, and blade front sight are brass. The Serial Number appears on the barrel lug (finish) and bottom of the wedge. Cylinder is marked " Colt's Patent No. 3117" over "Pat. Sept 10th 1850" on "Colt New York U.S. America". Grip exhibits few dings and scratches and the inspector's cartouche is visible but not legible. There is an "H" stamped in the brass behind the trigger guard. This revolver is housed in a standard military issue leather holster with plugged end. Stitching is tight tooling on flap. Leather closer tab present but repaired. Brass finish mechanically sound.

Condition: Good. Iron parts have a generally even patina with minor pitting. Traces of blemish remain on frame and loading lever. Same holster wear on muzzle. Grips show modest wear. Holster shows surface cracking throughout.

Estimate: $1,000-$1,500

72257   A REMINGTON NEW MODEL 1858 PATENT .44 REVOLVER − The Remington Model 1858 .44 caliber six-shot revolver was the major competitor to the Colt Model 1860 Army during the Civil War. This is a fine example of the Remington and bears a serial number of "98455" stamped under the 8" octagonal barrel. The walnut grips are in good condition and the gun has an overall dark gray patina and a nice contrasting brass trigger guard. The top of the barrel is stamped "Patented Sept. 14, 1858 E. Remington & Sons, Ilion, New York, U.S.A. New Model". This revolver comes with a light brown leather period holster with a brass finial. It has a 3" belt loop at the rear and a flap cover that is missing approximately 3" of the leather at the top and is open at the end.

This was the last percussion model Remington made in .44 caliber and was used extensively during the Civil War. Along with the holster it makes an excellent presentation piece.

Estimate: $6,000-$7,000

72258   A RARE CASED MORTON PINFIRE REVOLVER – This Irish made Morton revolver is cased in a beautiful mahogany case which includes the cleaning rod and tools, complete in the blue felt-lined compartments. The pinfire revolvers originated in France and incorporated a design where the hammer strikes the cartridge at a right angle causing a charge to detonate and fire the round. W. Morton and Son were makers of fine firearms and were located at 2 Ellen Street in Limerick, Ireland. This double-action six-shot revolver retains 80% of its bluing and has a nickel hammer and trigger which folds up toward the barrel. The front sight is missing. However, this revolver is an attractive display piece.

Estimate: $3,000-$4,000

72259 A REMINGTON REVOLVING PERCUSSION RIFLE − This Remington revolving percussion rifle in .36 caliber has a 29½" octagon barrel and dates from about 1865. Produced by D. T. Seeley of Delhi, New York as stamped on the top of the barrel, the attractive stock is made of walnut. Seeley produced weapons from about 1864 to 1874. The trigger guard is of German silver and the gun has an elevated rear sight. The metal of the gun has a dark brown patina with some denting on the barrel. The stock is loose at its connection to the gun but the action functions properly. This is a very rare and attractive piece that dates from the end of the Civil War.

Estimate: $4,000-$5,000

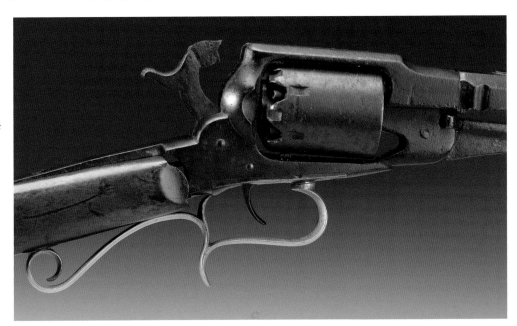

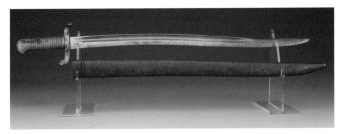

72260 A BAYONET FOR A COLT REVOLVING RIFLE − This bayonet manufactured by the S&K Company for the Colt revolving rifle has a 22¼" blade and 4¼" brass grip. It is rare to find a bayonet that fits the Colt revolving rifle and this one is in fair to good condition. The metal scabbard shows considerable wear with some rusting and a 4" crack on the bottom near the tip.

Estimate: $300-$500

72261 A NELSON LEWIS CIVIL WAR SHARPSHOOTER RIFLE FITTED WITH A WILLIAM MALCOLM TELESCOPIC SIGHT

– Nelson Lewis of Troy, New York began manufacturing target rifles in his shop in 1843 at the corner of Congress and Church Streets. By the time of the Civil War he was adept at the production of super-accurate weapons such as this one fitted with a William Malcolm telescopic sight.

Made famous by the Winslow Homer drawing he completed in 1862 for Harper's Weekly, this type of sniper's rifle was used for distant, impersonal killing that the new rifled technology had brought to the battlefield. This image so moved Homer that he made it the subject of his first oil painting since he had looked through the telescopic sight of one these rifles and remarked, "…the impression struck me as being as near murder as anything I could think of in connection with the army and I always had the horror of that branch (sharpshooters) of the service". A copy of this lithograph which appeared in the November 15, 1862 edition of Harper's Weekly accompanies this rifle.

Nelson Lewis purchased his very heavy octagonal target barrels from E. Remington and Son and he rifled them himself to perfection using equal width of grooves and lands. The end of the barrel is fitted for a false muzzle giving an extra edge to the sharpshooter in accuracy. The 27½" barrel of this rifle is marked "N. Lewis, Maker, Troy, New York" on the top under the telescopic sight which extends a full 5" toward the stock. Lewis' son Kilby produced the Monte Carlo walnut stock terminated by an elaborate nickel-plated buttplate. The hammer, and double set triggers set within the elaborate scrollwork trigger guard function perfectly.

Adding value and historical importance to the rifle is the William Malcolm 32" telescopic sight affixed to the top of the Lewis barrel. Malcolm, who had worked for a telescope manufacturer began production of his achromatic lenses and rifle telescopes in 1855 at Syracuse, New York. His optics were in standard use during the Civil War by sharpshooter units as evidenced in the Winslow Homer picture. Adjustable for windage and elevation through use of metal wheels and screws, when combined with the accuracy of the Lewis rifle, they became a deadly combination. This is a rare surviving example of the Civil War sharpshooter's weapon.

Provenance: *The Tharpe Collection of American Military History*

Exhibited: *The Liberty Heritage Society Museum*

Estimate: $10,000-$15,000

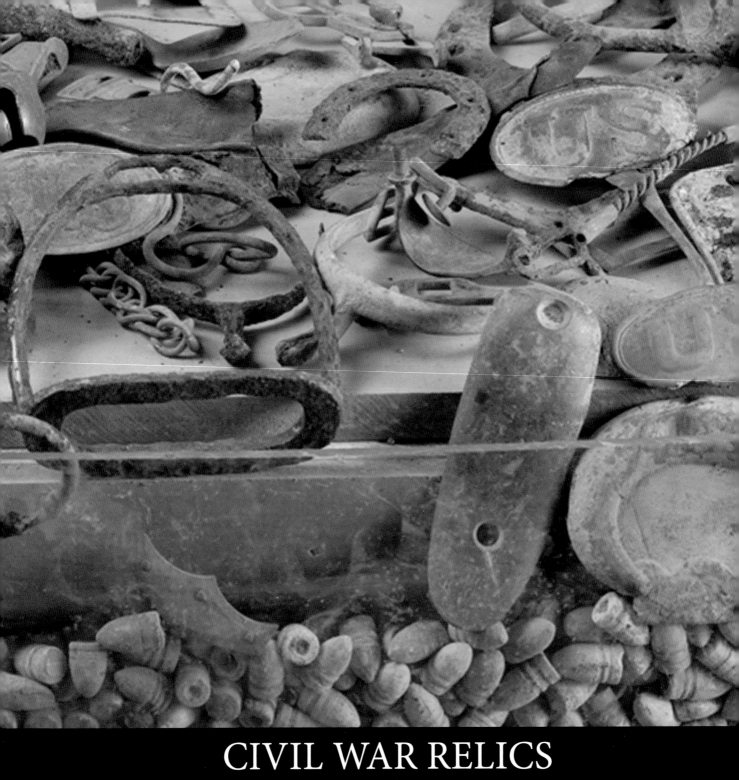

CIVIL WAR RELICS

72262   HUGE COLLECTION OF DUG CIVIL WAR RELICS FROM NORTHERN VIRGINIA − A 20" x 21 x 11" Plexiglas display case contains a hoard of over a thousand relics just as found. Nothing has been cleaned, treated or sorted. The grouping's hundreds of dropped bullets contain a good mix of Yankee three-ringers, Confederate Gardners and assorted carbine rounds. (A quick glance showed a nice Washington Arsenal star-base minie ball.) Brass items include a few US oval plates, eagle plates, civilian buckles, bayonet scabbard tips, artillery fuses, two butt plates, spurs, a set of Union Army shoulder scales, knapsack hooks, rivets and the like. Iron relics are dominated by a broken musket barrel having its hammer and lockplate. There are also gun parts, gun tools, a watering bit and horseshoes. A splendid array of once common items that are becoming increasingly scarce.

Provenance: *The Tharpe Collection of American Military History*

Exhibited: *The Liberty Heritage Society Museum*

Estimate: $6,000-$8,000

72263   THE DOOR HANDLE FROM LIBBY PRISON, RICHMOND, VIRGINIA – 5.25" x 19.5". This large section of a black pine door retains its handle, two keyhole covers, a bar fitting, a latch and a lock. These metallic elements are all iron save for one of the keyhole covers, which is of brass and filled in. This item is identified by a crude carving on its face, which reads: *"Libby Pris. Vir."*. All iron has a deep patina with only the lightest rusting. The paint is crazed and chipped throughout.

Libby Prison was the unwelcome destination for many of the US Army officers captured in Virginia. Built as a Richmond dockside warehouse, the building was appropriated by the Confederate government in order to help accommodate the huge influx of captured Yankees into the city. Overcrowding and privation accelerated as the war progressed, with Libby achieving great notoriety in the Northern press. On February 10, 1864 over one hundred prisoners escaped with 59 reaching Union lines. This morale-boosting event was rightly celebrated by a war-weary public and even dramatized for television a century later. The Libby building itself was dismantled in 1889 and re-built in Chicago to house a Civil Museum that remained open for the rest of the century. The museum, too, is now long gone with only a handful of Libby relics surviving into the present time, especially with this being the front door to the prison.

Provenance: *The Tharpe Collection of American Military History*

Estimate: $6,000-$8,000

72264   SCARCE NORTH CAROLINA "WALLPAPER" EDITION OF A GENERAL ORDER. One page, 5" x 20", Richmond, Virginia, February 21, 1865. This is the printed portion of General Orders Number 6, being the proclamation of Governor Vance to the citizens of North Carolina, printed in one column from the *Richmond Enquirer*. Before and during the Civil War, the South was almost entirely dependent on the North for its paper supply. As a result of Northern blockades, editors in the South were occasionally forced to use wallpaper to print their editions. Contrary to common belief, the wallpaper was not ripped off the walls of loyal Confederate plantation owners' homes. Instead, new rolls of wallpaper were used. Virtually all such known "wallpaper editions" were printed in Louisiana, making this Virginia printing quite unusual. The document is fine, with general wear present as well as a few small holes, not affecting the overall appearance. A number of folds are present, with some wear at the folds, mostly on the edges. A fascinating and scarce version of Civil War printing history.

Estimate: $1,000-$1,500

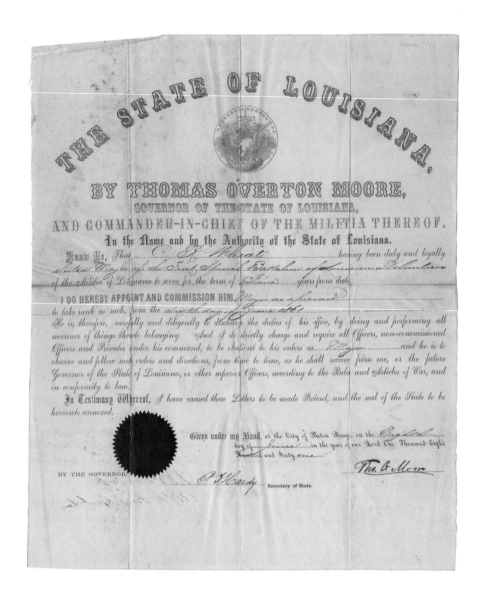

72265 BLOODSTAINED COMMISSION OF CONFEDERATE MAJOR BOB WHEAT OF THE 'LOUISIANA TIGERS' – FOUND ON GAINES' MILL BATTLEFIELD – Partially printed Document Signed "*Tho. O. Moore*", Governor of Louisiana, 13" x 16", Baton Rouge, Louisiana, June 8, 1861. This State of Louisiana commission names C. R. Wheat *"Major of the First Special Battalion of Louisiana Volunteers"*. It carries a vignette of the Louisiana State Seal and is affixed with a secondary red paper seal in the lower left corner. Folds, aging and old separation archivally repaired. Two verso panels appear to be smeared with mud, blood, or both. This document was found on the battlefield where Wheat received his mortal wound. It is conceivable that this document, being on his person, was tossed as the dying major was attended to.

Chatham Roberdeau 'Bob' Wheat was born in Virginia, practiced law in Louisiana, and served in the Louisiana legislature before being commissioned a Major at the outbreak of the Civil War. Wheat was known as an adventurer having traveled around the world as a military officer, first in Latin America and then in Italy serving under Garibaldi. He returned to the South to recruit the Louisiana battalion made up of rough-neck New Orleans men.

The unit saw action at Manassas where Wheat was shot through both lungs. Obviously a serious wound, Wheat struggled to recover and fought in the Shenandoah Valley campaign. He was killed at the Battle of Gaines' Mill, his unit disbanded thereafter since they had lost the only leader that could control their rough behavior.

Perhaps the best characterization of Wheat came from the August 1912 issue of *Confederate Veteran* as the magazine described the great men each state had contributed to the Confederacy. Wheat was included as follows:

"Louisiana gave the incomparable Bob Wheat, the white-plumed Knight of Navarre of the Army of Virginia, who fell at the Battle of Gaines' Mill while bravely cheering on his "Louisiana Tigers", waving aloft the sword presented to him by his State and clasping to his bosom the Bible given him by his Christian mother."

A handwritten sleeve in which this commission was found has the inscription *"Gen Robert Wheat Commission found on the battlefield of Antietam (later struck through and corrected 'Gaines' Mill') where he was killed."*

Estimate: $6,000-$8,000

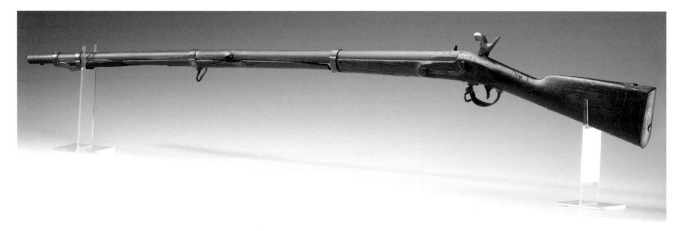

72266   THE ULTIMATE CIVIL WAR RELIC: PERCUSSION CONVERSION MUSKET STRUCK BY THREE BULLETS. A true battlefield pick-up, this contract .69 caliber Model 1816 musket was slammed on its right side at or near the barrel three times. The first hit has gouged the wood and dented the barrel above the middle band; the second bullet has gone clear through the barrel between the first and second bands; the final shot has bent the barrel band nearest the breech and has shattered the adjacent wood. The nature of these "wounds" indicate an ambush or flank attack. The original owner of this weapon must have surely fallen. The musket, converted from flintlock to percussion, has a 41" barrel and is 56" overall. The lockplate is stamped with an American eagle above "L. POMEROY" and has "1841 U.S." behind the hammer. A condition report is really only a formality in a case such as this, but the weapon has the usual light pitting and patina of an attic find.

Provenance: *The Tharpe Collection of American Military History*

Exhibited: *The Liberty Heritage Society Museum*

Estimate: $4,000-$6,000

72267   A CHIMBORAZO HOSPITAL CHEST FROM THE FAMOUS CONFEDERATE HOSPITAL AT RICHMOND – PUBLISHED IN WILLIAM ALBAUGH'S BOOK – This hospital chest manufactured by Samuel Sutherland's Gun and Pistol Emporium of Richmond, Virginia was used at the famous Chimborazo Confederate Hospital in Richmond, Virginia. Owned by Confederate Surgeon Captain W. H. Pugh of Division One, the mahogany chest has been published in noted historian William Albaugh's book and comes from his personal collection.

The Chimborazo Hospital was built in 1861 to start handling the casualties from the first Battle of Manassas. Now the site of the National Park Service building, the location was chosen on a high hill in Richmond near the James River. Supposedly named for a volcano in South America, Chimborazo had plenty of fresh water from nearby springs and was easily supplied through the use of the Kanawha Canal. Covering 40 acres, and handling almost 80,000 patients during the course of the war, the hospital was divided into five divisions within 120 buildings, making it one of the largest hospitals ever constructed by the Confederacy.

According to National Archives records Confederate Surgeon W. H. Pugh of Norfolk, Virginia was assigned to Division One as the assistant to Surgeon-in-Charge P. F. Browne. Conditions were harsh in the hospital as the number of wounded grew throughout the war and supplies became scarce. Chief Surgeon Dr. James McGraw, a brilliant manager did all he could to provide for the wounded but his surgeons such as Captain W. H. Pugh were inundated by the numbers of men resulting in a 20% death rate, actually quite good for a wartime hospital in the mid 19th century.

This mahogany box still bears the Samuel Sutherland's maker's label inside the top lid of the box. Originally a gun maker and gun supply business located at 132 Main Street in Richmond, Sutherland was an ardent Southerner and supporter of the Confederacy. The wording on the label states in part:

> Prices to suit all customers and a guarantee that Sutherland Mark rifles will kill a Yankee or Abolitionist at one hundred yards!

With two removable drawers inside and one bottom drawer, the chest retains its original hardware including two handles, the bottom drawer pull and original hinges. Stenciled on the front of the chest is "Capt. W. H. Pugh Asst. Surgeon" in block letters. On the top of the chest is stenciled "Chimborazo Hospital Division No. 1". This hospital chest is from the famous William Albaugh Collection and was published in his book, making this a rare and authenticated treasure from the famous Confederate hospital in Richmond.

Provenance: *The William Turner Collection*

Estimate: $8,000-$12,000

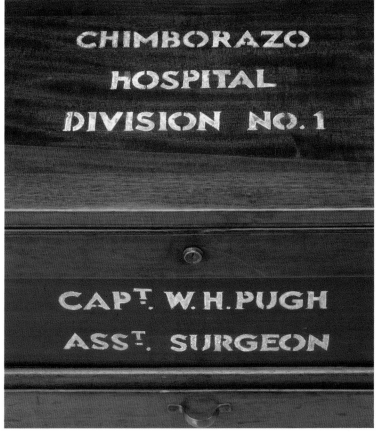

72268   CONFEDERATE MAJOR GENERAL JOHN AUSTIN WHARTON ARCHIVE – TERRY'S TEXAS RANGERS – Major General John Austin Wharton led Terry's Texas Rangers, the famed Confederate Cavalry regiment after the deaths of the regiment's former leaders, Colonel Benjamin F. Terry and Lieutenant Colonel Thomas S. Lubbock. Born in Nashville, Tennessee in 1828, Wharton moved to Texas at an early age and grew up on a plantation at Brazoria, Texas. From 1846 to 1850 he attended South Carolina College, now the University of South Carolina where he was commander of the student cadet corps. He returned to Texas and studied law under United States Senator William Preston and practiced law with Clint Terry, Benjamin F. Terry's brother at Brazoria. At the outbreak of the Civil War he owned 135 slaves in Brazoria County.

This ambrotype of Wharton was taken early in the war and is the only one of him at this age known to exist. Hand-tinted in its copper frame and ½ of its original leather case, there is some fading at the face, but this is undoubtedly General Wharton early in the war. On June 23, 1861 Wharton traveled to Richmond, Virginia and met with Confederate President Jefferson Davis and James Longstreet seeking permission to organize a company of Texas cavalry. Reportedly, Davis did not give his permission and Wharton returned to Texas. He passed through New Orleans and it is believed that this is where this ambrotype was taken as the backdrop is typical of the photographs from that era and place. Leaving New Orleans on a ship named the Shark bound for Texas, Wharton was captured by Union troops aboard the *USS South Carolina*. He was permitted to travel on to Texas by Union Commander James Alden and undoubtedly saved this ambrotype through the capture.

Back in Texas, Wharton was elected captain of the Terry's Ranger unit, formally known as the Eighth Texas Cavalry. After the Battle of Shiloh where he was wounded, he was promoted to Brigadier General. His bravery at the Battle of Chickamauga earned him his promotion to Major General.

While visiting the command of General John B. Magruder at the Fannin Hotel in Houston, Wharton quarreled with fellow Confederate officer Colonel George W. Baylor over a personal matter. Reportedly Baylor shot the unarmed General Wharton with his revolver killing him instantly. Baylor was acquitted of the killing and went on to enjoy an illustrious career as a Texas Ranger.

This archive of Major General John Austin Wharton includes this ambrotype and other family photographs including four nicely cased ambrotypes, letters with war content and other documents from the Wharton family. Also included is a photo album containing 48 tintype photographs of Wharton family members. Included with this group is a very interesting tintype of Samuel W. Wharton who fought with the 16th Texas Cavalry in the Civil War. Samuel W. Wharton is shown with an I. B. Smith and both are dressed in British Army officers' uniforms. Etched into the reverse of the photograph is a notation indicating that Wharton not only served with the 16th Texas Cavalry but also that he fought with the British Army at one time.

This is a very rare ambrotype of the Terry's Texas Rangers Major General from early in the war along with an interesting and attractive archive of family photographs and documents.

Estimate: $8,000-$12,000

72269   AN ORNATELY CARVED IVORY CARD CASE OF JEFFERSON DAVIS HELD BY A PRISONER OF WAR – This Civil War era card case has a highly carved ivory, bas-relief scene on the front of the case. Measuring 2½" x 4". The carved front is an artistic masterpiece of ivory carving. The scene depicts a young man and woman in a playful stance on either side of a lamppost. Floral and foliate effects at the top are accented by very detailed work of the ground on which the figures stand. The interior of the case is equally ornate and beautiful. Wafer-thin ivory leaves separate the compartments where one could place cards or photographs. Purple silk lines the inside of the case and is still in fine condition. The silver clasp of the case has a dark patina and still functions perfectly. There is some tearing of the ivory binding on the spine of the case but the case is overall intact and a functional work of art.

The case came from a Hampton Roads, Virginia African-American family whose ancestor "took possession" of it while Davis was imprisoned at Fortress Monroe and retained it as a memento of the passed rebellion.

Provenance: *The Tharpe Collection of American Military History*

Exhibited: *The Liberty Heritage Society Museum*

Estimate: $6,000-$8,000

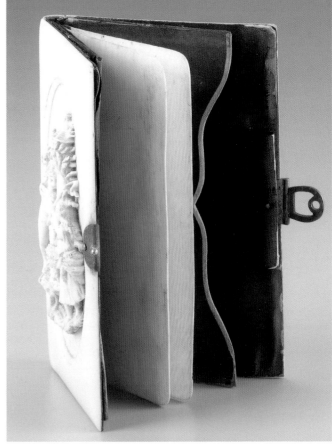

CANNONS

72270   12 POUNDER AMERICAN REVOLUTIONARY WAR "UNFINISHED" IRON CANNON, CA. 1770s − Early American Iron Cannon, "unfinished" and not bored out, with the casting chuck still in the barrel. It was buried on purpose in a unfinished state. It may have been that the foundry was overrun by British troops and the canon maker had planned on unearthing it to finish it and put into use in the field. The cannon is excavated and heavily corroded; the trunnions and the cascabel are in excellent condition. Behind the casting chuck must exist a near perfect unfired barrel! One can only speculate the history of this cannon; it is certainly one of the earliest American made iron canons from a small foundry. 78" in length, inclusive of the casting chuck.

Provenance: *The Crow Art Partnership Collection*

Estimate: $12,000-$16,000

72271 REVOLUTIONARY WAR "GRASS HOPPER" CANNON CARRIAGE, CA. 1750 – A rare Revolutionary War "grass hopper" carriage with a twin trailer. Completely original, the iron mounted wheels and spokes and iron hubs are all intact, which is quite rare. This carriage would have help a small 6 pound battlefield cannon. Interestingly, carriages are much rarer than canons. Only a few have survived both the extremities of war and time.

Provenance: *The Crow Art Partnership Collection (Dallas, Texas)*

Estimate: $3,000-$4,000

72272   6 POUNDER IRON NAVAL CANNON "HOPE FURNACE – RHODE ISLAND" CA. 1800 – A rare British style 6 pound naval cannon that has been overstruck "H.F." for the Hope Furnace Foundry in Rhode Island. With a shortage of both foundries and cannons, the American Navy utilized captured cannons from British, French and Spanish frigates that were taken as prizes by American privateers operating on the high seas. They would in turn use these same cannons to arm American merchant vessels sailing from New York & Boston. It is 62" in length with a 3.75" bore and is marked "H.F." on the breech.

Provenance: *The Crow Art Partnership Collection (Dallas, Texas)*

Estimate: $10,000-$12,000

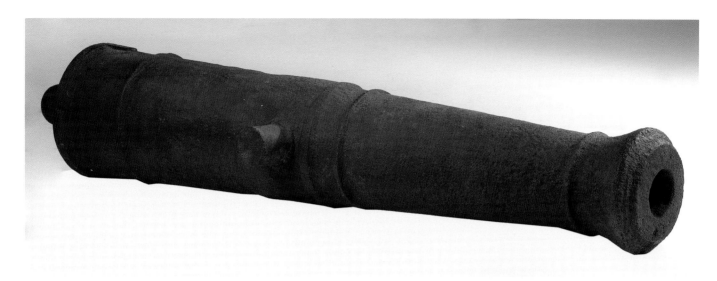

**72273   12 POUNDER IRON NAVAL CANNON
"HOPE FURNACE – RHODE ISLAND" CA. 1800 –** A
rare British style 12 pound naval cannon that has been
overstruck "H.F." for the Hope Furnace Foundry in Rhode
Island. With a shortage of both foundries and cannons, the
American Navy utilized captured cannons from British,
French and Spanish frigates that were taken as prizes by
American privateers operating on the high seas. They
would in turn use these same cannons to arm American
merchant vessels sailing from New York and Boston. The
cannon measures 82" in length with a 4.5" bore and is
marked "H.F." on the breech.

Provenance: *The Crow Art Partnership Collection (Dallas,
Texas)*

Estimate: $10,000-$12,000

72274   3 POUNDER IRON NAVY SWIVEL GUN CA. 1820 – British Navy swivel gun, used on deck of Frigates and Merchant Marines, easily stored and aimed. They are rarely offered.

The gun measures 20.5 inches in length with a 1.5 inch bore.

Provenance: *The Crow Art Partnership Collection (Dallas, Texas)*

Estimate: $1,500-$2,000

72275   6 POUNDER AMERICAN IRON CANNON, CA. 1840-1860
– An unmarked American Iron 6 pound field cannon in excellent condition.
Although completely unmarked, it is stylistically American made, heavily
cast with 3 inch trunnions. The fire hole is clear and the cascabel is intact.
Certainly used by US Forces from the Mexican War to the Civil War.

Provenance: *The Crow Art Partnership Collection (Dallas, Texas)*

Estimate: $8,000-$12,000

Please visit _HA.com_ to view other collectibles auctions. _A 19.5% Buyer's Premium ($9 min.) Applies To All Lots_

1838 EXPERIMENTAL IRON SIX POUNDER CANNON

IDENTICAL TO THE MODEL 1841 BRONZE 12 POUNDER, THIS GUN REPRESENTS AN ATTEMPT IN 1837 TO PRODUCE A STRONG BARREL WITH IRON. IRON BARRELS HAD A TENDENCY TO BURST IN USE, AND ALTHOUGH BRONZE TUBES WERE AVAILABLE, THEY WERE MORE EXPENSIVE AS ITS MAIN COMPONENT - TIN - HAD TO BE IMPORTED, WHILE IRON WAS ABUNDANT IN THE UNITED STATES.

CYRUS ALGER INVENTED A PROCESS TO PRODUCE AN EXTREMELY STRONG BARREL WITH EXTENDED HEAT TREATMENT WHILE STILL IN THE MOLD, THUS REMOVING MOST OF THE CARBON FROM THE IRON, PRODUCING A METAL SIMILAR TO CRUCIBLE STEEL. IN 1837, 8 BARRELS WERE CAST AT THE SOUTH BOSTON IRON COMPANY, WEIGHING APPROXIMATELY 787 POUNDS EACH, AND SERIAL NUMBERED 1 THROUGH 8. THESE WERE INSPECTED BY GEORGE TALCOT, WHOSE INITIALS CAN BE FOUND ON THE GUN, ALONG WITH A SERIAL NO. 8. ALGER DELIVERED EIGHT "MALLEABLE IRON" BARRELS TO THE GOVERNMENT ON JANUARY 27, 1838. LITTLE IS KNOWN AS TO THEIR DISPOSITION AFTER THAT TIME.

72276   AN 'EXPERIMENTAL' IRON SIX POUNDER CANNON, ONE OF EIGHT MADE – This 1838 six pounder experimental cannon was only one of eight made by Cyrus Alger from iron rather than bronze. Identical to the model 1841 bronze 12 pounder, this gun represents an attempt in 1837 to produce a strong barrel with iron. Iron barrels had a tendency to burst in use, and although bronze tubes were available, they were more expensive as its main component - tin- had to be imported, whereas iron was abundant in the United States.

Cyrus Alger invented a process to produce an extremely strong barrel with extended heat treatment while still in the mold, thus removing most of the carbon from the iron, producing a metal similar to crucible steel. In 1837, 8 barrels were cast at the South Boston Iron Company, weighing approximately 787 pounds each, and serial numbered one through eight. These were inspected by George Talcot, whose initials can be found on the gun, along with a serial number "8". Alger delivered eight malleable iron barrels to the government on January 27, 1838. Little is known as to their disposition after that time.

Accompanied by brass display plaques that read as follows:

"Gun serial no. 8 was found in Maryland in 1959 and purchased by an officer at Aberdeen Proving Ground for research, since no guns of that period had ever been found. After research, it was discovered that the iron in the gun was unlike that of any ever seen before, and it was as good as, or superior to, a bronze gun.

"In 1980, the New Hampshire division of Parks and Recreation discovered that one of their guns was of the same type. It had been purchased in 1840 and is serial number 5. Recently, serial number 4 showed up in the town of Lancaster in New Hampshire.

"In 1841, the iron age of guns came to an end and would not appear again in field artillery until just prior to the Civil War in the form of wrought iron or wrought iron reinforced cast iron, but never identical to gun number 8.

"In 1960, gun number 8 was loaned to Reuben Darby of Harper's Ferry, West Virginia. It was displayed at the museum and used in living history demonstrations. "At this time, General Mark Clark, commandant of the Citadel in Charleston, South Carolina, was asked to conduct the first reenactment of the Civil War Centennial, the firing on the "Star of the West" in Charleston Harbor. Gun number 8 was loaned to General Clark, and had the honor of firing the first shot of the Civil War Centennial of 1961-1965.

"While at Harper's Ferry, it was used in live and blank firing and it is estimated that over 1000 rounds were put through it. In 1965, it was returned to Aberdeen, where it was displayed in the Ordnance Museum.

"The unusual weapon sat in the museum until 1979 when it was sold into private hands and used by the 15th New Jersey Volunteers of the North/South Skirmish Association.

"A second group of 'malleable' guns was delivered in December of 1838, but none have yet surfaced, and their pattern is unknown.

"Experimental gun number 8 is the only one of its type in private hands, and the only surviving one which has seen true service for over 145 years. It is still fully serviceable and can be used with live or blank charges."

The gun is on a carriage in good mechanical condition and is a wonderful and historical museum piece.

Provenance: *The Crow Art Partnership Collection (Dallas, Texas)*

Estimate: $80,000-$120,000

72277   A LIMBER CHEST FROM THE 2ND LIGHT BATTERY OF THE VERMONT VOLUNTEERS, CIRCA 1863 – This limber chest was used by the 2nd Vermont Light Artillery in the Civil War. Used to carry ammunition for cannon in the field, in this case a six-pounder cannon, this copper and iron chest would ride atop the limber, a two-wheeled cart with an axle with a framework designed to hold the limber chest and an apparatus to receive the tongue of the gun carriage or caisson which also would carry limber chests.

The 2nd Vermont Light Artillery was organized at Brandon, Vermont in December 1861 and moved to Boston where they took the steamer *Idaho* for Ship Island, Louisiana where they were attached to Phelps' Brigade. They had the distinction of being the first battery to occupy New Orleans. They later saw action at Galveston, Plains Store and the Siege of Port Hudson and participated in the surrender of the Confederate forces there.

This heavy iron and copper chest has seen much duty. Measuring 42" x 17" x 20". The upraised handles measure 9" x 11". There is stenciling in white on the front of "Light 6 Pounder". On both ends the unit's name "2nd Lt. Battery Vermont Vols." is stenciled as well. The front has a hasp closure for the placing of a lock.

This is an historic piece of artillery equipment that was used to occupy New Orleans. Limber chests from the Civil War are very rare.

Provenance: *The Crow Art Partnership Collection (Dallas, Texas)*

Estimate: $12,000-$16,000

72278   AN ENGLISH 3' NAVAL CANNON, CIRCA 1840 – This 38" tube naval cannon has a 3" bore and is in good condition. The gun has a raised crown stamped into the barrel between the trunnions. It was made circa 1840 and comes with a period carriage and four Whitworth style shells along with the ammunition rack. This is an excellent presentation cannon and makes a great display weapon.

Provenance: *The Crow Art Partnership Collection (Dallas, Texas)*

Estimate: $12,000-$16,000

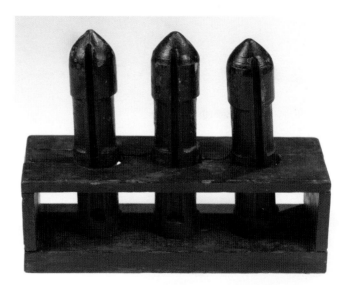

Please visit _HA.com_ to view other collectibles auctions. *A 19.5% Buyer's Premium ($9 min.) Applies To All Lots*

72279 **GRAND ARMY OF THE REPUBLIC CEREMONIAL SALUTE GUN,** cast bronze, 2.25" bore; 35" overall, made by W. H. Nutt, Athens, Pennsylvania, ordered by a Charles T. Hull, May, 1887. Heavily engraved tube includes large "GAR" above breech. Resting on an antique carriage retaining much of its original yellow paint. This cannon is in working order. The Grand Army of the Republic, founded in 1866, was the largest Civil War veterans' organization, boasting a peak membership of some 400,000 former Union soldiers and sailors. The last G.A.R. member, Albert Wollson, died in 1956. The gentleman who ordered this cannon was likely former Sergeant Charles Hull (1835-1910), Co. "E", 141st Pennsylvania Infantry. Hull, like the cannon's maker, was from Athens, Pennsylvania.

Provenance: *The Crow Art Partnership Collection (Dallas, Texas)*

Estimate: $8,000-$12,000

End of Session One

HERITAGE
CITY OF HARRISBURG
WESTERN PHOTOGRAPHS - GUNS - HISTORICAL ITEMS

Auction Week During October at The Hilton Anatole Dallas, TX